COLLAPSE V

Published in 2009 in an edition of 1000
comprising numbered copies 1-950
and 50 *hors-commerce* copies.

559

No ....

ISBN 978-0-9553087-4-1

Published by Urbanomic,
14 Harbour Terrace,
Falmouth, TR11 2AN,
United Kingdom.

Printed by Athenæum Press

www.urbanomic.com

COLLAPSE

Philosophical Research and Development

VOLUME V

Edited by

Damian Veal

URBANOMIC

FALMOUTH

COLLAPSE V

January 2009

EDITOR: Damian Veal

ASSOCIATE EDITORS: Robin Mackay, Ray Brassier

Editorial Introduction

Damian Veal[1]

[T]hough the medieval world was [...] immense, relatively to man and his planet, it was nevertheless definitely limited and fenced about. It was therefore essentially picturable; the perspectives which it presented, however great, were not wholly baffling to the imagination.[2]

Copernicanism tore asunder the fit between the world and man's organs: the congruence between reality and visibility [...] The breakdown of the postulate of visibility – taken in its widest sense – is brought to a point by a kind of reversal: The visible world is not only a tiny section of physical reality, but it is also, qualitatively, the mere foreground of this reality, its insignificant surface, on which the outcome of processes and forces is only symptomatically displayed. Visibility itself is an eccentric configuration, the accidental convergence of hetero-geneous sequences of physical events.[3]

Almost five hundred years after Nicolaus Copernicus' death, the notion of 'Copernicanism' continues to be a compelling one for science, philosophy and the popular imagination alike. However 'Copernicanism' stands for a

---

1. I would like to extend my thanks to Robin Mackay for his comments and contributions to this introduction, in particular the sections on the work of Nigel Cooke and Keith Tyson. Thanks also to Ray Brassier for his critical comments.

2. Arthur Lovejoy, *The Great Chain of Being* (Cambridge, Mass.,: Harvard University Press, 1936), 101.

3. Hans Blumenberg, *The Genesis of the Copernican World* (Cambridge, Mass.: MIT Press, 1987), 642.

legacy which is still contested, as the multiple perspectives collected in this, the fifth volume of **COLLAPSE,** reveal; and as was amply demonstrated by some recent events.

While in the penultimate stages of editing this volume in late November 2008, it was widely reported in the world's media that researchers in Poland had identified the remains of Nicolaus Copernicus by comparing DNA from a skeleton with that of a hair retrieved from one of the sixteenth-century astronomer's books. The findings, it was reported, were 'the culmination of four years of investigation and centuries of speculation about the final resting place of the man who challenged the Bible and medieval teachings of the church'.[4] The Catholic bishop who had instigated the archaeological search, however, knowing full well that Copernicus had never harboured any such heretical intentions, used the opportunity to point out that Copernicus had in fact been 'a deeply religious clergyman and cathedral canon who dedicated his main work to the Pope and presented his faith clearly'.[5]

The bishop of course neglected to mention the fact that it had taken no less than four and a half centuries and a succession of forty-four popes before one of latter took it upon himself to officially admit that Copernicus may actually have had a point.[6] Instead, he proposed that the discovery should lead humanity to reflect that centuries of conflict between scripture and empirical science had really

4. *The Guardian,* Friday 21 November 2008.

5. 'Bishop: Discovery of Copernicus' remains highlights his contributions', *Total Catholic,* 2 December, 2008.

6. 'Vatican Science Panel Told By Pope: Galileo Was Right', *New York Times,* 1 November, 1992.

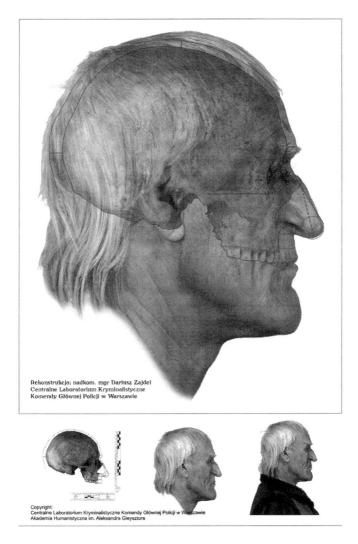

Rekonstrukcja: nadkom. mgr Dariusz Zajdel
Centralne Laboratorium Kryminalistyczne
Komendy Głównej Policji w Warszawie

Copyright:
Centralne Laboratorium Kryminalistyczne Komendy Głównej Policji w Warszawie
Akademia Humanistyczna im. Aleksandra Gieysztora

Digital reconstruction of the head of Nicolaus Copernicus, on the basis of remains identified by Polish scientists in late 2008 as being those of the sixteenth-century astronomer.

only been a lot of fuss about nothing – a 'great misunder-standing' brought about by the fact that people had 'made the mistake of absolutising one philosophical vision without reflecting on new insights and discoveries'.[7] The implication, of course, was that no 'philosophical vision' ought to be so absolutised, and that we must finally come to understand that there is really no substantive conflict between science and Church doctrine at all – a conciliatory sentiment fittingly symbolised by the fact that Copernicus' remains, identified by means of advances made in late twentieth-century genetics and computer technology, are now set to be reinterred during the celebrations planned for Frombork Cathedral's 750th anniversary in 2010.[8] In thus ceremoniously returning Copernicus' remains to the consecrated grounds of this ancient place of worship, perhaps it is hoped that 'Copernicanism' itself, and the unholy forces it unleashed, might finally be buried as well.

Remarkably enough, this was not the only news report involving Copernicanism and the Catholic Church to appear during the final stages of the preparation of this volume. Just five days after the story about the identification of Copernicus' remains, *The Times* put out the headline 'Vatican Seeks to Rehabilitate Galileo Galilei', while *The Boston Pilot* ran with 'Vatican Official Says Galileo Was a Man of Faith'.[9] The occasion this time was the appearance of an article entitled 'Thank you, Galileo' on the front page of the Vatican's official newspaper, announcing a series of

---

7. 'Bishop', *Total Catholic*, op. cit.

8. Ibid.

9. *Times Online*, 26 November, 2008; *The Boston Pilot*, 5 December 2008.

events planned by the Vatican for 2009 to coincide with the celebrations surrounding the 400th anniversary of Galileo's first observations with a telescope. Earlier in 2008, Pope Benedict XVI had been obliged to cancel a planned visit to Rome's principal university due to vehement protests from academics and students who had accused him of hostility towards science, citing his alleged endorsement of the Inquisition's condemnation of Galileo. (In a speech in 1990, the then Cardinal Ratzinger had cited the philosopher of science turned anarchist-cum-Dadaist Paul Feyerabend's comment that the verdict against Galileo had been 'rational and just'.)[10] Given the negative press following from this incident, it seems that the Vatican had thought it expedient to publicly 'reclaim' Galileo for the Church, very much in the way that the Polish bishop had used the identification of Copernicus' remains as an opportunity to posthumously bring him back within the fold.

Citing Pope Benedict XVI's statement that Galileo had been 'a man of faith who saw nature as a Book written by God', the author of the Vatican's newspaper article reiterated the sentiment of the Polish bishop, insisting that the Galileo celebrations should 'encourage people to consider seriously the relationship between faith and science; lead scientists to recognize the role faith played in Galileo's life; and lead theologians to recognize the contributions Galileo made to the church's attitude toward science'.[11] Having announced

---

10. See, e.g., 'Pope pulls out of visit to Rome university after outrage at his views on Galileo and science', *The Guardian*, 16 January, 2008. The passage cited by Ratzinger is taken from Paul Feyerabend, *Wider den Methodenzwang*, 2nd ed. (Frankfurt am Main: Suhrkamp, 1983), 206. For helpful scholarly (rather than journalistic) treatment of the Feyerabend passage, and Ratzinger's citation of it, see Ernan McMullin, 'Quoting Feyerabend on Galileo', *Irish Theological Quarterly* 73, 2008: 164-73.

11. 'Vatican Official Says Galileo Was a Man of Faith', *The Boston Pilot*, op. cit.

in November that a statue of Galileo was to be erected in the Vatican gardens, the Pope then used the onset of the Winter solstice on the 21st of December as an opportunity to remark upon not only the coincidence of Christmas with the solstice and 'the function of astronomy in marking out the rhythm of prayer', but to once again praise Galileo and his telescope for the way in which they had stimulated appreciation of God's work: 'If the heavens', said the Pope, 'according to the beautiful words of the psalmist, "proclaim the glory of God" (Psalm 19 [18]: 2), then the laws of nature, which over the course of the centuries many men and women of science have helped us to understand better, are also a great stimulus to contemplate with gratitude the works of the Lord.'[12] One can only surmise what the official Vatican line will be with respect to the imminent celebrations for the 200th anniversary of Darwin's birth and the 150th anniversary of *The Origin of Species* in 2009. Will it be claimed that Darwin too had been a 'man of faith', and that evolution likewise bears witness to the glory of the Lord's Creation?[13]

Of course, that Nicolaus Copernicus and Galileo Galilei were 'men of faith' is uncontroversial. Indeed, given that the Pope's comments were made in connection with the quatercentenary of Galileo's first use of the telescope, he

---

12. See the news headlines for 21 December 2008: 'Pope Praises Galileo's Astronomy' (*BBC News*), 'From Heretic to Hero: Pope Pays Tribute to Galileo' (*ABC Online*), 'Pope Benedict XVI Celebrates Galileo's Astronomy' (*The Telegraph*).

13. Given the fact that in April 2007 Pope Benedict gently 'corrected' Pope John Paul II's 1996 statement that evolution was 'more than a hypothesis', stating that while his predecessor 'had his reasons for saying this, it is also true that the theory of evolution is not a scientifically proven theory', this seems rather less than likely. See 'Pope Stokes Debate on Darwin and Evolution', *Times Online*, April 12, 2007.

might have done well to point out that, in his 1610 *Sidereus nuncius* (i.e., the book in which his first telescopic observations were reported), Galileo had enthusiastically declared that he had devised the telescope 'after being illuminated by divine grace.'[14] Moreover, as Hans Blumenberg and Karsten Harries have documented, the advent of the telescope in the seventeenth century was seized upon by the likes of Francis Bacon and Joseph Glanvill as an invention which promised a technological restitution of the perfect clarity of vision which humanity had supposedly lost with Adam's fall. Adam, surmised Glanvill,

> needed no Spectacles. The acuteness of his natural Opticks (if conjecture may have credit) shew'd much of the Coelestial magnificence and bravery without a Galilaeo's tube: And 'tis most probable that his naked eyes could reach near as much of the upper world, as we with all the advantages of art. It may be 'twas as absurd even in the judgement of his senses, that the Sun and Stars should be so very much less than this Globe, as the contrary seems in ours; and 'tis not unlikely that he held as clear a perception of the earth's motion, as we think we have of its quiescence.[15]

Glanvill's book was published just fifteen years before Olaf Römer's discovery of the finite speed of light in 1676 – a discovery scarcely less momentous than that of the

---

14. 'All these facts were discovered by me not many days ago with the aid of a spyglass which I devised, after being illuminated by divine grace.' Galileo Galilei, *The Starry Messenger*, in *Discoveries and Opinions of Galileo*, trans. S. Drake (New York: Anchor Books, 1957), 28.

15. Joseph Glanvill, *The Vanity of Dogmatizing* (1661), cited in Harries, *Infinity and Perspective*, op. cit., 106. On seventeenth-century attitudes toward both the telescope and microscope, see also Catherine Wilson, *The Invisible World: Early Modern philosophy and the Invention of the Microscope* (Princeton: Princeton University Press, 1995).

Copernican revolution itself, and which was later adverted to in Mark Twain's posthumously published *Letters from the Earth*, wherein Satan, in one of the most cruelly cynical tirades against human vanity ever written, points out that at the beginning of Creation not even a single star would have been visible in the sky over the biblical Paradise, and that even at the end of a thousand years there still would not have been enough to 'make a show'.[16] Yet as Blumenberg suggests, Bacon's idea of making the recovery of Paradise into the goal of historical progress through science, and Glanvill's expectation that the telescope might ultimately enable man to recoup his prelapsarian intuitive prowess, should be understood less as the secularisation of an originally religious idea and more as a way of safeguarding an anthropology in which man and cosmos are seen as 'coordinated in such a way that no essential incongruence can be assumed between man's organic equipment and the constituents of reality'.[17] No wonder, then, that Bacon, the anti-Copernican, expressed such alarm at the idea of the finite speed of light:

> It seemed to him shocking (*dubitatio plane monstrosa*) that in looking at the starry heavens we could catch sight only of the past, something that might have long since ceased to be real – that the *tempus visum* and *tempus verum* [apparent time and true time] could split apart arbitrarily [...] that the presentation of the starry heavens, which man had so long related to himself as the one who was called to observe it, could be a mere appearance

---

16. Mark Twain, *Letters from the Earth* (New York: Harper & Row, 1962), 15. Twain wrote the book in 1909; it was not published until 1962.

17. *The Genesis of the Copernican World*, op. cit., 629, cf. 635 and Part VI, Chapter 1: 'How Horizons of Visibility Are Conditioned by Views of Man', 622-642 *passim*.

also in that it was not the homogeneous total reality that it presents itself as in intuition, but instead was nothing but an accidental section through the many layered depths of huge temporal differences.[18]

According to Blumenberg, the epochal significance not only of Copernicanism but also of what we might call 'Römerianism', is thus not so much that it entailed 'man's removal from the centre',[19] but rather that it rendered obsolete once and for all the medieval equation of reality and visibility,[20] thus revealing a seemingly unbridgeable chasm between our biologically-inherited perceptual faculties and the sheer scale and complexity of the universe. While Copernicus himself could still employ as a premise in arguing for the truth (rather than mere empirical adequacy)

---

18. Ibid., 542.

19. As scores of historians have not failed to point out, this standard narrative is inherently implausible inasmuch as the medieval conception of the cosmos was less anthropocentric than *diabolocentric*, the earth being regarded as 'the filth and mire of the world, the worst, lowest, most lifeless part of the universe, the bottom story of the house' (Montaigne as quoted by Arthur Lovejoy, *The Great Chain of Being*, op. cit., 102) and the actual centre of the universe being identified with hell. As late as 1640 an English supporter of Copernicanism recognised one of the strongest current arguments against heliocentrism as proceeding from 'the vileness of our earth, because it consists of a more sordid and base matter than any other part of the world; and therefore must be situated in the centre, which is the worst place' (ibid.). Galileo himself, in the work already cited, took himself to be furnishing a refutation of 'those who argue that the earth must be excluded from the dancing swirl of stars for the specific reason that it is devoid of motion and of light. We shall prove the earth to be a wandering body surpassing the moon in splendor, and not the sink of all dull refuse of the universe; this we shall support by an infinitude of arguments drawn from nature' (*The Starry Messenger*, op. cit., 43). Thus, from the perspective of pre-modern cosmology and theology, Copernicanism, far from entailing the *demotion* of the earth and of man, actually amounted to their *exaltation*. For a brief but helpful survey of the evidence, see Dennis Danielson, 'The Great Copernican Cliché', *American Journal of Physics* 69 (1), 2001: 1029-35.

20. This is what Blumenberg calls 'the postulate of visibility' in our epigraph.

11

of his theory the idea that the universe had been created 'on our behalf' or 'for our sake' (*propter nos*) by a supremely good and orderly Creator,[21] such a teleological, anthropocentric conception of the universe became increasingly difficult to maintain in the wake of Römer's demonstration of the finite speed of light – that is, at least, for those who were cognizant of its implications. How, after all, could one continue to regard man as the privileged *contemplator caeli*, as the specially appointed witness of the wonders of creation, when the time required for the light to reach him from unknown star systems was longer than the entire duration of the earth?

In this regard, the fact that UNESCO elected 2009 as the International Year of Astronomy on the grounds that it is the 400th anniversary of Galileo's first telescopic observations speaks volumes with regard to what Blumenberg called 'man's optical neediness',[22] and is symptomatic of the extent to which we are still in thrall to what Popper called 'the Baconian myth' – that is, the idea 'that all science starts from observation and then slowly and cautiously proceeds

---

21. In the Preface to *De Revolutionibus*, Copernicus states that the reason he set out to see if the assumption of a moving Earth would provide better explanations of celestial phenomena was that he had been 'annoyed with the philosophers, who while in other respects had made a very careful scrutiny of the least details of the world, had discovered no sure scheme for the movements of the machinery of the world, which was built for us by the Best and Most Orderly Workman of all' (*On the Revolution of Heavenly Spheres*, in [ed.] Stephen Hawking, *Standing on the Shoulders of Giants: The Great Works of Physics and Astronomy*, London & New York: Penguin Books, 2002, 10). The seeming paradox of this unequivocal statement of teleological anthropocentrism ('built for us' or 'on our behalf') as the motivating reason for the Copernican revolution is examined at length in Blumenberg's *The Genesis of the Copernican World*, op. cit.

22. Blumenberg, *The Genesis of the Copernican World*, op. cit., 632.

to theories'.[23] Galileo's telescopic observations – observations which first made visible the moons of Jupiter, the ring of Saturn, the phases of Venus, and the craters and mountains of the moon – were certainly of great scientific and historical significance. However, 1609 witnessed another breakthrough in astronomy which was even more portentous, yet which has not even so much as been mentioned in relation to the forthcoming quatercentenary celebrations: namely, the publication of Kepler's *Astronomia nova.* Not only did this book lay the very foundations of modern astronomy and physics, but it did so on the basis of precisely that kind of resolute refusal to be taken in by the self-evidences of sensible intuition which Galileo professed to so admire in Copernicus.[24] Indeed, in comparison with Kepler's break with tradition in abandoning the 'Platonic' requirement that all celestial orbits be circular, Galileo's telescopic observation of the Jupiter system 'seems extremely conventional [...] an attempted *coup de main* of intuition, by means of the telescope, to carry the day for Copernicanism', with Galileo's medieval faith in what he

23. Karl Popper, *Conjectures and Refutations* (London and New York: Routledge, 1963), 185.

24. In his *Dialogue Concerning the Two Chief World Systems,* in response to Sagredo's expression of surprise that Pythagoreanism 'has found so few followers in the course of centuries' and that 'even Copernicus is not having any better luck with it in these latter days', Galileo-Salviato replies: 'No, Sagredo, my surprise is very different from yours. You wonder that there are so few followers of the Pythagorean opinion, whereas I am astonished that there have been any up to this day who have embraced and followed it. Nor can I ever sufficiently admire the outstanding acumen of those who have taken hold of this opinion and accepted it as true; they have through sheer force of intellect done such violence to their own senses as to prefer what reason told them over that which sensible experience plainly showed them to the contrary.' (This quotation is from the Third Day of Galileo's *Dialogue Concerning the Two Chief World Systems* [1632]; the English translation of the full text by Stillman Drake is available online at http://www.law.umkc.edu/faculty/projects/ftrials/galileo/dialogue.html.)

called 'the certainly of sense evidence'[25] blinding him to the momentous achievements of Kepler.

The idea that direct, first-person observation provides not only the ultimate *source* of knowledge but also its *fulfilment*, that reason and theory are only ever an anticipation of intuition (the latter being regarded as the very essence of a fully realised relation to reality), is one that has very deep roots in Western philosophy. Indeed, it is one which governs the traditional historiography of science whenever the demise of the Aristotelian philosophy of nature is attributed to the latter's allegedly speculative, non-empirical stance, being superseded by a thoroughly empirical approach to science. But on the contrary, as Blumenberg suggests, the downfall of Aristotelian physics is better described by the lapidary sentence of Heinrich Scholz: 'It perished as a result of its positivism'.[26] It is well known that the Aristotelian physics is in fact very close to the commonsense 'folk physics' of everyday experience, and 'is familiar to us in a way that Galileo's and Newton's never can be'.[27] What was needed to overcome the Aristotelian philosophy of nature was not simply more experience, or greater attention to the way things appear, but rather a different *kind* of experience, 'an experience which was already directed toward specific premises – selected and arranged in accordance with them – and placed under definite conditions: in other words, *experimental* experience':

25. Galileo Galilei, *The Starry Messenger*, op. cit., 28.

26. Blumenberg, *The Genesis of the Copernican World*, op. cit., 394.

27. Lewis Wolpert, *The Unnatural Nature of Science* (Cambridge, Mass.: Harvard University Press, 1991), 3.

This type of experience never presents itself immediately, and is not exhausted in intuitive givenness. It confirms or disproves assumptions in regard to a definite and, at least in principle, measurable aspect of a total phenomenon. Experience that is controlled – not to say prepared or dissected – in this way cannot stand at the beginning of radical theoretical change. Instead, what stands at this beginning is a distancing from the immediacy of the life-world.[28]

It was precisely this transformation of the notion of experience that Kant recognised as the revolution which placed the study of nature 'on the secure path of a science', and upon which he modelled his own 'transcendental' revolution in metaphysics:

When Galileo caused balls, the weights of which he had himself previously determined, to roll down an inclined plane; when Torricelli made the air carry a weight which he had calculated beforehand to be equal to that of a definite volume of water; or in more recent times, when Stahl changed metal into lime, and lime back into metal, by withdrawing something and then restoring it, a light broke upon all students of nature. They learned that reason has insight only into that which it produces after a plan of its own, and that it must not allow itself to be kept, as it were, in nature's leading-strings, but must itself show the way with principles of judgement based upon fixed laws, constraining nature to give answer to questions of reason's own determining. Accidental observations, made in obedience to no previously thought-out plan, can never be made to yield a necessary law, which alone reason is concerned to discover.[29]

28. Blumenberg, *The Genesis of the Copernican World*, op. cit., 394.

29. Immanuel Kant, *Critique of Pure Reason*, trans. N. K. Smith (London: Macmillan, 1929), Bxii-xiii.

While one might agree with Popper that Kant's statement that '[o]ur intellect does not draw its laws from nature [...] but imposes them upon nature' must be modified as 'but tries – with varying degrees of success – to impose upon nature laws which it freely invents',[30] Kant's statement is significant for its recognition of the way in which the history of science refutes the Baconian myth that all science starts from pure observation. Once modified in the way suggested, one ends up with Popper's notion of science as the forwarding of risky conjectures and bold speculations which, while they may be 'in striking contrast to the everyday world of common experience', are 'yet able to explain some aspects of this world of common experience'.[31] This is a tradition to be valued for 'its ability to free our minds from old beliefs, old prejudices, and old certainties, and to offer us in their stead new conjectures and daring hypotheses'.[32] Such speculatively audacious attempts to '*explain the known by the unknown*' have immeasurably extended the realm of the known, adding to the facts of our everyday world 'the invisible air, the antipodes, the circulation of the blood, the worlds of the telescope and the microscope, of electricity, and of tracer atoms showing us in detail the movements of matter within living bodies'.[33]

It is precisely this willingness to question and even radically overturn the commonsense or intuitive image of the world that **CARLO ROVELLI** identifies as the essence

---

30. Popper, *Conjectures and Refutation*, op. cit., 259; emphasis added.

31. Ibid., 137.

32. Ibid., 136-7.

33. Ibid.

of the scientific enterprise in the first essay of the present volume, 'Anaximander's Legacy'. Drawing upon both his extensive historical erudition and his first-hand experience of research at the cutting-edge of contemporary theoretical physics, Rovelli meditates on the question 'What is Scientific Thinking?' and takes us on a tour through some of the most profound conceptual revolutions of the history of science. As one of the founders of loop quantum gravity – today widely recognized as the leading rival to string theory in the quest to unify general relativity and quantum mechanics – there is scarcely anyone alive today in a better position to reflect upon the counterintuitive nature of modern science than Rovelli. Providing as it does a stimulating overview of the way in which science continually 'redraws the image of the world' based on its perpetual 'rebellion against what appears obvious', Rovelli's essay is a fitting introduction to the 'Copernican imperative' to which this volume of COLLAPSE is devoted.

By all accounts, Anaximander's studies were vast in scope, comprising a cosmogony, a history of the earth and the heavenly bodies, a proto-Darwinian account of the development of living organisms and the origin of species, studies in astronomy, meteorology and biology, a geography, as well as the first attempt to describe the structure of the universe in mathematical terms. But it was Anaximander's conjecture that the earth 'is held up by nothing, but remains stationary owing to the fact that it is equally distance from all other things'[34] that Rovelli singles out as the 'gigantic leap in our understanding of the world' which set in motion the naturalistic inquiry that

34. Quoted in Popper, *Conjectures and Refutation*, op. cit., 186.

ultimately evolved into modern science. Popper described this hypothesis as 'one of the boldest, most revolutionary, and most portentous ideas in the whole history of human thought',[35] and it is not hard to see why. While every account of which we have a record, including that of Anaximander's teacher Thales, pictures the earth as resting upon some support or other, Anaximander boldly conjectures, against the evidence of sense experience, that the earth is suspended in mid-space. Faced with the mutually contradictory commonsense beliefs that everything moves downwards, and yet that the earth is at rest, Anaximander in effect accepts the latter of these conflicting judgments and rejects the application of the former to the earth, and he does so on the basis of considerations of symmetry and geometrical structure. In short, Anaximander's ingenious answer to the conflicting judgements of common sense amounts to the first application of the Principle of Sufficient Reason of which we have any trace the history of thought: The earth does not fall, conjectures Anaximander, because has no *reason* to move in one direction rather than other. As Rovelli suggests, Anaximander's willingness to reject observation-based judgements in favour of mathematical and logical considerations in constructing his theory amounts to the invention of a completely new grammar for understanding the spatial structure of the universe, one in which the idea of *absolute direction* is abolished. By 'subverting the meaning of "up" and "down", which had provided the most intuitive and elementary way of organizing space and reality for countless generations of humans hitherto', Anaximander 'inaugurates the very process of *rethinking the*

---

35. Popper, *Conjectures and Refutation*, op. cit., 186.

image of the world – the path of investigation of the world which is based on the rebellion against what is obvious' that is characteristic of the scientific enterprise.

How did Anaximander arrive at this remarkable theory? 'Certainly not', writes Popper, 'by observation'[36] but rather by critical engagement with his predecessor Thales – a type of critical engagement which, as Rovelli also suggests, seems to have been invented by the Ionian school. Thales founded a new school in which there was a new relation between master and pupil, one in which the former tolerated, perhaps even encouraged, criticism, one generation after another. It would be difficult to exaggerate the momentousness of this innovation in the history of human thought, representing as it does a break with dogmatic tradition and an admittance of a plurality of competing doctrines which all try to approach the truth by means of critical discussion. As Popper points out, this leads almost by necessity to the realization 'that our attempts to see and to find the truth are not final, but open to improvement; that our knowledge, our doctrine, is conjectural; that it consists of guesses, of hypotheses, rather than final and certain truths; and that criticism and critical discussion are our only means of getting nearer to the truth'.[37] This is a sentiment also strongly endorsed by Rovelli, according to whom it is the Ionian school's 'realization that we can have *valuable* knowledge, but at the same time that this knowledge can be partially wrong' that 'opens up the path for the immense development of subsequent speculation, which is the basis of Greek philosophy and modern science'.

---

36. Ibid., 187.

37. Ibid., 203.

According to Rovelli, today we are 'in the midst of a reconceptualization of our world which is likely to prove every bit as far-reaching as those of Anaximander and Copernicus'. The revolutions of twentieth-century physics, if properly digested, entail 'a change of image of the world far more dramatic than that of Copernicus, and also a change of image of ourselves far more far-reaching than Darwin'.[38] Perhaps most dramatically, Rovelli predicts that we will discover that space and time do not exist at the most fundamental level, that they are in effect a reflection of our ignorance, 'convenient macroscopic approximations, flimsy but illusory and insufficient screens that our mind uses to organize reality'.[39] Moreover, he predicts that we will have to give up the notion that there are 'things' altogether, in favour of a way of thinking about nature that 'refers only to interactions between systems and not to states or changes of individual systems'[40] – an idea also ultimately prepared for by Anaximander's 'gigantic leap', and one which is has a strong affinity with those defended by Julian Barbour, James Ladyman and Gabriel Catren, also in this volume.

---

38. *Edge: World Question Center*, Annual Question 2006: 'What is Your Dangerous Idea?', online at http://www.edge.org/q2006/q06_print.html#rovelli.

39. *Edge: World Question Center*, Annual Question 2005: 'What Do You Believe is True Even Though You Cannot Prove it?, online at http://www.edge.org/q2005/q05_2.html#rovelli.

40. Ibid. For detailed treatment of these ideas see for example Carlo Rovelli, *Quantum Gravity* (Oxford: Clarendon Press, 2003); Carlo Rovelli, 'Halfway Through the Woods: Contemporary Research on Space and Time' in J. Earman & J. Norton (eds), *The Cosmos of Science* (Pittsburgh: University of Pittsburgh Press, 1997), 180-223; and 'Quantum Spacetime: What do we know?' in C. Callender and N. Huggett (eds), *Physics Meets Philosophy at the Planck Scale* (Cambridge: Cambridge University Press, 2001), 101-22.

The question Rovelli raises towards the end of his paper – namely, '*Is it possible to think a world without time?*' – is one that has preoccupied theoretical physicist and historian of physics JULIAN BARBOUR for the best part of five decades. Like the great philosopher-physicists of a century ago such as Ernst Mach, Henri Poincaré and Pierre Duhem, Barbour is not only a physicist but also an eminent historian of science, and it is clear that the breakthroughs he has been able to make in rethinking the foundations of physics are owed in no small part to his considerable historical and epistemological erudition. Having sacrificed a promising career in academia in order to devote himself to exploring his interest in dynamics unencumbered by the 'publish-or-perish syndrome', Barbour set himself the task of a fundamental rethinking of two basic questions that he felt had seldom been seriously asked, let alone satisfactorily answered: 'What is time?', and 'What is motion?' These are precisely the two questions that Leibniz and Mach had raised in their critique of Newton's absolute concepts, but had not answered definitively, and Barbour's entire adult life has been devoted to resolving them. In our interview we discuss with him the way in which his early reading of Mach provided a crucial stimulus to his life's work, ultimately leading him to the most counterintuitive conclusion imaginable: namely, that time *does not exist*. This is of course not a thesis which anyone is likely to take on trust, and in our interview Barbour not only recounts the motivations and influences that led him to embrace it, but also responds to some of the inevitable criticisms that have been voiced in connection with it. Of all the commonsense-defying ideas to be encountered in this volume, Barbour's are surely the most difficult to intuitively digest; and yet, as the reader will discover, they are also ideas to which those working in the most advanced areas of contemporary quantum gravity research, whether it be string theory or loop quantum gravity, are increasingly being drawn.

The problem of the relationship between a mathematicized reality and a human intuition which persists in asking 'how to make sense of this?' is also explored, visually and conceptually, in a unique collaboration between artist **CONRAD SHAWCROSS** and philosopher **ROBIN MACKAY** in 'Shadows of Copernicanism'. As Mackay suggests, Shawcross's remarkable 2006 work *Binary Star* provides a potent visual challenge to the heliotropic tendency of the philosophical imaginary, an imaginary in which the sun has always stood as the metaphor for a singular *lumen naturale*, a unique source of enlightenment. For Mackay, *Binary Star* raises questions regarding the philosophical tradition's metaphorical anchorage of thought to apparently fixed and permanent characteristics of the physical world. If Rovelli suggests that the search for 'a fixed point on which to rest is [...] naïve, useless, and counterproductive for the development of science'[41] and Barbour's theory demands that we 'learn how to find our bearings when the solid reassuring framework of the Earth is not there',[42] Mackay suggests that the challenge of philosophical thought today amounts to coming to terms with a scientific worldview 'which disabuses us of every illusion of fixity and permanence'. In this regard, Shawcross's *Binary Star*

---

41. 'Quantum Spacetime: What do we know?', op. cit., 121.

42. *The End of Time*, op. cit., 71.

demonstrates how the 'Copernican cliché' of a 'reversal of perspective between two heavenly bodies' remains tied to 'terrestrial' tropes of thought. If Tycho Brahe's destruction of the crystal spheres prompted Kepler to remark (as quoted by Barbour in our interview) that '[f]rom now on, the planets must find their way through the void like birds through the air' – a remarkably prescient comment in view of the recent discovery of enormous numbers of planet-sized bodies roaming freely in the void between the stars[43] – the physical picture of the world furnished by general relativity is one in which localisation with respect to a background spacetime, or to any fixed external reference system, has no meaning. Mackay suggests that art, given to the image and what is humanly intuitable, insistently inhabits the terrain of this fractured ground, of the gap opened up between mathematical models freed from the contingencies of human visibility and the efforts of intuition and the imagination to make sense of them; and that Shawcross's works mimic the efforts which philosophy must make to incorporate mathematical-scientific models of reality into the grain of language without ceding the latter entirely to mathematical abstraction. Thus the most profound content of the work, suggests Mackay, lies in a vacillation between object and model that indexes its necessary 'failure'.

The idea that there exists an intimate correlation between reality and visibility, or between the actual and the intuitable, is not one which was left behind with the Middle Ages. Rather, it is one which remains deeply rooted in the

43. See, e.g., P. W. Lucas & P. F. Roche, 'A population of very young brown dwarfs and free-floating planets in Orion', *Monthly Notices of the Royal Astronomical Society* 314 (4), 2002: 858-64; and H. Cheongho, 'Secure Identification of Free-floating Planets', *The Astrophysical Journal* 644 (2), 2006: 1232-6.

human psyche. Not only for the first-person perspective of common sense, for which degrees of phenomenal avail-ability are experienced as degrees of 'realness',[44] but even for significant numbers of contemporary philosophers, 'reality' and 'manifestation' are treated as highly correlative concepts, often even being employed interchangeably. While traditional empiricist and positivist philosophies took the limits of the real to coincide with the boundaries of the (humanly) observable, many self-styled 'critical' philoso-phers – philosophers, that is, who typically pride themselves upon their overcoming of the 'naïveté' of positivism – continue to persist in the opinion that phenomenology is ontology enough. While earlier philosophers, beginning with Kant, based their critical inquiries upon an extensive familiarity with the best scientific knowledge of their times, many contemporary philosophers, perhaps daunted by the vast and highly-specialised edifice of contemporary science, seem to believe that they can afford to forego the difficult task of acquainting themselves with the methods and results of the sciences altogether.

However, as JAMES LADYMAN makes clear in our interview 'Who's Afraid of Scientism?', it is not only philosophers working in the Continental tradition who are guilty of such negligence. According to Ladyman and Don Ross in their recent book *Every Thing Must Go: Metaphysics Naturalized*,[45] many of the standard debates in contem-porary analytic metaphysics – debates concerning, for

---

44. Thomas Metzinger, *Being No One: The Self-Model Theory of Subjectivity* (Cambridge, Mass.: MIT Press, 2004), 75.

45. James Ladyman and Don Ross with David Spurrett and John Collier, *Every Thing Must Go: Metaphysics Naturalized* (Oxford: Oxford University Press, 2007).

example, causation, identity, part-whole relations, and the nature of time – typically involve little more actual science than was available to the early modern philosophers, or even the pre-Socratics.[46] In this regard, what today passes for metaphysics, whether in the Continental or analytic tradition, amounts to a continuation of what Ladyman and Ross call 'the metaphysics of domestication', a tradition 'which aims at domesticating scientific discoveries so as to render them compatible with intuitive or "folk" pictures of structural composition and causation'.[47] While such efforts at domestication are typically defended on the grounds that they provide *understanding* (read: 'rendering more familiar'), in contrast to science itself, which allegedly allows only for *explanation*, Ladyman and Ross argue that such metaphysics cannot be defended 'on the grounds that psychological repose and cultural familiarity are values that might be defended against the objective truth'.[48] However much 'the objective truth' might always be open to revision and correction, such refinement and extension of our knowledge is itself a process which is *internal* to the ongoing project of science itself, and not something that might be achieved by adopting an imaginary stance of philosophical anteriority floating entirely free of the sciences.

In our interview, Ladyman expresses his exasperation with philosophers unable or unwilling to abandon the constraints of intuition and the manifest image, and who stubbornly insist upon pursuing metaphysics as if modern

---

46. Ibid., 20.

47. Ibid., 1 and Chapter One *passim*.

48. Ibid., 4.

science had never happened. While many philosophers habitually decry any philosophical position that goes beyond a vague science-friendliness as 'scientistic', Ladyman argues forcefully for a radically naturalistic metaphysics based upon what he and Ross have provocatively called 'the scientistic stance'. As well as explaining why he believes it is incumbent upon philosophers to free themselves from the parochial conceptual prejudices devolving from an uncritical embrace of categories rooted in the manifest image, Ladyman also challenges the all too popular *doxa* that would align science with ideological conservatism. While some philosophers may still dream of 'some kind of new age spirituality that will re-enchant nature, de-alienate us and inaugurate some kind of postmodern arcadia', Ladyman argues that 'the actual alternatives to science are the ideologies of bigotry and superstition'.

As one of the leading voices in current debates in the philosophy of science, Ladyman has developed, along with Steven French, a distinctive brand of scientific realism he calls 'ontic structural realism', a position that would synthesize the virtues of empiricism and realism by denying the ontological priority of individual objects and properties in favour of the primacy of relational structures. While structural realism in the philosophy of science goes back at least as far as Henri Poincaré a century ago, Ladyman's position is distinctive inasmuch as it construes structural realism as a metaphysical rather than as a merely epistemological thesis. In other words, while Poincaré held that all that we can *know* are the structures of or relations holding between inscrutable objects in themselves, Ladyman argues that these structures are *all that there is*, thus closing the gap between epistemology and metaphysics entailed by Poincaré's quasi-Kantian position. Motivated as it is not only by the problem of theoretical change in the history of science, but also by reflection upon quantum mechanics and general relativity, one might expect that Ladyman's eliminativism with regard to individual objects and intrinsic properties entails a reductive physicalism. However, the project developed in *Every Thing Must Go*, whilst granting to physics a definite epistemological and ontological priority, aims at a unification of the sciences which proceeds by way of consilience rather than reduction. But how is it possible to defend a physics-based metaphysics which holds that there are no such things as 'things' without impugning the reality of the everyday lifeworld or the special sciences, both of which are of course richly populated with individual objects? This is just one of the questions explored in our interview.

As physics uncovers more and more of a reality which simply does not work according to the models of our intuitive picture of the world, cognitive neuroscience increasingly reveals the extent to which these models themselves depend more upon the nature of our cognitive processing systems than on the world which they purport to represent. In an interview with **THOMAS METZINGER**, we discuss the radical thesis presented in his magnum opus *Being No One* that 'no such things as selves exist in the world: Nobody ever *was* or *had* a self'.[49] Metzinger discusses the bases for and the ramifications of his position, and responds to

---

49. Thomas Metzinger, *Being No One: The Self-Model Theory of Subjectivity* (Cambridge, Mass.: the MIT Press), 1. See also J. Trafford, 'The Shadow of a Puppet Dance', in **COLLAPSE** IV (Falmouth: Urbanomic, 2008), 185-206.

criticisms of his radical eliminativist position with regard to the existence of selves. Like Ladyman, Metzinger too takes philosophers to task for prioritising 'armchair intuitions' about the nature of the mind over scientific discoveries, but also reflects upon the evolutionary provenance of such intuitions; that is, how 'certain forms of self-deception were adaptive and became superbly robust, spilling over into the enterprise of philosophy and science itself'. But if the 'Copernicanism' of neuroscience consists in its subtracting the real substrate of our 'selves' from all intuitive 'visibility', rendering it incongruent with our biologically-inherited patterns of thinking and rebarbative to efforts to 'make sense' of the world and our fellow humans, is there any way for our *cultural* fabric to 'digest' its deliverances? Here, Metzinger proves more than ready to address the potential social and cultural ramifications of his position: Against the frightening possibilities many find in the prospect of an accomplished science of the mind, he argues that, although it will inevitably entail a profound transformation in our self-understanding, advances such as his self-model theory present potential opportunities for ushering in a new age where society and politics can be informed by scientific discovery: 'Enlightenment 2.0'.

This question of the 'toxicity' of Copernican thought makes explicit the connection between this volume's theme and that of its predecessor, with its suggestion that between the adventures of reason and the comfort of intuition may lurk 'concept horrors' best explored in the imaginings of writers and artists.[50] Painter **NIGEL COOKE**'s

---

50. See **COLLAPSE** IV. Readers who enjoyed the perspective suggested by this volume may be interested to hear of R. Scott Bakker's *Neuropath* (London: Orion, 2008),

contribution gives us a glimpse of the territory in-between the two volumes. Over the last decade, Cooke's massive canvases have introduced their viewers to an 'interzone' of representation, where painting enters into a dialogue with its past that eschews the progressive dialectic of artistic modernism. With formal ingenuity and wit Cooke has invented a mode of landscape painting that depicts the landscape of representation itself, a plane of uneasy coexistence (cartoon vegetables suck disconsolately on cigarettes alongside severed heads smiling up from the undergrowth, before vast walls which serve as a support for weeping graffiti brains ...) whose effect is to disturb and parody received notions of the relative sophistication, meaning and value of images. The contemporary painter, suggests Cooke, faces an objectively 'moronic and hysteri-cal'[51] situation which can be transmuted into opportunity only through a concerted complicity with its groundless condition. Accordingly, Cooke's latest works, exhibited as 'New Accursed Art Club', found the character of 'The Painter' himself absorbed into the canvas, as a vagrant stumbling through the remains of representation, a derelict motif encompassed in his own disorienting predicament. The new paintings Cooke has made for this volume of COLLAPSE, entitled 'Thinker Dejecta', are haunted by a close relative of this shambolic figure – The Thinker, overbur-dened and undermined by what Julian Barbour describes as 'a journey into the totally unknown, in which shock

---

a 'techno-thriller' inspired by Metzinger's work, which prompted Metzinger himself to warn, in hyperbolic mode: 'You should think twice before reading this – there could be some scientific and philosophical possibilities you don't want to know!'

51. See the absorbing interview with Cooke in S. Malik, D. Leader, N. Cooke, and S. Goetz, *Nigel Cooke: Paintings 01-06* (London: Koenig Books, 2006).

follows shock', slogging on with an intellectual labour that only ever seems to bring him further down in the world. Nonplussed by the puzzling connection between his lofty intellectual flights and the degeneration of his condition, Cooke's thinker drifts in a wasteland, Kant's 'rational delight'[52] a distant memory, while a psychotic sun (recalling Shawcross's experiments in helio-eccentrism) beats down mercilessly on his fevered brow. As in Cooke's other work, the density of reflection compacted into these apparently cartoonish vignettes indexes the entangled motivations, glories and disorienting turns of philosophical thought, that enigmatic mélange of hubris, masochism, and addiction: A compulsion, Cooke suggests, whose crowning insight will be that man was ever its confused instrument rather than its master.

While many philosophers, especially those unacquainted with philosophy of science, assume that naturalism (or 'scientism') entails a radical kind of physicalist reductionism which is constitutively incapable of doing justice to the manifest image of the *Lebenswelt*, as James Ladyman makes clear, and as biologist **JACK COHEN** and mathematician **IAN STEWART** also affirm in our interview 'Alien Science', scientific realism does not necessarily entail impugning the status of everyday macroscopic objects. Cohen and Stewart's collaboration has produced a series of popular science books which are remarkable in their scope, epistemological subtlety and conceptual inventiveness. Much of their work has consisted in a close examination of the development in recent decades of the sciences of chaos and complexity, which seek to systematically account for

52. See Kant, 'On Creation ...', this volume, 399.

the 'emergence' of high-level natural properties on the basis of the abstract microphysical principles described by modern science. It seems that reductionism alone cannot do justice to these macroscopic patterns, which retain a certain autonomy from their component parts, but the precise nature of their 'emergence' remains a vexed question. While Ladyman prefers to avoid the fuzzy term 'emergence' altogether, Cohen and Stewart have sought to develop a theory of emergence that avoids the invocation of any 'magical' properties that would not be fully causally determined by their underlying microphysical properties. Against the accusation that emergentism privileges those features which happen to be phenomenologically available to human beings, they insist that, far from being an anthropomorphic notion, emergentism rather registers our ignorance of the underlying mechanisms. If much of what we perceive is the result of the 'quick and dirty feature-detection systems' of the brain, this is only one of the ways in which nature, of which the human brain/mind is a part, 'collapses' the underlying chaos. Crucially for Cohen and Stewart, it is not only the human brain that perceives nature in terms of high-level structures and features: Just as the scientist singles out specific features of Mars, such as its orbit, position and mass, and models those features mathematically as a curve, a point and a number respectively, so does the sun 'see' Mars as a concentrated mass exerting a gravitational force, rather than as a collection of atoms and force vectors.[53] The human brain is a part of the natural world and the way in which it 'caricatures' the things which

---

53. Jack Cohen and Ian Stewart, *The Collapse of Chaos: Discovering Simplicity in a Complex World* (London: Penguin Books, 1994), 430.

it comes into contact with is not unique to it. This recalls a position familiar to readers of **COLLAPSE**, as Graham Harman has developed in previous volumes the argument that with an understanding of this 'caricaturing' one can prosecute realism in the macroscopic domain.[54] However, while Harman continues to reserve a special place for an a priori metaphysics which would treat of 'the same world as that of the various sciences but in a different manner',[55] and holds the categories of the manifest world to retain an ontological primacy over the discoveries of science, the work of Ladyman and Cohen and Stewart alike seems to suggest a metaphysics developed entirely on the basis of the deliverances of the sciences, without need for any such metaphysical 'overlay'.

As well as recounting the origins and significance of the key conceptual innovations of their co-authored works ('complicity', 'Ant Country', 'privilege', 'extelligence', etc.), and discussing the relationship of their work to philosophy, in our interview Cohen and Stewart also explain their criticisms of what they see as the overly conservative and unimaginative nature of much of contemporary astrobiology and cosmology. If, according to Rovelli, the strength of science 'resides not in any putative certainties uncovered, but rather *in a radical awareness of our ignorance*', one of the ways which contemporary cosmology has attempted to take into account the intrinsic limitations of the human perspective has been in terms of what is known as 'anthropic

---

54. See Harman's 'Vicarious Causality', in R. Mackay (ed.), **COLLAPSE** II (Oxford: Urbanomic, 2007), 171-205 ', and 'On the Horror of Phenomenology: Lovecraft and Husserl', in **COLLAPSE** IV, op. cit., 333-64.

55. 'Vicarious Causality', op. cit., 174.

reasoning', which aims to rigorously take into account the fact that our evidence about the universe is restricted by the conditions which must be in place for us to be there to observe it in the first place. As Barrow and Tipler have pointed out, the Copernican revolution itself was initiated by the application of what is known as the 'weak anthropic principle': Copernicus rendered redundant the hypothesis of epicycles by explaining that the retrograde motion of the planets was due to the 'anthropic selection effect' consequent upon the fact that we were observing the planetary motion from the vantage point of the moving earth.[56] Subsequent to Brandon Carter's invention of the term 'anthropic principle' in the early seventies, an increasing number of scientists have turned to anthropic reasoning in order to account for the extreme unlikelihood of the advent of life and intelligence which seems to follow from the 'fine-tuned' nature of the fundamental physical constants of our universe. However, Cohen and Stewart have long been critical of the very idea that our universe is in any way 'fine-tuned', and in our interview they explain their charge that the very notion rests on little more than 'bad logic'.

While Cohen and Stewart are vitriolically dismissive of the very idea of the putative 'fine-tuning' of our universe, astrophysicist **MILAN ĆIRKOVIĆ** remains unconvinced by their criticisms, which he regards as being largely based upon the outdated idea that anthropic reasoning is necessarily teleological and anthropocentric. In his 'Sailing the Archipelago', Ćirković sketches the philosophical foundations for an epistemologically and

---

56. Barrow and Tipler, *The Cosmological Anthropic Principle* (Oxford: Oxford University Press, 1986), 3-4.

scientifically sophisticated approach to anthropic reasoning and fine-tuning which, while acutely aware of the kinds of problems emphasized by Cohen and Stewart, does not lead to the conclusion that anthropic reasoning is forlorn. Against the accusation that anthropic reasoning necessarily entails an anti-Copernican privileging of *Homo sapiens*, or of terrestrial, carbon-based life as the only possible kind, Ćirković begins his inquiries by taking seriously the idea that our own universe is only one region of a possibly infinite multiverse, thus 'dealing with the widest conceivable ensemble in which our universe can be embedded, in order to avoid assigning it any special status'. If during the history of science since the Copernican revolution we have witnessed the loss of special status for ever-wider and more encompassing environments, Ćirković suggests that now, in the twenty-first century, 'we should not be surprised to learn that there is nothing special about the whole of our cosmological domain – our universe – either'.

Comparing contemporary cosmologists, astrophysicists and astrobiologists to the great explorers of the European Age of Exploration, Ćirković argues that the fact that earlier voyages had come to the premature conclusion that our island is the only habitable one in no way suggests that the voyage itself is misbegotten: If they were wrong, it was not because of 'some ulterior and heinous agenda [...] [I]t was perfectly reasonable for them to think so – we might compare their rationality to that of a hypothetical ancient philosopher of Easter Island, pondering the huge ocean surrounding his home'. If we think of the range of possible parameters governing the laws of physics as describing a landscape of 'possible universes', then, Ćirković suggests, we have so far only charted the very small 'island' that is 'habitable' for us. However, this does not mean that we live on the *only* island in this space, or that the type of life for which our universe appears to be 'fine-tuned' is the only type of life possible. If a little humility is appropriate, argues Ćirković, given that we are only beginning to chart this vast topography, it would be absolutely premature to conclude that we are its only possible inhabitants.

While the detractors continue to accuse anthropic reasoning of anti-Copernicanism, Ćirković finds in their criticisms the relics of a Cartesian dualism which fails to take into account the fact that human bodies are 'measuring instruments whose self-selection properties *must* be taken into account, just as astronomers *must* take into account the self-selection properties of optical telescopes'.[57] After all, if the human animal is fully a part of the natural world which science investigates, having evolved through various physical, chemical and biological processes, how can one justify ignoring their properties, or failing to take into account the very special nature of the conditions which had to be in place for those properties to evolve in the first place? Is all science which takes account of the nature of human beings *eo ipso* 'subjective' or 'anthropocentric', or might it not rather be the case that science *needs* to mention human

---

57. 'Such telescopes tell us about the radiation in the visible band of the electromagnetic spectrum, but it would be completely illegitimate to conclude from purely optical observations that all of the electromagnetic energy in the Universe is in the visible band. Only when one is aware of the self-selection of optical telescopes is it possible to consider the possibility that non-visible radiation exists. Similarly, it is essential to be aware of the self-selection which results from us being *Homo sapiens* when trying to draw conclusions about the nature of the Universe.' (Barrow and Tipler, *The Anthropic Cosmological Principle*, op. cit., 3-4).

beings in order to *be* objective?[58] Thus, far from being a prop to human self-importance, a 'reactivation [of] finalist thought', or a reversion to the doctrine of Copernicus' own teleological anthropology (as Quentin Meillassoux argued in an earlier volume of **COLLAPSE**),[59] Ćirković's work demonstrates how anthropic thinking merely stems from a deepening of the 'Copernican imperative' which imposes itself once physics begins to consider landscapes of physical possibility beyond the actual universe. Thus, contrary to the critics' charges, the anthropic programme of the investigation of observation selection effects, far from amounting to a 'betrayal of the Enlightenment', is rather 'the continuation of the Copernican revolutionary spirit in overcoming not only the apparent specialness of the Earth and of life on it, including humans, but of the very special laws, associated mathematical structures, and our universe in general'. While it may take generations of astrobiologists before quantitative precision is reached, Ćirković argues that the enormity of the task 'should not detract from the fact that the problem is a well-defined one from the start'.

Whereas Cohen and Stewart enthuse about the possibility of the discovery of alien life – '[f]inding aliens (even bacteria) would be fantastic [; c]omplex aliens, at the level of a snail, would be amazing [; t]he level of intelligence of a cat – awe-inspiring' – transhumanist philosopher

---

58. This is a point forcefully made by Sherrilyn Roush in her excellent 'Copernicus, Kant, and the anthropic cosmological principles' in *Studies in the History and Philosophy of Modern Physics* 34 (2003), 5-35. This paper also sheds further helpful light on many of the connections between Copernicanism, Kantianism, and anthropic reasoning explored in this volume.

59. Q. Meillassoux 'Potentiality and Virtuality', in R. Mackay (ed.) **COLLAPSE II** (Oxford: Urbanomic, 2007), 55-81, 78.

NICK BOSTROM argues in 'Where Are They?' that such findings, far from being a cause for celebration, would in fact augur very badly for the future of the human race. Bostrom's work as an analyst of 'existential risk' here dovetails with his work on anthropic thinking, as he unravels the consequences that would follow from such a discovery. Were traces of life discovered elsewhere in our solar system – on Mars, say, or upon Jupiter's moon Europa – most people would of course be thrilled, perhaps even comforted to learn that we are not entirely alone in the cosmos. However, for Bostrom, no such news could be good news, and indeed the more complex life we found, the more depressing that news would be. On the basis of two well-known facts – namely, that our galaxy alone harbours billions of potential germination points for life, and yet that decades-worth of searching for traces of extraterrestrial life has consistently failed to detect any signs of intelligent life – Bostrom argues that there must exist a 'Great Filter' that renders the existence of advanced technological civilisations exceptionally improbable. The crucial question then becomes where this Great Filter might be located. If it is located in our evolutionary past, this would be good news, since it would suggest that the great fluke which ushered us into existence had already taken place. However, should we ever find evidence of life on other planets, and especially were we to find it to have independently evolved somewhere in our own solar neighbourhood, this would of course suggest that life is commonplace, meaning that the Great Filter still awaits us: a prospect that would leave our future chances of survival looking very bleak indeed.

Speaking about his early exposure to physics and mathematics, artist **KEITH TYSON** has said: 'once I could see myself as part of a network everything became clearer'.[60] But in using the structures of scientific experience to 'explore the myth of individuality', he adamantly maintains his right to creatively transform them. His work thus marries a keen attentiveness to the concepts of contemporary science with a tendency to appropriate them into conceptual 'machines' to steer his artistic practice, as in projects such as *Geno/Pheno* (2005).[61] Refusing to grant scientific conceptualisation any overarching role in his work, he instead sites it within a broader, transversal network of ideas whose dazzling multiplicity is reflected in works such as 2006's *Large Field Array*. This work – whose title adverts to the Very Large Array on the plains of San Agustin, New Mexico, where twenty-seven massive radio telescopes combine their multiple viewpoints to produce high-resolution astrophysical imaging – consists of a 'rhizome' or 'huge soup' of elements arrayed in a vast grid according to lines of affinity traced by Tyson himself, and reflecting his own multiple interests, memories and experiences. Thus Tyson extends the cosmological ambition to address 'everything' to extra-physical forces: 'We are the things that are carrying those forces. Including history. Including energy. All sorts of fields. So everything is the sum of all possible paths. And that's what [*Large Field Array*] is about. All those intricate interrelations.'

The conceit of Tyson's contribution to **COLLAPSE** lies in making a short series of images stand for a similarly

60. K. Tyson *Studio Wall Drawings 1997-2007* (London: Haunch of Venison, 2007), 2.

61. See K. Tyson *Geno/Pheno* (NY: Pace Wildenstein, 2005).

megalomaniacal ambition – that of employing the entire history of the universe as a pool of 'time-based media'. The work draws upon the Einsteinian model of four-dimensional spacetime, or 'blocktime' – Tyson explains: 'If we accept blocktime as a working model in which any position in time, space and possibility is a frame within a 3D animation, we could splice together single frames in the celestial cutting room as a kind of random sampler'. Ironically, the presentation of such an 'animation' as a series of stills on the page is all the more apt given Julian Barbour's thesis of the 'unreality of time', entailing as it does a modification of Einsteinian blocktime whereby Tyson's 'animation' would cease to be animated at all. Meanwhile, the inclusion in the images delivered by his 'random splicing' of disproportionately many images of our planet is perhaps as unlikely ('uncopernican') as it is comforting: but, as Tyson – an erstwhile gambler – has said, he doesn't believe in chance, or at least only as a name for a human constraint which is there to be explored. Here again, the universal reach of science is twinned with a sanguine acceptance of the artist's own unique location in time, space and history.[62]

Of course, for many philosophers the notion of 'Copernicanism' as entailing a subtraction of scientific knowledge from the conditions of intuition will seem utterly alien. For 'Copernicanism' in philosophy has become a byword for what is in effect understood, in Kant, to be a recentring of the universe precisely around the power of cognitive synthesis harboured by the knowing subject. By making phenomenal reality orbit around a transcendental subject

---

62. 'The Wu Way', interview with Dominic van den Boogard, available online at http://www.keithtyson.com/#/projects/largefieldarray/writings/.

which is supposedly distinct from and yet indissociable from the human subject, Kant is deemed to have inaugurated what Quentin Meillassoux has recently denounced as a 'Ptolemaic counter-revolution' that re-installed human experience at the centre from which Copernicanism had displaced it.[63] However, in his 'The Phoenix of Nature: Kant and the Big Bounce', **MARTIN SCHÖNFELD** presents us with a vivid picture of Kant profoundly at odds with this recent popular characterisation of him as a conservative, anti-Copernican thinker, by way of an examination of his 1755 work *Universal History of Nature and Theory of the Skies*.[64] Here we encounter a radically anti-anthropocentric, anti-Christian, naturalistic, and speculatively audacious Kant who pushes 'Copernicanism' to its limits, abolishing the hand of God from the Newtonian cosmos and introducing history and evolution into it. This is Kant as the Copernican revolutionary who as early as 1755 strongly anticipates the fundaments of what became the Standard Model of modern cosmology only in the 1920s. More specifically, Schönfeld introduces the reader to an undeservedly neglected idea from Kant's early cosmology ('the Phoenix of Nature'), one which takes on surprising significance in view of the very latest hypotheses and findings of contemporary (quantum loop) cosmology: 'the Big Bounce'.

---

63. See Quentin Meillassoux, *After Finitude: An Essay on the Necessity of Contingency*, Tr. R. Brassier (London and New York: Continuum 2008), Chapter Five.

64. It is strongly recommended that this essay be read in connection with Schönfeld's more in-depth treatment of Kant's 1755 work and its context in his superb 'Kant's Early Cosmology' in G. Bird (ed.), *A Companion to Kant* (Oxford: Blackwell, 2006), 47-62. See also Schönfeld's *The Philosophy of the Young Kant* (Oxford: Oxford University Press, 2000), and his entry for the *Stanford Encyclopedia of Philosophy*, 'Kant's Philosophical Development', online at http://plato.stanford.edu/entries/kant-development/

To accompany his piece, Schönfeld also provides a new translation of the chapter from the *Universal History of Nature* in which the Phoenix of Nature appears: 'On Creation in the Total Extent of its Infinity in Space and Time'. This work will certainly come as a surprise to those familiar only with Kant's critical works, or with a contemporary *doxa* aligning Kant unproblematically with an idealism that is constitutively incapable of breaking out of the 'correlational circle' in order to take the measure of the 'Great Outside'.[65] Its astonishingly prescient cosmology of 'island universes' and the birth and death of 'worlds' presents a truly awe-inspiring vision of the cosmos, thought-provoking even to those familiar with the latest developments in astrophysics. Popper called the *Universal History of Nature* 'one of the greatest contributions ever made to cosmology and cosmogony',[66] and as Schönfeld notes, Kant's daring conjectures have been to a significant extent vindicated in their general outlines by modern cosmology.

Embarking as it does upon what Kant, with tangible enthusiasm, calls 'the greatest and most awesome subject imaginable',[67] the *Universal History of Nature* sketches what Blumenberg calls 'a monumental panorama of the endless evolution of worlds, still from the point of view of a faculty of reason that, so to speak, adopts the standpoint of divinity and identifies itself with the divine view of the world'.[68]

---

65. Again, see Meillassoux, *After Finitude*, op. cit.

66. Popper, *Conjectures and Refutations*, op. cit., 240.

67. From the Preface of *Universal Natural History and Theory of Heaven*, trans. Ian Johnston, available online at http://records.viu.ca/~johnstoi/kant/kant2e.htm.

68. Hans Blumenberg, *The Legitimacy of the Modern Age* (Cambridge, Mass.: MIT Press, 1985), 212. The following passage contains several close paraphrases of Blumenberg's text; sources are indicated in the footnotes.

Here man appears, 'among the immense vortices of the self-propagating worlds, as but an ephemeral episode. This whole infinite extravagance of a "world of worlds", of galaxies and supergalaxies, is conceived in relation to omnipotence, as the latter's demonstration of itself to itself'.[69] Though still partially in thrall to the teleological metaphysics of the 'great chain of being', and speaking of 'degrees of perfection', it is clear that Kant sees no connection between man's history and this process of improvement. Whereas Romantic thinkers such as Friedrich Schlegel took the unfinished nature of the world to indicate that man's vocation was to play a role in completing it, for Kant there is no such anthropocentric teleology in play. That the world is ever 'unfinished' has nothing to do with human action but is due to its having been created by an inexhaustible power, which Kant speaks of, in Spinozistic fashion, as either 'God' or 'Nature'. Man, 'who seems to be the masterpiece of creation', finds his place with the 'world of worlds' precisely where there is an already 'perfected world structure', among others still in the process of coming into being or disintegrating.[70] In a startling anticipation of Ćirković's position, Kant holds that the universe is not made for man, but that the infinite process of the evolution of worlds creates temporary 'habitable zones'. Habitability is not a lasting and ubiquitous feature of the bodies of the universe, but is only the result of the fact that the total reality, in analogy to the distribution of habitability on the earth, also has its 'temperate zones'.[71]

69. Ibid.

70. Ibid., 212-3.

71. Blumenberg, *The Genesis of the Copernican World*, op. cit., 591.

As Kant explains in one of his letters, it was the cosmological problem of the finitude or infinitude of the universe
that led him to his theory of knowledge in the first *Critique*,[72]
and as Schönfeld suggests, one should not underestimate
the degree of continuity between this early work and the
later critical philosophy. This is borne out by a comparison
of the two passages below, the first from the *Universal History
of Nature*, the second from the *Critique of Pure Reason*:

If the size of a planetary system in which the Earth is hardly
seen as a grain of sand fills the understanding with astonish-
ment, how delightfully astounded we will be when we examine
the infinite crowd of worlds and systems which fill the totality
of the Milky Way. But how much greater this wonder when we
know that all these immeasurable arrangements of stars once
again create a numbered unity, whose end we do not know and
which is perhaps, like the previous one, inconceivably large
and yet, once again, only a unit in a new numbered system. We
see the first links of a progressive relationship of worlds and
systems, and the first part of this unending progression already
allows us to recognize what we are to assume about the totality.
Here there is no end, but an abyss of a true infinity, in which all
capacity of human thought sinks, even when it is uplifted with
the help of mathematics.[73]

The observations and calculations of astronomers have taught
us much that is wonderful; but the most important lesson that
they have taught is has been by revealing the abyss of our
ignorance, which otherwise would never have been conceived
to be so great. Reflection on the ignorance thus disclosed must

72. As noted by Popper, *Conjectures and Refutations*, op. cit., 240-1.

73. *Universal Natural History and Theory of Heaven*, op. cit., Part One, 'On the Systematic
Arrangement of the Fixed Stars'.

produce a great change in our estimate in the purposes for which our reason should be employed.[74]

If Rovelli suggests that the problem is that we 'use concepts that we have developed in our very special environment (characterized by low velocities, low energy ...) and we think the world as if it was all like that',[75] this is also a sentiment shared by Kant, who puts the order and structure we see down to 'anthropic' considerations regarding our spatial and temporal location in the universe. Whereas 'from our perspective in the Universe, it would seem as if we looked at wholly completed creation and, so to speak, at an infinite array of systematically connected world-orders [...] if we could step outside this evolved sphere, we would see chaos' and a 'random scattering of elements'.[76] Similarly, in Part Three of *Universal History of Nature*, itself devoted to speculations regarding the inhabitants of other planets, Kant compares the worldview of human beings with that of a louse inhabiting the head of a vagrant:

Let us judge in an unprejudiced manner. This insect, which in its way of living as well as in its lack of worth expresses very well the condition of most human beings, can be used for such a comparison with good results. Since, according to the louse's imagination, nature is endlessly well suited to its existence, it considers irrelevant all the rest of creation which does not have a precise goal related to its species as the central point of nature's purposes. The human being, who similarly stands

---

74. *Critique of Pure Reason*, op. cit., A575/B603.

75. *Edge: World Question Center*, Annual Question 2006: 'What is Your Dangerous Idea?', op. cit.

76. See Kant, 'On Creation ...', this volume, 396.

infinitely far from the highest stages of being, is sufficiently bold to flatter himself with the same imaginative picture of his existence as essential.[77]

It should be borne in mind that Kant never completely abandoned even some of the most speculative views expressed in the *Universal History of Nature*. Thus, in the celebrated conclusion of the *Critique of Practical Reason* he speaks of 'an unbounded magnitude with worlds upon worlds and systems of systems',[78] and in the *Critique of the Power of Judgement* likewise of 'the Milky Way, and the immeasurable multitude of such Milky Way systems, called nebulae'.[79] Indeed, as **IAIN HAMILTON GRANT** points out in his 'Prospects for Post-Copernican Dogmatism', it would be a matter of considerable irony if a *soi-disant* 'Copernican' revolution in philosophy should have put an end to the project of a *Universal History of Nature*. However, there is of course no doubt that the critical philosophy brought about a hugely significant transformation in Kant's epistemological approach, and in this regard Grant suggests that the 'dogmatism' against which Kant contrasts his critical conception of philosophy is none other than the naturalism of his own 'pre-critical' writings. This raises a number of important questions regarding the relationship between transcendental philosophy and a naturalistic ontology, questions which are skilfully examined in Grant's paper.

77. *Universal Natural History and Theory of Heaven*, op. cit., Part Three, 'An Attempt, Based On Natural Analogies, at a Comparison Between the Inhabitants of Different Planets'.

78. *Critique of Practical Reason* (Cambridge: Cambridge University Press, 1997), 133 [*Ak*: 162].

79. *Critique of the Power of Judgement* (Cambridge: Cambridge University Press, 2000), 140 [*Ak*: 256].

Exploring the paradoxes and antinomies that result from the attempted combination of transcendental philosophy and a physics-based ontology as it arises in Kant and post-Kantianism, Grant finds transcendental philosophy, as defended by both Kant and Fichte, to be itself 'dogmatic' according to its very own criteria. Taking into account Kant's late revisions of his critical philosophy in the light of advances in the natural sciences, Grant argues that transcendentalism's susceptibility to naturalistically driven ontological change inevitably pushes a rationally consistent transcendental philosophy in the direction of Schelling's 'transcendental naturalism'.

In 'A Throw of the Quantum Dice Will Never Overturn the Copernican Revolution', GABRIEL CATREN also draws upon Schelling's *Naturphilosophie* in proposing what he calls a 'speculative overcoming' of recent quasi-Kantian interpretations of quantum mechanics. Rather than being limited to a mathematical account of the correlations between 'observed' systems and their 'observers', or pointing to the inherent 'transcendental limits' of physical knowledge, Catren argues that quantum mechanics furnishes a complete and realistic description of the intrinsic properties of physical systems, an ontology which exemplifies the Copernican deanthropomorphisation of nature. While Catren is sympathetic to Quentin Meillassoux's suggestion that Kant's Copernican revolution ultimately eventuated in a kind of 'Ptolemaic Counter-Revolution', and argues for an explicitly 'pre-critical' approach to the interpretation of quantum mechanics, he is also severely critical of Meillassoux's a priori arguments regarding 'necessary contingency'. Indeed, Catren finds Meillassoux guilty of recapitulating a paradigmatic gesture of 'Kantian' critique: that is, of presuming to stipulate, in purely philosophical terms, what physicists will never be able to do. Through an ingenious appropriation of resources from the history of philosophy and the models of mathematical physics, Catren succeeds in providing an interpretation of quantum mechanics that seems able to satisfy the often mutually-exclusive requirements of philosophical intelligibility *and* mathematical coherence. While Catren's interpretation is doubtless controversial in its suggestion that it enables us to recover the 'classical' notions of 'decontextualised objects' and 'intrinsic properties' from within quantum mechanics – a thesis which would seem to run directly counter to the kind of interpretation developed by the likes of Ladyman – there is no doubt that Catren's essay presents a challenging thesis, and outlines a project for a 'speculative physics' that deserves to be followed closely.

If in Cooke's errant figure of the dejected cognitive labourer wandering a scorched earth we see the human thinker bent under the epochal 'humiliations' dealt by Copernicus, Darwin and Freud, **ALBERTO GUALANDI** discovers a certain 'errancy of the human' to be the very source of its cognitive prowess. In contrast to Grant and Catren's bold proposals for a Schelling-inspired 'speculative physics' which would push the Copernican deanthropo-morphisation of nature to its limits, Gualandi argues for the need to establish a new 'circular and communicative' theoretical interface between science and philosophy which would be capable of both integrating the natural and the human sciences and overcoming the antinomy between Kant's 'Copernican revolution' and that of Copernicus himself. Exploring the features common to certain speculative philosophies of nature in 1960s France and problems facing current evolutionary biologists, Gualandi introduces a 'neotenic conception of the human animal' capable of taking into account what he calls 'the necessary complementarity between the *critical* and *eccentric* dimension of man'. While it would be impossible to do justice to this superbly rich and thought-provoking paper here, we would note that it brings into focus the many reasons why the notion of 'Copernicanism' is still important for philosophy and for the sciences today, and will certainly repay careful and repeated reading.

Whereas Gualandi insists on the human and embodied nature of all knowledge, and adverts to the unsurpassability of Kant's Copernican revolution, PAUL HUMPHREYS proposes that computational science is fast displacing humans from the centre of the epistemological universe, a revolution which will eventually produce as radical a transformation in our self-image as did the Copernican revolution itself. Beyond the implicitly anthropocentric epistemologies of an empiricism which would limit the knowable to what is accessible to a set of biologically-contingent devices and a realism whose criterion of reality invokes independence from human minds, Humphreys considers the possibility of a purely automated science for which the division between what is and what is not accessible to the human mind would be, ironically, an entirely 'artificial' one. While Kant rejected the idea of obtaining knowledge of the world as it is in itself on the grounds that it would require us to have 'a faculty of knowledge altogether different from the human [...] in other words, that we should be not men but beings of whom we are unable to say whether they are even possible, much less how they are constituted',[80] Humphreys' paper suggests that such beings may already be among us. If we have not yet entirely relinquished the hope of one day being able to 'finally penetrate the barriers that have stood between between us and the rest of reality', Humphreys argues that the sooner we understand how 'some instruments and some computers confront reality non-conceptually' the better. Might not this also prove to be a necessary part of the task of what Metzinger calls 'Enlightenment 2.0'? In this regard, it seems appropriate to close this introduction with a citation from the conclusion to Kant's *Universal History of Nature*: 'We do not really know what the human being truly is today. [...] How much less would we be able to guess what a human being is to become in the future!'

We would like to conclude by offering our most sincere gratitude to all of our contributors and collaborators, whose wholehearted commitment to this project has consistently been above and beyond the call of duty. We hope that the fragments of the 'big picture' assembled in this unique volume will compensate them for their efforts.

Damian Veal,

Mexico City, January 2009.

---

80. *Critique of Pure Reason*, op. cit., A277-8/B333-34.

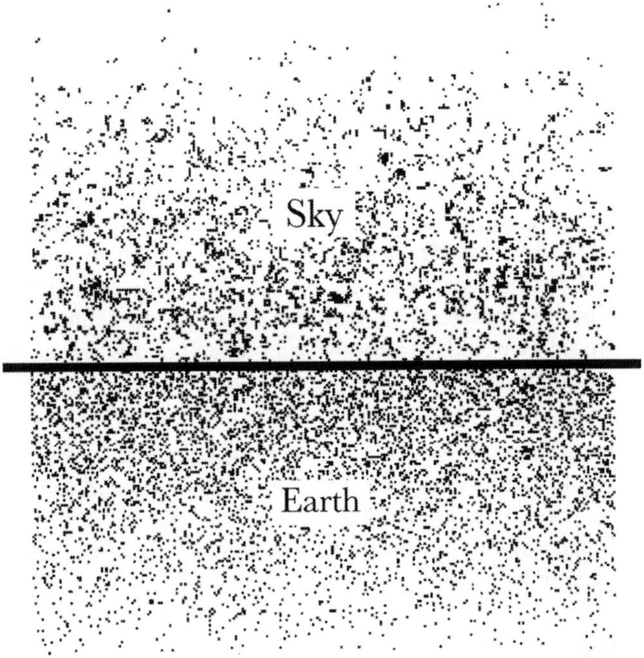

Figure 1

Anaximander's Legacy[1]

Carlo Rovelli

I. ANAXIMANDER

It all started twenty-six centuries ago, on the coast of what is now Turkey. Every civilization in the world had an image of the world like that in Fig. 1: *Up* there is the sky, *down* there is the Earth. Below the Earth, to prevent it from falling, there is more Earth. Or else a turtle standing upon an elephant, as in some Asian myths; or maybe gigantic columns, like those mentioned in the Bible. This was the picture of the world common to the civilizations of Egypt, Babylon, India, China, Africa; as well as to the Jews of the Old Testament, the natives of Australia and North America, the Mayans, the Incas, and every other ancient culture of which we have a trace.

---

1. Freely extracted from the forthcoming book, *Anaximander of Miletus and the Nature of Scientific Thinking*. (Text revised by Ray Brassier and Damian Veal.)

Then came a man, living in Miletus, who suggested something else: the world is rather more like this:

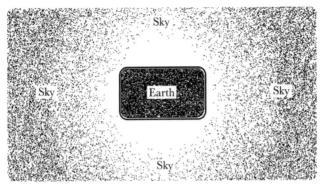

Figure 2

That is, the sky is not just above us: it is all around us, including below us. The Earth is not the lower half of the universe: it a big stone, floating in the middle of the sky without falling. The man who proposed this major change in our understanding of the world was Αναξιμανδρος, Anaximander. In a rather short time, Anaximander's idea is recognized as correct. Only a generation later, Pythagoras, or someone of his school, improves upon the model by making the Earth spherical (an easy move, after Anaximander's step). Another couple of generations later and Plato, in the *Phaedo*, presents the idea as the most reasonable one and shortly after Aristotle proposes very convincing arguments, based upon observations, in support of the idea. The idea becomes universally accepted around the Mediterranean, and subsequently by all other civilizations, one by one, as they come into contact with it.

How was Anaximander able to make this gigantic leap in our understanding of the world? At first sight, it doesn't seem too hard: evidence abounds. For instance, the Sun sets in the west in the evening and reappears in the east in the morning: so where does it go? More precisely, if we observe a starry night, we see all the stars rotating slowly and magnificently around the Polar star. Some stars, close to the Pole star, are always up in the sky; others, a bit further away, hide for a while beyond far-away mountains; still others disappear for a short while beyond the horizon, only to reappear a little further east. Isn't it rather obvious that there must be empty space, down there, so they can keep going?

Image: © Josch Hambsch

But if it was so obvious, why did it take until Anaximander to understand that the sky above us continues below us? Civilization had existed for millennia by Anaximander's time. Why had nobody realized this earlier?

Why had no-one among the Egyptians, or Babylonians, or Jews, all undoubtedly clever people, noticed this? Why had the Chinese, with their splendid civilization and with several millennia of the Imperial Astronomical Institute, failed to understand that the Earth floats in the sky, so that they had to wait until as late as the seventeen-century, when Jesuit astronomers arrived in China, to realize it? Evidently, this was not such an easy step to take. So why was it so hard?

Because it contradicts common-sense. If there is nothing below the Earth, why doesn't the Earth fall? Anaximander's genius, and the reason why he was able to convince the world of his idea, consisted in coming up with an answer to the obvious objection to the idea of a floating Earth. His answer was marvellous: The Earth does not fall, because it has no *reason* to fall; things fall 'towards the Earth', but the Earth itself has no preferred direction or any special reason to fall. In other words, Anaximander proposed a completely new grammar for understanding the spatial structure of the universe. There is no longer a universal 'up' and 'down' (Fig. 3) – rather, 'up' and 'down' are *relative* to the Earth (Fig. 4). Things fall towards the Earth itself. Hence the Earth itself has no special reason, or preferred direction, for falling.

Anaximander's greatness consists in this: Starting from remarkably little, he redraws the entire cosmos. He transforms the very grammar of the way we understand the universe, subverting the meaning of 'up' and 'down', which had provided the most intuitive and elementary way of organising space and reality for countless generations of humans hitherto.

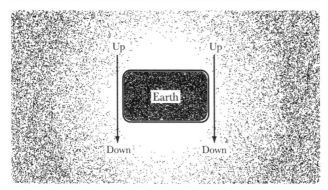

Figure 3

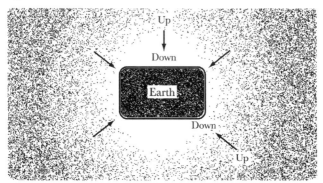

Figure 4

No, says Anaximander: *Things are not as they appear to us.* The world differs from the way it seems at first sight. Common sense is deeply misleading. Our intuitions are based upon our limited experience: Think more openly, look further away. There is no 'up' or 'down' in the universe; only in our little garden do things seem to be that way.

When properly utilized, reason liberates us from our partial and limited point of view, profoundly restructuring our understanding of the world. This is what science does.

Anaximander's idea that the Earth is in fact floating in the middle of the sky alone would suffice to make him one of the most decisive figures in the entire history of human thought. But in fact his heritage is considerably broader than that. Anaximander also paves the way for astronomy, geography, meteorology and biology. With Thales, he initiates the naturalistic enquiry which, over the centuries, will slowly evolve into modern science. More importantly, however, in doing so he also inaugurates the very process of *rethinking the image of the world* – the path of investigation of the world which is based on the rebellion against what appears obvious; the recognition that knowledge begins with the realisation that common sense can be misleading. In this regard, Anaximander is one of the major wellsprings of all scientific and, more generally, rational thinking.

II. WHAT IS SCIENTIFIC THINKING?

Scientific thinking is a passionate exploration of new ways of conceiving the world. Its strength resides not in any putative certainties uncovered, but in *a radical awareness of our ignorance*. It is this awareness that allows us to continuously question what we think we know, and thereby to learn more. Such thinking is fluid and capable of continuous evolution. It has the capacity to subvert the order of things and to continuously redraw the world.

Scientific theories are not arbitrary constructions whose only truth content lies in their verifiable and verified consequences. Rather, they are the eyes through which we view and understand the world. Science can neither be grounded in, nor its truth-value reduced to, its verifiable predictions – nor to its hypothetical-deductive method, or to its operational protocols. Quantitative predictions, calculations, techniques, operations, falsifications ... all these are *tools*: important and incisive tools; pieces of evidence; instruments of clarity; ways to try to avoid mistakes; techniques to detect false assumptions; and so on. But they are only *tools*, and only some of the tools which come into play in science. They serve an intellectual activity whose substance is to be found elsewhere.

Numbers, techniques, predictions and calculations are all indispensable for suggesting, for testing, for validating, for confirming, and for utilizing discoveries. But there is nothing technical in the content of these discoveries: the Earth floats in space; the cosmos does not pivot around the Earth; matter is made up of protons, electrons and neutrons; there are hundreds of thousands of galaxies in the universe, each made up of hundreds of thousands of stars; rainwater comes from the evaporation of water from seas and rivers (another discovery by Anaximander); fifteen billions years ago the entire visible universe was compressed into a ball of fire; similarities between parents and children are transmitted by a DNA molecule which is carried by each of our cells; our brains comprise a million million synapses that jump when we think; the unlimited complexity of chemistry basically consists in combinations of simple electrical forces between protons and electrons; since all living beings on our small planet have common ancestors, we are related to ladybugs ... These are all *facts* about nature which were deeply counterintuitive for our common-sense worldview not so long ago; facts which have effected a profound change in our vision of the world and of ourselves. Their scope and relevance is vast, direct, and inhuman. This is what science is.

Scientific knowledge is the ongoing process that brings about an in-depth modification of our way of conceptualising the world by selectively questioning our assumptions and beliefs the better to propose new ones that promise to be more effective. Scientific thinking consists in re-drawing the world anew over and over again before our eyes. It is learning how to look further; learning how to conceive and envisage the world differently. Science is primarily an exploration of new forms of thinking.

Thus, before being technical, science is visionary. Anaximander, who was ignorant of mathematics, was the necessary step before we could arrive at the sophisticated mathematical astronomy of Hipparchus and Ptolemy. Nicholas of Cusa and Giordano Bruno opened up the way for Galileo and Hubble. The young Einstein asked what the world would look like if observed while riding a light wave, and told us in his best work of popularization that he saw spacetime as a huge jellyfish. Science is always conjuring up new worlds, before going on to discover that some of these fit reality better than our old prejudices.

Science's reconceptualisation of the world is continuous. The great conceptual revolutions, like those of Anaximander, Copernicus, Darwin or Einstein, are only its most visible moments. But the way in which we structure and conceive our understanding of the world today is profoundly at odds with that of a citizen of Babylon three thousand years ago.

And this transformation is the result of the gradual accumulation of many small modifications. Some of these steps represent definitive acquisitions: We no longer dance when we want it to rain. Others are only partially established: we know that our universe has been expanding rapidly for around fifteen billion years, but some still stubbornly insist that the world has only existed for six thousand or so years simply because the Bible says so. And other steps have been made by the research community, but have yet to become common currency: The structure of spacetime revealed by Einstein's work is quite different from the one with which most of us are familiar. It will take time to adapt, just as it took time to accept Copernicus' discovery. But the world will keep changing around us, as we discover more and more aspects of it. The visionary force of scientific thinking lies in its capacity to see further, and to expose our innumerable prejudices.

But in our attempt to think the world and to uncover hitherto unexpected aspects of it, we never begin entirely from scratch: We are always guided by the enormous amount of knowledge that we have already acquired. Our awareness that there might be something wrong with this knowledge – with the very conceptual structure in terms of which it is formulated – does not alter the fact that this knowledge provides the basis for everything we think and is the source of our intellectual strength. We can only transform it from within; not from the outside. As we compare this knowledge with our ever-changing experience of the world, as we confront different parts of our vast and complex body of knowledge with one another, our knowledge is increased, consolidated and strengthened.

This means that scientific advances are never simply directed against past knowledge: They are always also grounded in it. When Einstein was faced with the problem of the apparent incompatibility between Maxwell's equations and Galilean relativity, he could, in good Kuhnian spirit, easily have dismissed the relativity of velocity; or, alternatively, the universal validity of Maxwell's equations. But that's not what he did. Rather, he steadfastly maintained his faith in the validity of the core factual content of *both* the Galilean and Maxwellian theories – precisely that core factual content which is supposed to change freely at every step forward, in Kuhn's *vulgata*. But Einstein assumed that these theories should be valid well beyond the regime in which they had been tested. The combination of these seemingly contradictory hypotheses was sufficient for him to derive a new synthesis, special relativity; but at the price of dropping a *third* hypothesis, previously always tacitly assumed but never made explicit: that of the absolute value of simultaneity. Until that moment, this third hypothesis had been construed as an *a priori* of thinking, a veritable pillar of common sense.

Einstein did not carry out his revolution by discarding the old theories and proposing a new one. Rather, he carried it through by taking the old theories seriously and by questioning something in the general conceptualisation of the world. He did not proceed by finding new solutions in a game with clearly defined rules, but rather by changing the rules of the game itself.

This is not an isolated example. Copernicus does not abandon Ptolemaic astronomy in order to re-organise the phenomena; rather, he absorbs Ptolemy's system in depth, preserving epicycles and deferents, and it is within the folds of the old theory that he discovers the golden key – something unexpected should be abandoned: the fixity of the Earth. Similarly, Dirac predicts anti-matter on the basis of his faith in special relativity and quantum theory; Newton derives universal gravitation by taking seriously Kepler's third law and Galilean acceleration, virtually without *any* additional empirical input. In Einstein's greatest *coup de génie*, 1915's general theory of relativity, he discovers that spacetime is curved solely on the basis of special relativity and Newtonian gravity. And so on. In all of these examples, it is faith in the factual content of previous theories (the factual content that much contemporary philosophy of science disdains) which leads to discovery. And it is common sense that pays the price at each step.

From this perspective, we cannot identify three centuries of Newtonian science with science *simpliciter*, as we so often do. Rather, the past three centuries have been more like a pause along the way, in the wake of a major success. In questioning Newton's conceptualisation of the world, Einstein did not question our ability to understand reality. He simply made a new beginning upon the existing path; the path that had been that of Maxwell and Faraday, of Newton, of Copernicus, of Ptolemy, of Hipparchus and of Anaximander; questioning over and over again our naïve image of the world in order to keep deepening and refining it; recognising that our common sense is superficial and misleading; that the world is more vast, more beautiful and ultimately more understandable than the little garden of our everyday intuitions. We learn to see further by recognizing our mistakes.

Each of the steps taken by these great figures, as well as those taken by many more minor figures, gradually transforms our image of the world – sometimes in great depth. They can even modify the very rules upon which we base our understanding of the world. At each step, we obtain an improvement in our map of reality, drawn in new colours. At each step, we understand the world a bit better.

Let me briefly return to Anaximander. Among his numerous major contributions to human knowledge, there is one which is purely methodological; one which is perhaps the least evident but also the most far-reaching. Anaximander has a 'Master': Thales. Thales was a major figure in ancient Greece, so revered as to be included in the list of the 'Seven Sages', together with Solon, who wrote the first democratic constitution of Athens, and various other personages that the Greeks considered as their *maîtres à penser*. Anaximander is a follower of Thales: he shares the same interests, the same naturalistic approach to the world, the same topics of investigation ('What is the principle out of which everything is made?'). It is clear that Anaximander's reflection begins from and is deeply rooted in that of Thales. This is not unusual in the ancient world, where great Masters (Confucius, Jesus, Pythagoras ...) often founded influential schools and had famous disciples (Mencius, Paul of Tarsus ...). But although such disciples would sometimes develop and expand the ideas of their Masters, they would certainly never question those ideas. Mencius never questions Confucius. Paul never questions Jesus. Not that criticism was absent from the ancient world: it was very present indeed, and sometimes bloody: just read what the

Bible has to say about Babylon's great culture. But there was no third way between ferocious criticisms and reverential study. This is where Anaximander's attitude towards Thales initiates a new approach. Anaximander accepts Thales' idea that everything in the world consists in a single 'principle', but rejects the idea that this principle could be water, as it was for Thales. He accepts the idea that the Earth might be like a large floating stone, but removes the ocean upon which Thales thought it was floating. And so on ...

This is to say that while Anaximander relies heavily upon Thales' speculation, building upon it, he does not hesitate to declare that Thales is wrong. There is a sophisticated theory of knowledge underlying this attitude: The realization that we can have *valuable* knowledge, but at the same time that this knowledge can be partially wrong; and, in any case, that it can always be improved. In other words, Anaximander realises that knowledge can be uncovered by relying upon what we know, but also by uncovering *mistakes* in what we believe to be true. This is precisely the attitude of any good detective. In adopting it, Anaximander opens up the path for the immense development of subsequent speculation, which is the basis of Greek philosophy and modern science. After Anaximander, Pandora's box is open: Every Greek feels free to challenge the received view and to propose an alternative in what might at first appear to be a cacophony, but is in fact the most spectacular development in the emergence of a formidable array of new and better ways of understanding the world.

III. The Current Revolution and Loop Quantum Gravity

Today, we are in the midst of a reconceptualisation of the world which is likely to prove every bit as far-reaching as those of Anaximander and Copernicus. Einstein's theory has effected a profound transformation in our understanding of what space and time are. Quantum mechanics has effected a profound transformation in our understanding of matter and energy. These theories are now almost a century old, and have been very widely corroborated: they furnish the basis for much modern technology. But we have not yet attained a fully credible theory within which the two theories can be coherently understood in their relation to one another. Our understanding of the world has once more become deeply confused and fragmented. There is currently an ongoing theoretical effort striving to discover the new sought-for synthesis and there are candidate theories which look promising, for instance the theory on which I work, called *loop quantum gravity*.

These theories demand of us, once again, a readiness to transform our understanding of the world in depth. Just as Anaximander asked his contemporaries to accept the idea that the Earth can float without falling, and Copernicus asked his contemporaries to believe that the Earth rotates on itself at great speed, once again our common sense is going to be questioned; once again, we cannot *and must not* rely too much upon our simple intuition, if we want to be able to see deeper into reality. We will have to rely instead upon our observations, our capacity for rational thought, and our imagination. We will have to rely upon our vast body of acquired knowledge about the world, which codes everything we know about it, even as we recognise that several pieces of the story might in fact be wrong. And we will have to keep searching. We have no fixed ground. Our intelligence is our only guide.

General relativity has taught us that space and time form a quasi-material continuum; a field very much like the electromagnetic field: A sort of fluid that suffuses everything. We have learnt with quantum mechanics that all fields, including the spacetime field, must have quantum properties, which means a granular structure and a probabilistic dynamics.

Loop quantum gravity is a tentative mathematical theory for describing this *granular* and *probabilistic* spacetime. The best way to understand it is to think about it as a substance formed by quanta ('atoms of space'), which fluctuate probabilistically and which are not to be thought of as immersed *in* space and evolving *in* time, but rather as what makes up space and whose relations make up time.

The resulting picture of the world is one in which space and time are no longer primary concepts. They are not the 'home' of reality and the 'flow' along which things happen. Rather, they are approximate and derivative concepts, like the concept of temperature or the concept of the surface of a liquid: Concepts which disappear in a more elementary description of reality. *Can we think the world without time?*

IV. Is There No Time in the Future?

Time is the hardest concept to modify in our intuition. We already know all too well from Einstein's work the extent to which our intuition that time flows equally and universally all over the universe is badly misleading: Two twin brothers can travel separately and meet again when they are different ages.

But if our current tentative theories about quantum gravity are correct, we will have to modify a good deal about our concept of time. Indeed, we will have to learn to think the world at its most elementary level (at least for the time being) *without making any reference to the notion of time at all.* This means that we must reinterpret dynamics as a theory of relations between variables, instead of as a theory of the evolution of variables in a preferred independent time-variable.

The only fragment that remains of the book written by Anaximander reads:

εξ ων δε η γενεσις εστι τοις ουσι, και την φθοραν εις
ταυτα γινεσθαι
κατα το χρεων
διδοναι γαρ αυτα δικην και τισιν αλληλοις της αδικιας
κατα την του χρονου ταξιν

Its (disputed) translation is as follows:

All things originated one from the other, and perish the ones into the others,
following necessity
And they render justice to one another, and pay one another for injustice
in conformity with the order of time

Much has been read into this text. It is possible that this is the first enunciation of the idea of natural law. Pythagoras, shortly after, added the remarkable idea that laws must be written in mathematical terms; Plato instructed his students to search for such mathematical laws in the regularities of the heavens, leading to that spectacular scientific success which is Alexandrian astronomy – which, in turn, once revived by Copernicus, paved the way for modern science.

For twenty-six centuries, Anaximander's prescription to search for laws that describe how things change *in time* ('in conformity with the order of time') has been strictly adhered to, and has proved immensely fruitful. But it may be that we now need to challenge even this most fundamental rule of the game: Today, the fundamental physical laws are no longer being sought in the form of laws of evolution in time, but rather in the form of laws of relations between physical variables.

In doing so, we are not betraying Anaximander's legacy, but celebrating it once again: knowledge is not attained by revering the Masters and scrupulously following their lead; it is attained by absorbing at the most profound level what the Masters have to teach, the better to uncover where they might be wrong.

V. What do we Know with Certainty?

If the condition of our search for knowledge is the recognition of the limitation and the uncertainty of our present understanding, where can we find the solid ground upon which to base our certainties?

I think that, notwithstanding the impressive amount of knowledge that we have been able to accumulate so far, there is nothing in our knowledge that is ultimately grounded in a solid bedrock. And it is my opinion that the attempt by philosophical inquiry to unearth a metaphysical or methodological starting-point from which some certain indubitable knowledge could be derived, is misbegotten.

We have learnt that there is no such thing as 'pure experience' – the experience which Bacon elevated into the principle of his new religion of science – capable of grounding certainty. Nor is there any 'pure reason' of the kind upon which Descartes hoped to rely, but which led him to such an erroneous physics. Both Baconian empiricism and Cartesian rationalism had a polemical objective: to supplant the tradition upon which Scholasticism had relied with a new source of epistemic validity. The explosive and liberating power of these philosophies freed thinking from the prison of tradition, reawakening the freedom of ancient Greek inquiry and opening the doors to modernity. This openness to criticism is their immense legacy. But today we know only too well that there is no absolutely certain foundation upon which to ground all our knowledge. Every time we believed ourselves to have uncovered one, we have been disappointed. Neither pure experience, nor pure reason, nor a transcendental inquiry into the conditions of knowledge, nor strict verificationism, nor anything else will be able to provide us with an absolute guarantee against the pervasive influence of our faulty ideas and limited assumptions.

But the antiscientific irrationalism that pervades so much of contemporary culture is, in my opinion, as short-sighted as the eighteenth-century faith in scientific certainties: the lack of certainty is not the weakness of scientific thinking, but rather its strength. Scientific theories are not credible because they are definitive: they are credible because they represent the best knowledge about the world we are able to attain at any given moment. And it is precisely because we refuse to consider them definitive that we are capable of constantly improving them. As John Stuart Mill put it in *On Liberty*:

> The beliefs which we have most warrant for, have no safeguard to rest on, but a standing invitation to the whole world to prove them unfounded.

'Reality' itself is a flimsy notion, but what an effective one! How could we do without it? Our thinking is thinking about reality. We refer to it, relate to it. What else we are dealing with if not reality? Everything we know is something we know about reality. That about which we know – that is reality. It is that which continues to surprise us, to disclose itself to us anew, and about which we imagine there is still so much to learn – perhaps aspects of which we will never learn about or be able to understand. Reality continues to appear to us other than we had thought. And in the evolution of our love story with it lies the growth of our knowledge. It has aspects of a dream but, as in the marvellous words of Hippolyta:[2]

> ... all the story [...] told over,
> And all their minds transfigur'd so together,
> More witnesseth than fancy images,
> And grows to something of great consistency;
> But, howsoever, strange and admirable.

I think that our mistake is to fear this fluidity and to search for certainty. To select a fixed point upon which our restlessness could finally come to rest would be not only naïve, indeed counterproductive for our thirst for knowing; it would be dishonest. Science is the human adventure that consists in exploring novel ways of thinking the world; it should always be ready to subvert any certitude we think we have gained thus far. The fearful side of this adventure consists in fully recognizing and assuming our ignorance. It is my conviction that to accept our ignorance is not only the royal road to knowledge: It is also the most honest and the most beautiful one. The emptiness and the corrigibility that it entails do not make our life and our knowledge less meaningful: They make it more precious. It is an adventure that was begun twenty-six centuries ago, so far as we can tell, by Anaximander – or, if not by him, by somebody else living in Miletus at that time. It is, I think, amongst the most enchanting of human adventures.

And of course, yes: Anaximander was right:

---

2. Shakespeare, A *Midsummer Night's Dream*, V, 1.

Earth seen from Apollo 17 (Image: NASA)

The View from Nowhen

Interview with Julian Barbour

In his first major book, The Discovery of Dynamics (1989), *theoretical physicist and historian of physics Julian Barbour described the process of discovery and progress in science as 'a journey into the totally unknown, in which shock follows shock'.[1] A decade on, in* The End of Time (1999)[2] *he put forth in popular form his thesis, developed over some decades, regarding what he had come to believe would be the next great shock to our commonsense picture of the world – namely, that the concept of time would cease to have any role in the foundations of physics. More starkly expressed, Barbour predicts that the next great revolution in our understanding of the universe will entail the realisation that time does not exist – a thesis which, if true, would be shocking indeed. The question, of course, is whether it is true; and, if it is, how we could ever possibly find a way to test and confirm such a seemingly outrageous hypothesis. In our interview with Barbour, we ask him about the motivations which led him to develop his radical position, the paradoxes and problems which arise in trying to make sense of it, and his own eccentric position in relation to mainstream academic theoretical physics.*

1. Julian Barbour, *The Discovery of Dynamics: A Study from a Machian Point of View of the Discovery and the Structure of Dynamical Theories* (Oxford: Oxford University Press, 2001), 58; originally published as *Absolute or Relative Motion? Vol. 1: The Discovery of Dynamics* (Cambridge: Cambridge University Press, 1989).

2. Julian Barbour, *The End of Time: The Next Revolution in our Understanding of the Universe* (London: Weidenfeld and Nicolson, 1999).

COLLAPSE: Before tackling the details of your thesis regarding time and timelessness, we would like to start by asking you to say something about your own intellectual journey 'into the totally unknown'. Your reading of Ernst Mach's *The Science of Mechanics* in 1963 seems to have been a crucial turning point. You have said that this book made a profound and lasting impression on you, and it's clear that your subsequent intellectual trajectory has been profoundly marked by Mach's ideas. What was it, precisely, about Mach's book that you initially found so compelling? Was it simply the persuasiveness of his arguments against the Newtonian notion of absolute space, or was there more to it than that?

JULIAN BARBOUR: It is certainly true that Mach's writings, especially his *Mechanics*, were extremely important in providing the stimulus for my life's work. I found his critique of Newton's notion of absolute space totally persuasive. Perhaps luckily for me, Mach never formulated in any detail an alternative to it, though he certainly gave suggestive hints. The field was therefore free for me to develop. However, in doing so I departed strongly from Mach's ideas about how one should actually do science. In his view, one should carefully observe natural phenomena, identify characteristic phenomena that recur repeatedly, and formulate science as the economic representation of these phenomena. Mach distrusted theory, especially the attempt to advance in science by means of analytical dynamics. In fact, I totally disregarded this aspect of Mach's thinking when formulating Machian theories. They rely heavily on the techniques of analytical mechanics, above all the principle of least action.

Mach was also important in strengthening my belief – already formed before encountering his work – that the Newtonian concept of time needed revision. Few people have noted that the first half of Mach's critique of Newton's concepts deals with time and includes his remark: 'It is utterly beyond our power to *measure* the changes of things by *time*. Quite the contrary, time is an abstraction, at which we arrive by means of the changes of things.'[3] Much of my work has been devoted to the transformation of this qualitative statement into a quantitative theory of duration. This also finally led me to the radical ideas presented in *The End of Time*.

C: One might be surprised here that you neglect to mention the fact that, while Mach indeed did not himself develop a detailed alternative to the Newtonian notion of space and time, *Einstein* certainly did, and that he did so on the basis, at least in part, of Machian ideas. While the degree to which, and in what precise respects, Mach's ideas exercised an influence on Einstein have long been a matter for debate, there is no doubt that Einstein himself was of the opinion that Machian epistemology had exercised a crucial influence upon him. In an article from 1916 he even went so far as to say that certain passages from Mach's *Mechanics* 'show that Mach clearly recognised the weak spots in Classical Mechanics and was not far from requiring a General Theory of Relativity', adding that '[i]t is not improbable that Mach would have come across Relativity if, at the time when he was in his prime, physicists had concerned themselves with

3. E. Mach *The Science of Mechanics: A Critical and Historical Account of Its Development*, trans. K. Menger & T. J. McCormack (Chicago: Open Court, 1988), 273.

the significance of the constancy of the speed of light'.[4]

Whether or not Einstein was correct about this, the popular view seems to be that, while Mach's ideas undoubtedly influenced Einstein to some extent, those ideas were nevertheless motivated by a combination of ideas which have long since been rendered obsolete by developments in both physics and the philosophy of science: not much more, then, than a mere historical curiosity. However, your early comparison of Mach's ideas with the papers which Einstein had written while he was developing his general theory of relativity led you to the conclusion that Einstein had been formulating his theory on lopsided foundations, and that it was the problems relating to what Einstein called 'Mach's Principle' which had been inadequately developed. You have described Mach's Principle as the idea that 'the locally observed inertial properties of particles arise not from some independently existing absolute space, but rather from the combined effect of all the dynamically significant masses in the universe.'[5]

JB: Yes, the idea that only *relative* configurations exist; a position that had already been adopted, incidentally, by Leibniz.[6]

---

4. Cited in Elie Zahar, 'Mach, Einstein, and the Rise of Modern Science', *British Journal for the Philosophy of Science* 28, 1977: 196.

5. Julian Barbour, 'The Development of Machian Themes in the Twentieth Century' in J. Butterfield (ed.), *The Arguments of Time* (Oxford: Oxford University Press, 1999), 83.

6. See Julian Barbour, 'The deep and suggestive principles of Leibnizian philosophy', *The Harvard Review of Philosophy* 11, Spring 2003: 58. This and other papers by Barbour which treat issues discussed in this interview are available to download at Barbour's website, platonia.com.

C: So you set out to explore what a truly 'Machian theory', wholly faithful to this principle, might look like. In order to directly confront problems that Einstein had failed to think through sufficiently, it would be necessary to return to first principles regarding the Machian problem of inertia. But how would this rethinking of the Machian foundations of general relativity ultimately lead you to the radical thesis of the total elimination of time and change from fundamental physics?

JB: You correctly summarize the reasons why I felt that it was necessary to go back to first principles. I very soon came to the conclusion that, while what Einstein had done in creating general relativity was brilliant, he had not clearly formulated what needed to be done in order to implement Mach's ideas directly. This led me to hope that a direct approach might lead to a new theory of gravity different from Einstein's. For several years Bruno Bertotti and I worked to create such a theory, only to discover that the theory we had found was general relativity in an unfamiliar guise. This was initially a disappointment for both of us; for a while I turned to politics, while Bertotti turned decisively to space-based searches for gravitational waves. Luckily for me, Lee Smolin encouraged me to consider the implications of our work for attempts to create a quantum theory of gravity. As the years pass, I become more and more hopeful that the Machian aspects of general relativity that Bertotti and I uncovered will prove to be useful in that regard.

I arrived at my radical idea in two stages, the first of which involved a theory of time in classical physics, the second a consideration of the implications of the insights gained in the first for a quantum theory of the universe.

A key notion in classical dynamics treated by the methods of variational mechanics is the configuration space of a closed dynamical system. It is the collection of all possible configurations that the system can have. One can take such a system to model a universe. In Newtonian particle dynamics, a configuration is defined by the separations between the particles as well as by the position and orientation of the complete collection of particles in absolute space. The first step to a Machian theory is to insist that the separations alone define the configurations. The Machian (relative) configuration space of the universe, then, is the set of all such relative configurations; I call it the RCS (of the universe). A *history of the universe* is any curve in its RCS.

Now we must think about time. According to Newton, it is absolute and flows uniformly without any reference to what is happening in the universe. But we could never say that time passes if we did not observe change. The hands of a clock must move. Moreover, the curve in the RCS is a record of *all* changes in the universe. There is no further change not already coded in the curve that would enable us to say how fast the universe moves along it. History is not the curve traversed at some speed; it *is* the curve.

In this Machian kinematics, the dubious aspects of Newtonian dynamics have been eliminated: overall position and orientation have been eliminated, as has the 'invisible flow' of time. However, geometrical separations are retained and so too is a unique succession of configurations. This is not a really radical change, since succession of configurations is the most important feature of time that we gain from direct experience. Using this Machian kinematics, Bertotti and I were able to create a Machian theory that differs in its predictions from Newtonian theory when applied to the complete universe but is able to reproduce Newtonian theory for a subsystem of the universe like a galaxy or the solar system.

The radical step comes when one considers potential applications to a quantum theory of the universe. In my view the greatest revolution in physics occurred when Schrödinger introduced his wave function. In classical physics, we have curves in some configuration space traversed at some speed with respect to an external time; in Schrödinger's wave mechanics we have a wave function on the same configuration space, and the wave function varies with respect to the same external time. But if there is no external time and we want to retain the notion of a wave function, which has been so outstandingly successful, it seems to me that we must take seriously the idea that in the quantum mechanics of the universe we have a *static* wave function defined on some relative configuration space. There is no external time with respect to which it can evolve.

The question then is how to make sense of that!

C: One of the ways in which you have attempted to make sense of it is by picturing this 'relative configuration space of the universe' in terms of what you call 'Platonia', which you describe as a kind of timeless and frameless arena comprising 'the collection of all possible Nows'. Before trying to come to grips with that, however, perhaps we can take a moment to unpack a little of what you have just said regarding the reasons you came to suspect that failure to resolve Mach's problem regarding inertia (with which Einstein had struggled between 1907 and 1918, but ultimately abandoned) might be intimately connected to the obstacles confronting the attempt to construct a workable quantum theory of gravity. You came to the conclusion that the lack of progress in resolving certain problems in the foundations of dynamics related to Mach's Principle, on the one hand, and stagnation in the field of quantum gravity research, on the other, might have a common origin. Einstein had favoured an indirect approach to the Machian problem based on his conviction that the history of science had demonstrated the impracticability of dispensing with coordinate systems. But the logic of Mach's own approach seemed to require precisely that they be dispensed with, in order to formulate the laws of motion directly in terms of relative distances and relative velocities without recourse to any distinguished local frames of reference. In effect, this would amount to a direct implementation of Mach's Principle, according to which the inertial properties of local matter are determined by the overall matter distribution in the universe. It was Einstein's early neglect of such explicitly *cosmological* considerations – that is, considerations regarding the universe as a whole understood as a single dynamical entity – which, you suggest, resulted in a failure to appreciate the deep 'relational' structure of general relativity. Could you spell out a little more what this strongly 'relational' interpretation of general relativity entails, and in what way you regard the previous failure to appreciate it as having posed a fundamental obstacle to progress in quantum gravity and quantum cosmology research?

JB: This is a longish story, so I will only give some of the essentials. From about 1911 Einstein always thought in terms of curved four-dimensional spacetime and believed that, if he could find a law describing the structure of spacetime that had the same form in all coordinate systems, Mach's requirement would be automatically satisfied. This is because such a law would not single out any special coordinate system in which the laws of nature take a distinguished simplest form in the way Newton's laws do in an inertial frame of reference. Einstein called his requirement the principle of general covariance and was convinced that it had deep physical significance. However, soon after general relativity had been created, Kretschmann pointed out that any law that makes physically meaningful statements about the world must be expressible in a generally covariant form. Einstein immediately accepted this argument and argued, rather feebly I believe, that it still had great heuristic value. It is also worth mentioning that the most important part of Einstein's theory, his tensor field equations, were not created by him but were taken over more or less intact from mathematicians. He did make one brilliant modification to the Ricci tensor that his friend Grossman proposed, but he never 'unpacked' the tensor that he employed (the Einstein tensor) to see exactly what it does do. Unlike Newton, he did not create his theory in its entirety *ab initio*.

To see what actually happens in general relativity, you have to work out how the structure of three-dimensional space changes as you move through spacetime. This was first described at the end of the 1950s by Dirac and Arnowitt, Deser, and Misner (in the ADM Hamiltonian formalism developed as a first step to the canonical quantization of general relativity). Without realizing there was any connection with this work, around 1979 Bertotti and I started to think what a Machian theory of the evolution of three-dimensional Riemannian geometry would be like. We constructed a theory in which not only spatial change but also time would be relational, only to discover a year later that we had effectively rediscovered general relativity in a Lagrangian form equivalent to the ADM formalism. This showed that in its most basic structure GR is Machian and, moreover, in a sense not anticipated at all by Einstein. More recent work that I have done with Niall O'Murchadha, Edward Anderson, Brendan Foster, and Bryan Kelleher[7] has shown that what I call the two Machian requirements – that both time and change are relational – are extremely powerful, much more so that Bertotti and I thought thirty years ago. They lead to conditions that any Machian theory must satisfy; in the case of dynamical Riemannian three-geometry, these are extremely restrictive.

C: Your interpretation of the radically relational structure of general relativity draws heavily upon not only Mach's ideas, but also those of Henri Poincaré. It was Poincaré, you suggest, who demonstrated more clearly even than Mach what the requirements of a theory of relative motion must be. In a thought experiment remarkably reminiscent of Plato's allegory of the cave which appears in the chapter entitled 'Relative and Absolute Motion' of his 1903 book *Science and Hypothesis*, Poincaré speculates about whether there would ever have been a Copernicus to infer the

7. Several papers related to this research can be accessed at Barbour's website, platonia.com.

motion of the earth on its axis if the latter were continually surrounded by a thick blanket of impenetrable clouds, and we thus had no means of observing the stars. Poincaré, of course, did not yet know anything of the possibilities of space travel or of non-optical (e.g. radio) astronomy; yet he argues that, while we would have had to wait a much longer time than we did for the coming of a Copernicus, 'this Copernicus would come at last'.[8] After centuries of accumulating complications analogous to Ptolemy's glass spheres in order to explain such phenomena as centrifugal forces, the flattening of the poles, the asymmetric motion of cyclones, and Foucault's pendulum experiment, suggests Poincaré, 'the long-expected Copernicus would sweep them all away with a single blow, saying it is much more simple to admit the earth turns round'.[9]

This is a remarkable thought experiment in many ways, not least with regard to Poincaré's suggestion that we might indeed be in an analogous situation, with regard to the universe as a whole, to that of these imaginary physicists in relation to the solar system – that is, that we might be mistaking for fundamental physical constants what a greater knowledge of our cosmic environment would reveal to be merely a function of our limited terrestrial perspective.[10] However, the main questions Poincaré seeks to raise with this thought experiment concern the Newtonian notion of absolute motion:

If the sky were covered with clouds, and if we had no means of

8. *Science and Hypothesis* in Henri Poincaré, *The Value of Science: Essential Writings of Henri Poincaré* (New York: The Modern Library, 2002), 89.

9. Ibid., 90.

10. Ibid., 92-3.

observing the stars, we might, nevertheless, conclude that the earth turns round [...] And yet, would there in this case be any meaning in saying that the earth turns round? If there is no absolute space, can a thing turn without turning with respect to something; and, on the other hand, how can we admit Newton's conclusion and believe in absolute space?"[11]

Would you like to comment on this thought experiment, and to say why you regard Poincaré's epistemological reflections on relative and absolute motion to have been so crucial in working out the necessary requirements for formulating a fully relational mechanics?

JB: Personally, I do not find this particular discussion quite so significant as the one, also in *Science and Hypothesis*, in which he pinpointed the way Newton's absolute space shows up in the evolution of the observable separations between the bodies of the solar system: the separations and the rates of change of the separations do not suffice to predict the future evolution as one would expect if only the separations had physical significance. Poincaré notes that even if astronomers could not see the stars, but only the sun and the planets, they could deduce absolute motions from their observable positions. The same thing holds, *mutatis mutandis*, for the example in which the earth is completely covered by clouds. The observable motions of the bodies that one can see can be represented so much more simply if one postulates an invisible absolute space. Poincaré was profoundly troubled by this, but being a conservative scientist he concluded that we must simply accept this fact

11. Ibid., 89.

that is so 'repugnant to the philosopher'. It is odd that he nowhere (to my knowledge, certainly not in *Science and Hypothesis*) mentions Mach, and did not conjecture that the universe as a whole might satisfy his improved form of the relativity principle free of the repugnant feature.

Reading your quote from Poincaré again, I note his question 'can a thing turn without turning with respect to something?' This suggests to me that he was unaware of the notion of an inertial system that Ludwig Lange had introduced in 1885 and to which Mach had given considerable prominence in later editions of the *Mechanics*. Lange had shown how an inertial system is determined by observable separations of material objects; objects meaningfully rotate relative to the matter-determined inertial system. The concept is sophisticated: moving matter itself determines the frame of reference in which the laws governing the motion take their simplest form. Mach still felt that although Lange had put Newton on a sound epistemological basis, his mechanics was not relative enough; this was a gut intuition that Poincaré shared.

Coming back to his analysis and why I think it is so important: because it provides a precise criterion that a Machian theory must satisfy. Consider a system of bodies. A relative configuration of these bodies, taken to represent the universe, is determined by a set of separations between them. The set of all relative configurations forms the relative configuration space (RCS) of the system. For mechanics to be fully rational, in Poincaré's view, a point in the RCS and a rate of change of that point in the RCS should determine the evolution uniquely. Such data do not suffice to do that in Newtonian theory because they contain no information about the angular momentum in the system; that is coded in the velocities in absolute space, which are not uniquely determined by the relative velocities. Poincaré still kept an external time in his analysis and spoke of the rate of change of the relative separations. In a timeless Machian theory, there should not be any such external time. Therefore, the condition for a fully Machian theory should be: a point and a *direction* at that point in the RCS of the universe should suffice to determine the evolution. Although Einstein read *Science and Hypothesis* closely, Poincaré's analysis seems to have made no impression on him. He never formulated Mach's principle in such a way. I think all the innumerable arguments about Mach's principle would never have arisen had Einstein been sensitive to what Poincaré had written. In a closed universe (for which arbitrary unnatural boundary conditions do not arise), Einstein's theory perfectly satisfies both parts of the Machian condition. Only if one insists that size should be relative does a very curious non-Machian feature of general relativity show up: expansion of the universe should have no meaning, in flagrant contradiction to all the successes of the modern theory of the expanding universe. Scale is absolute in general relativity – a last vestige of Newton's absolute space.

C: Are you claiming, then, that the observable universe is *not* in fact expanding? If that is the case, how then to account for the masses of mutually corroborative evidence, starting with cosmological redshift observations, which suggest that it is?

JB: I admit that much evidence supports the theory of the expanding universe very impressively. The point that I want to make is that this is mysterious. A notion of absolute size is built into the mathematics of general relativity and matches observations very well. In accordance with our present picture, the universe is doing *two* things: it is getting larger and changing its shape (it is becoming more inhomogeneous). I would be much happier with a theory in which the universe is only changing its shape and through a presently unknown mechanism this is giving rise to the effects currently explained by expansion. I live in hope of finding such a theory, or stimulating someone to do so, but am not optimistic given the success of the standard model.

C: But even if such an explanation someday becomes possible, so that we drop the hypothesis of expansion and are left only with the idea that the universe is 'changing shape' and 'becoming more heterogeneous', how is it possible to think the latter without presupposing notions of time and motion? Or to put the question in more general terms, how, in a theory according to which there is no time, change or motion in the universe, is one to account for the apparent ubiquity of such phenomena? Doesn't the suggestion that time, motion and change do not really exist run the risk of landing oneself in a rather extreme form of idealism? One might of course say that such experiences are an 'illusion', but even illusions – indeed, we might even say, *especially* illusions – require explanations, and all the more so when what is being claimed to be illusory is that which we have always taken to constitute the fundamental fabric of reality.

JB: Your question only becomes acute when we pass from classical physics to my conjecture of a static quantum universe. In this context, we have to understand how our familiar notions of time and motion arise. Now evidence for time and motion comes in two forms. First, we directly see things move; second, we deduce passage of time and change from records, which in themselves are unchanging. The latter evidence for time is no threat to my idea. As to the former, I think it need be little different from the fact that we see colour. Scientists do not think colour exists in the physical world but do not deny that it is somehow given to us in consciousness. I put motion on a par with colour. Since Galileo, we have had the distinction between primary and secondary qualities. The primary qualities, related to geometry, shape, and motion, are believed to exist in the material world while colours and sounds exist only as mental states. The primary qualities are believed to 'excite' the secondary qualities in our minds. Scientists work happily with the division of qualities and the conjectured relationship between them. I am proposing that motion should cease to be a primary quality and become a secondary one.

C: But even if we can somehow make sense of the idea that motion is a secondary quality pertaining, as you say, only to mental states – a proposal which would obviously involve enormous difficulties compared to the case of colours, heat and so on – isn't it the case that those mental states themselves, those *experiences* of primary qualities, must always have a certain *temporal duration?*

JB: I do not think this is necessarily so. A theory like mine must propose structure in the physical world that is correlated consistently with experience. If I have in front of me simultaneously two snapshots showing a football match with the players and ball in slightly different positions, I can work out from that static information how each player and the ball have moved between the two snapshots. I argue that the physical correlate of what we experience as motion is stored in the instantaneous brain configuration as two (or more) such 'snapshots'.

C: Regarding 'snapshots': In *The End of Time* you claim that the world is made up of 'instants of time' which you call 'Nows', and you liken them to 'three-dimensional snapshots' such as 'could be constructed if many different people took ordinary two-dimensional snapshots of a scene as the same instant'. As an example, you write: 'I feel an itch at the same time as seeing a moving object in a certain position. All the things I see, hear, smell and taste are knit together in a whole. "Knitting together" seems to me the defining property of an instant. It gives it unity'.[12] However, again, even if it makes sense to speak of a durationless visual 'snapshot', surely hearing a sound, at least, is not something which can happen without a certain duration? Moreover, if what I see when I feel an itch is a star many millions of light-years away, while my experience of seeing the light from the star and feeling the itch might be said to be simultaneous, the idea that the star and I make up a unified 'instantaneous present' is obviously false. In this respect, then, the 'Now' would seem to be something which

12. *The End of Time*, op. cit., 18.

has its locus only in one's experience of the world, yet you are surely not claiming that reality is somehow dependent upon experience or consciousness – which, again, would amount to a very extreme form of idealism. Doubtless these questions at least partially result from taking the metaphor of a 'snapshot' too literally, but then could you say something by way of warding off such (perhaps somewhat inevitable) misinterpretations of your position? Perhaps your idea of 'time capsules' might shed some light on this?

JB: One can argue that all concepts in theoretical physics, including the most abstract ones in quantum mechanics, are suggested by experience. Here 'suggested' is vital. Close your eyes and open them for about half a second before closing them again. You do experience something very like seeing a snapshot. Accumulated experience then leads us to the idea that bodies have instantaneous positions in space and that a collection of bodies is characterized at each given instant by a configuration that can be likened to a 3D 'snapshot'. In the theoretical concept, geometry plays a decisive role; it holds the world together. For me the key notion is of a plurality within a unity (a deeply suggestive expression often used by Leibniz). As I employ it, the notion comes from direct experience but is honed by abstraction to a precise theoretical concept. For example, before the finite speed of the propagation of light was discovered it was natural to assume that we see everything at the same instant, even the most distant star. Astronomers take account of the speed of light to correct apparent positions and obtain instantaneous positions in some particular frame of reference. Although it is often argued that configurations at some instant lost physical significance in Einstein's relativity theories, especially the general theory, this is not true because appropriate initial data on a spacelike surface determine a complete spacetime in general relativity. The spacelike surface is in fact a 3D curved Riemannian space. Thus, after much abstraction (which nevertheless retains the essential idea of unity within plurality) my 'snapshot' becomes such a space with matter distributed within it. The collection of all possible such 'snapshots' is my Platonia, the space of possible configurations of the universe. The reason why I identify this space – the config-uration space of the universe – as all-important is because it plays a central role in both general relativity and quantum mechanics. Though others might not agree, I do not see how either theory can survive if it is not retained in some form or other.

Thus, when I speak of itches and sounds experienced simultaneously with images of objects, that is only to get across the idea of an instantaneous plurality within a unity. The insistence on 'instantaneous' in the refined concept comes from the success of the notion of instanta-neous configuration in both relativity theory and quantum mechanics. In *The End of Time* I attempt to close the circle and show how our experiences might be explained by the special configurations that I call 'time capsules'. If, as I conjecture, the quantum mechanics of the universe gives a high weight (probability) to time capsules, which are instantaneous configurations that contain what seem to be mutually consistent records of a past that unfolded in accordance with the currently known laws of physics, and if conscious experience is correlated with instantaneous configurations, then one can understand how experience suggests refined concepts and a theory that in turn has the potential to explain the original experiences.

C: Isn't it empirically incoherent to claim that the empirical conditions necessary in order to confirm a given hypothesis are, according to the very hypothesis itself, non-existent or illusory? In order to even qualify as a candidate theory, is it not required that the would-be theory make novel and testable predictions? And yet, doesn't the very notion of testing a prediction fundamentally presuppose the notion of time, and of the identity of a world and an observer over time? For without these, what sense would it make to say that a prediction unconfirmed at an *earlier* time had come to be confirmed or falsified at a *later* time? In this regard, the philosopher Richard Healey has suggested that your interpretation of general relativity ends up under-cutting its own epistemic credentials, since 'we can have no empirical reason to believe such a theory if it cannot explain even the possibility of our performing observa-tions and experiments capable of providing evidence to support it'.[13]

JB: Think of Copernicus: The motion of the sun across the sky and the retrograde motions of the planets relative to the stars are empirical conditions and were used by Copernicus

---

13. Richard Healey, 'Can Physics Coherently Deny the Reality of Time?' in Craig Callender (ed.) *Time, Reality and Experience* (Cambridge: Cambridge University Press, 2002), 308; cf. Jeffrey Barrett, 'Empirical Adequacy and the Availability of Reliable Records in Quantum Mechanics', *Philosophy of Science*, 63, 1996: 49-64; and Jeffrey Barrett, *The Quantum Mechanics of Minds and Worlds* (Oxford: Oxford University Press, 1999), esp. 162.

to argue that they were illusions. Ultimately, science is not really about prediction but *explanation* and *confirmation*. A theory is confirmed by comparing in the same instant data that we call the outcome of an experiment and data that we call a record of the earlier conditions. Theories are always confirmed in the present. Geologists, for example, developed a theory of the deep past without making any experiments. All their conclusions were drawn from present data. Cosmologists are currently developing an account of cosmology in the same way. Even experiments at the LHC are ultimately interpreted by theoreticians from data sets acquired from the experimentalists. Records are always a vital part of the story. Information is all of the same kind; we divide some of it into effects and some into records.

I may add that John Bell (of the famous inequalities) remarked, in a discussion of Everett's 'many worlds' interpretation of quantum mechanics, that 'we have no access to the past, but only to present memories. A present memory of a correct experiment having been performed should be associated with a present memory of a correct result having been obtained. If physical theory can account for such correlations in present memories it has done enough – at least in the spirit of Everett'.[14] This seems to me a complete and succinct response to Richard Healey's difficulty. It seems to me that it is for psychological reasons that people have difficulty with such a position as mine; I do not see where there is a flaw in the logic or methodology of science properly understood. Indeed Bell himself had difficulties in this respect, in my view. In later comments on Everett

14. John S. Bell, *Speakable and Unspeakable in Quantum Mechanics* (Cambridge: Cambridge University Press, 1988), 95-6.

93

he says that in his opinion the 'really novel [but unappreciated] element in the Everett theory [...] is a repudiation of the concept of the "past", which could be considered in the same liberating tradition as Einstein's repudiation of absolute simultaneity'.[15] He goes on to give a wonderful account (on which I draw heavily in *The End of Time*) of how time capsules as I define them can emerge with high probability from a timeless quantum-mechanical treatment of the formation of alpha-particle tracks in cloud chambers. But when he comes to the end, he dismisses Everett's theory (despite the brilliant support his gloss has given to it) as a 'radical solipsism [...] It is always interesting to find that solipsists and positivists, when they have children, have life insurance'.[16] This is clearly rejection for psychological reasons. For my part, I am not a solipsist and retain virtually all the ontology of impeccable realists – except that ever-elusive time.

C: The mathematician and cosmologist George Ellis has charged you with 'sneaking in a standard concept of time through the back door' since the very idea of 'the reading of records in some order presupposes a concept of time operational in the mind – which surely cannot occur if the brain is part of a static, unchanging world.'[17] Ellis thus finds you guilty of exempting the mind from the physics which you claim governs the way things work, and thus of

---

15. Ibid., 118.

16. Ibid., 136.

17. George Ellis, book review in *Studies in History and Philosophy of Modern Physics* 33, 2002: 380.

'allowing the human mind to transcend the basic worldview that is supposed to govern the way nature works'.[18] Do you reserve a special ontological place for the conscious mind?

JB: We are clearly learning a great deal about the workings of the brain, but how anything ultimately comes into consciousness is, to my knowledge, still a complete unknown. However, let me make this comment: Boltzmann's explanation for our sense of the direction of time relies on difference of structure: a state with higher entropy is perceived as being later in time than one with lower entropy. This implies that the brain compares two structures and on the basis of the structures alone decides which is later and presents it to us later in consciousness. My view is hardly different; in fact I am not sure if it is in any way different. I propose that, in the immense complexity of our brain, there are, in any instant, configurations of neurons that in the traditional view scientists would regard as occurring in a definite time-order. I am merely saying that they can be put naturally in that order solely using their intrinsic structure; in the process of presenting the stored information to us in consciousness, the brain does not need access to an externally supplied time-order. It constructs it from the information available in one instant. I put such arguments in *The End of Time*, especially Chapter Two, and still think they are reasonable, despite what George says. He argues that I allow 'the human mind to transcend the basic worldview that is supposed to govern the way nature works'. I would answer that, when it comes

18. Ibid.

to essentials, I am in the good company of Boltzmann, and that the Wheeler-DeWitt equation (which is the putative fundamental equation of quantum gravity) suggests that it is the 'basic worldview' that may need to be changed.

C: Ought we take this as a kind of avowal, then, that you are indeed suggesting that the mind in some way transcends the physical world? There are, of course, very many neuro-scientists, cognitive scientists, evolutionary biologists and philosophers who will strongly demur at your suggestion that the nature of the relationship between consciousness and the brain is still 'a complete unknown'. But even if that *were* the case, wouldn't even a superficial knowledge of the history of science over the past two centuries lead one to expect that we are not dealing with anything essentially refractory to physical explanation here, or anything intrin-sically more 'mysterious' than, say, motor control? Before the advent of molecular biology, for example, many people thought it was unimaginable that to be a living thing could consist in a particular organization of 'dead' molecules, and many today have similar difficulty imagining how consciousness could be a function of the brain, and it's hard not to see the two cases as being closely analogous. As the philosopher of neuroscience Patricia Churchland points out, '[f]rom the vantage point of considerable ignorance, failure to imagine some possibility is only that: a failure of imagination – one psychological capacity amongst others [...] It is not an interesting metaphysical fact about the universe nor even an epistemological fact about the limits of scientific knowledge'.[19] Of course, you know this very well, since your own thesis is so radically counterintuitive. But the point is that any form of metaphysical dualism just doesn't look like a scientifically respectable option nowadays.

JB: I certainly grant that very exciting advances are being made in the study of the relationship between brain activity and conscious experience. But this always leads to the recognition of *correlations*. Kepler remarked long ago that if certain phenomena are invariably correlated, this may occur for two reasons: certain of the phenomena are the cause of the others, or else all the phenomena have a common unidentified cause. Thus, it is not necessarily the case that the correlations now being found *explain* the conscious state. Your example of motor control shows that complex automata can and do exist, but I do not think that understanding of the control mechanism could ever suggest that an automaton is self-aware. As Leibniz said in his *Monadology*, '*perception* [...] *cannot be explained mechanically*, that is to say by figures and motions. Suppose that there were a machine so constructed as to produce thought, feeling, and perception, we could imagine it increased in size while retaining the same proportions, so that one could enter as one might a mill. On going inside we should only see the parts impinging upon one another; we should not see anything which would explain a perception.'[20]

19. Patricia Churchland, 'Can Neurobiology Teach Us Anything About Consciousness?', *Proceedings and Addresses of the APA* 67 (4), 1993: 27.

20. G. W. Leibniz, *Monadology* paragraph 17, in *Philosophical Writings* (London and Vermont: Everyman, 1973), 181.

Despite all the recent advances in brain research, I do not think anything overthrows Leibniz's argument.

Thus, I believe one should keep an open mind about the true connection between the brain and experience. As to metaphysical dualism, it seems to me deeply rooted in modern quantum mechanics, which posits a *wave function* defined over *the space of possible configurations* (of whatever physical system that one is considering). I do not see how one can get more dualistic than that. Moreover, the precise connection between these two remains obscure because of the profound interpretational problems in quantum mechanics. Of course, the dualism I have just mentioned is not between mind and matter, but it is still a fundamental dualism.

C: I note that when talking about the way in which the psychological impression of time and motion is created a moment ago, you spoke about the *brain* rather than the mind doing all the work, and thus seem to accept that consciousness is indeed subserved by neurobiological mechanisms.

JB: This is more or less correct. If I use the word *mind*, it is inadvertently (except in idioms). I prefer *experience* or Leibniz's term, *perception*. But I would say *correlated with*, not *subserved by*. The position that I adopted in *The End of Time* is conventional: the conscious state is correlated with the brain state, by which I mean with an instantaneous configuration (positions of atoms) of the brain. The only role of the wave function that I attributed to experience is to make it (the wave function) determine the probability of particular experiences. I am now wondering if the wave function might not play a richer part in experience alongside the instantaneous configuration. But these are all tentative ideas. The only difference between my view and the conventional one is that I remove *motion* from the overall state of the physical world with which I propose experience to be correlated. This contrasts with the standard view that correlates experience with *positions* and *motions*. Position is clearly much more fundamental than motion, for motion is change of position.

I may also mention that there are people with what is said to be a neurological malfunction that makes them see the world as a succession of snapshots. I know one such person; she is currently cured of the problem, but it was so extreme in her case that she would sometimes experience the snapshots in the wrong chronological order, so that crossing a road was life threatening. She contacted me having read my book and found that my concept of Nows resonated deeply with her experience. This suggests to me that deepest-level experience may be snapshot-like and that continuous experience is a higher-level phenomenon.

C: One might wish to maintain, in quasi-Kantian terms, that time is only a mode of intuiting reality rather than something pertaining to the world as it is in-itself. However, it's still rather difficult to see how even that mode of perception – understood as an *internally* rather than *externally* supplied time-order – can take place in a entirely static world. You say that 'in the process of presenting the stored information to us in consciousness, the brain does not need access to an externally supplied time-order', but even here one cannot help but be struck by the fact that you are still talking about a *process* – namely, a process of making comparisons and drawing inferences about relative temporal ordering. It's difficult to see how that can be squared with the idea that the physical world is entirely static – unless, that is, we somehow exempt the activity of brain from the very physical world of which it forms a very minute part, an idea which seems inherently absurd.

JB: No, I would not advocate that. Of course, I do have difficulty in expressing atemporal notions in familiar language, which is so permeated by temporality. A French man did write a whole book without using the letter *e*, but writing one using only the verb *to be* does not appeal to me. It may help to note that for millennia theologians and millions of believers have been happy with the idea that God is eternal, unchanging, and omniscient (and therefore presumably self-aware). I do not want to invoke theology to bolster a scientific theory, but this does at least show that my basic proposal is not without precedent. I believe I am part of a universe far larger than myself; I know I am self-aware; ergo I conclude that the universe is self-aware. We have long lived with the idea of the block universe that results from taking Einstein's relativity seriously. So self awareness resides in eternity.

C: What happens to the idea of *evolution* according to your theory, whether we're talking about the evolution of the universe, or biological evolution? How could a brain, for example, evolve in a purely static world, and why would it be fitted out with sophisticated but delusive experiences of a world of change in which things have happened, and indeed which are happening now? What, after all, could these experiences be *good for?* – a question for which the theory of evolution by natural selection provides an extremely plausible set of answers, but which seems inherently baffling on the basis of your own conjecture of a timeless universe.[21] Does your theory require one to 'explain away' the massive amounts of mutually corroborative evidence for evolution, just as it would seem to require explaining away all the evidence which seems to indicate that the universe is expanding, or do you think it might be possible in some way to construct a 'timeless' theory of evolution?

JB. We are talking about such big issues, we must take one thing at a time. The theory of evolution relies heavily on chemistry and that posits for the (classical) universe an extraordinarily special beginning, for otherwise there are great difficulties with the second law of thermodynamics and the arrow of time, which is deeply reflected in all of evolutionary theory. Now, in *The End of Time* I did put forward what I believe is the first potential explanation for the arrow of time from first principles. It is based on a quantum theory of the universe from which the appearance of a classical universe can in principle arise. I relate the great asymmetry of experience – between the past and the future – to an inescapable profound asymmetry in the space of possible configurations of the universe. Although my book has clearly attracted much interest because of its denial of time, virtually no one has commented on this idea.

21. This objection is borrowed from Jeremy Butterfield's extensive review of Barbour's book, 'The End of Time?', *British Journal for the Philosophy of Science* 53 (2), 2002: 289-330.

As to chemistry, many researchers in quantum gravity have proposed a mechanism whereby timeless quantum gravity can be compatible with the emergence of the conditions for chemistry governed by standard quantum mechanics. Thus I think I can provide the broad framework needed for evolution to be represented in eternity. The point is that every possible configuration of the universe is present in my Platonia: actual dinosaurs in one place in Platonia and fossils of dinosaurs in different configurations in another place, both of which can in principle have high probability as measured by the wave function of the universe. In principle, that is enough to have evolution emerge. Of course, there is a huge way to go from a qualitative outline to detailed confirmation.

C: While you said you earlier that you think science is more about explanation and confirmation than prediction, you of course do not deny that any candidate theory in physics must be able to make novel predictions, and in *The End of Time* you say that 'even clear disproof of my theory would be exciting for me'.[22] Hypothetically, then, what kinds of findings might be able to disprove or falsify your theory? Could you provide examples? What would *testing* your theory involve?

JB: I am hesitant to say that my theory makes any predictions at the moment because it is as yet more in the nature of an outline of a theory. However, I do have the clear proposal that there is a static wave function of the universe that concentrates its associated probabilities

22. *The End of Time*, op. cit., 17.

on configurations of the universe that I call *time capsules*. These are static material configurations containing what appear to be mutually consistent records of a history that unfolded from a special past (highly uniform Big Bang) into the universe that we see around us. In principle, this suggestion could be supported or clearly disproved by mathematics. It is certainly the case that time capsules as I define them are ubiquitous. So this is the most obvious field for testing of my theory. I also think it is just possible that developments in brain research might support my conjecture that experience of motion is correlated with instantaneous brain configurations.

C: At the beginning of *The End of Time* you compare your theory of the non-existence of time to the Copernican revolution in cosmology in the following terms:

> The pattern of the first great revolution will be repeated. Copernicus, Galileo and Kepler taught us that the earth moves and rotates while the heavens stand still, but this does not change by one iota our direct perception that the heavens do move and that the Earth does not budge. Our grasp of the interconnections of things was, however, eventually changed out of recognition in ways that were impossible to foresee. Now I think we must, in an ironic twist of the Copernican revolution, go further, to a deeper reality in which nothing at all, neither heaven nor Earth, moves. Stillness reigns.[23]

A further comparison with Copernicanism appears at the beginning of the fifth chapter, where you suggest that the kind of mental preparation needed to understand Poincaré's ideas requires one to undertake a radical transformation in

---

23. *The End of Time*, op. cit., 14.

one's biologically-inherited mode of thinking:

> I hope you will be able to change from a way of thinking to which we have been conditioned by the fact that we evolved on the stable surface of the Earth to a more abstract way of thinking that would have been forced upon us had we evolved from creatures that roamed in space between objects moving through it in all directions. We have to learn to find our bearings when the solid reassuring framework of the Earth is not there.[24]

If the total disappearance of time from our worldview indeed turns out to be the ultimate denouement of Copernicanism – that is, if time itself, rather than being retained in our world-picture, albeit at some less fundamental level, must rather 'go the way of the [Ptolemaic] epicycles'[25] – what are the implications of this for our commonsense, intuitive picture of the world? Is it really possible that a creature whose imagination and cognitive capacities evolved, as you say, on the stable and reassuring surface of the earth, could ever be capable of coming to terms with the implications of such a revolution in anything more than the most purely abstract way? The philosopher Paul Churchland has suggested a way in which we might train ourselves to perceive our place in the solar system in properly 'Copernican' terms, thereby freeing not only our minds but also our *eyes* from 'the tyranny of a flat immobile Earth' and finding ourselves 'at home in the solar system for the first time'.[26] However, the prospect that we might

24. *The End of Time*, op. cit., 71.

25. http://www.edge.org/discourse/davies_loops.html

26. Paul Churchland, *Scientific Realism and the Plasticity of Mind* (Cambridge: Cambridge University Press, 1979), 30, 34 and Chapter Two *passim*.

ultimately be able to undertake an analogous experiment in the 'expansion of perceptual consciousness' in such a way as to become at home in a physical universe in which time does not exist seems not only remote, but fanciful in the extreme.

JB: Half of my ontology is very conservative and barely different from Newton's: the universe can exist in many different configurations. They can be thought of as like snapshots that a child can pick up and examine. I am not introducing a difficult concept here. A continuous succession of such snapshots is epistemologically identical to a Newtonian history of the universe if it satisfies a certain law that can be formulated without any notion of enduring time. Our direct experience of time is not of duration but of succession, and I can easily show that a timeless lawful succession leads to the emergence of a well-defined duration effectively identical to Newton's absolute time.

The other half of my ontology comes from quantum mechanics and will be easy for physicists, if not children, to grasp: the wave function defined on a configuration space. I think it is highly relevant for my programme that Schrödinger originally found a *timeless* equation for his wave function. It explains *all* nuclear, atomic, and molecular structures that we find around us. It was even used by Max Born (before Schrödinger proposed an equation that describes evolution of the wave function in Newtonian time) to describe processes regarded as dynamic.

I regard quantum mechanics as a theory that explains structure. Close and open your eyes for a second; you see a structure, a snapshot. What I aim at is a theory that explains the presentation to us of such structures that involves only a timeless comparison of such structures and does not posit *evolutionary* laws and their initial conditions. The fundamental law is a law of structure selection in which structures are favoured by virtue of their structure and nothing else. It is not totally unlike a child selecting the most interesting snapshots among a large collection. To make the connection with experience I propose that awareness is correlated with single snapshots (which can be arbitrarily complex and contain, as it were, snapshots within snapshots). The standard view is that awareness is correlated with a succession of snapshots, which I replace by my 'snapshots-within-snapshots' snapshots. This idea is beautifully illustrated in the film about my ideas shown on Dutch television, *Killing Time*.[27]

Perhaps it will help if I say that Newtonian theory (and even Einstein's theories to a large degree) is like a law that forces an object to follow a path at a definite speed through a landscape once it is set going at some point in the landscape with a definite direction and speed; this is the initial condition, without which nothing can be done with the law. It is easy to show that the speed part of this initial condition is redundant if one considers the whole universe. History is then not a path traversed as some speed but merely a path. The huge change introduced by quantum mechanics is that the notion of a definite path is eliminated and replaced by the wave function that 'samples', or 'looks at', all possible points in the landscape. This can be done in a timeless fashion that is precisely analogous to the way

---

27. A link to this film can be found on Barbour's website, platonia.com; it is also available via *YouTube*.

that quantum mechanics determines atomic and molecular structures.

C: While it's of course impossible to predict the eventual social and cultural ramifications of any scientific revolution, I wonder if you have anything to say about the possible consequences which the notion of 'the end of time' might bring about were it ultimately to become as widely accepted as the idea that the earth revolves around the sun is for us today?

JB: That is impossible to answer. All I can say is that life could be less hectic and more contemplative. People in the parts of Platonia where my theory is accepted should cherish the Now more than in this overworked region. To go back to what I said about theology: In the Middle Ages busy kings still spent hours in daily prayer because they believed deeply in eternity and its primary importance. Today, many would reject their beliefs. However, mathematicians have rational grounds for believing in eternal mathematical truths. Theoretical physics has a definite tendency to go in the same direction – on rational grounds. Indeed, it can hardly avoid doing so, since it uses mathematics, and mathematics that is only occasionally true is not much use.

C: You have already mentioned Leibniz a few times, and at the outset of *The End of Time* you describe your 'central idea' as being inspired by the Leibnizian idea that the world is to be understood 'not in the dualistic terms of atoms (one kind of thing) that move in the framework and container of space and time (another quite different kind of thing), but in terms of more fundamental entities that fuse space and matter into the single notion of a possible arrangement, or configuration, of the entire universe'.[28] According to this Leibnizian notion, 'the world does not consist of infinitely many essentially identical things – atoms moving in space – but is in reality a collection of infinitely many things, each constructed according to a common principle yet all different from one another. Space and time emerge from the way in which these ultimate entities mirror each other'.[29] This is an idea which, you suggest 'has the potential to turn physics inside out – to make the interestingly structured appear probable rather than improbable'.[30]

One might be surprised to see a contemporary theoretical physicist drawing so explicitly upon early eighteenth-century rationalist metaphysics in order to rethink the foundations of contemporary physics in this way. However, far from being a mere eccentricity on your part, your application of Leibnizian ideas to fundamental physics and cosmology have exercised a considerable influence upon leading contemporary physicists and cosmologists. Lee Smolin, for example, to whom you introduced Leibnizian and Machian ideas when he was visiting Oxford in 1980, and with whom you subsequently collaborated in an attempting to formulate Leibnizian monadological ideas in precise mathematical form, has gone on to develop, along with Carlo Rovelli and

28. *The End of Time*, op. cit., 16.

29. *The End of Time*, op. cit., 240.

30. Ibid.

others, relational theories of quantum gravity and quantum cosmology which are today regarded as the principal rivals to string theory. In this way, in the form of Loop Quantum Gravity and Relational Quantum Mechanics, ideas of distinctly Leibnizian inspiration stand at the very cutting-edge of contemporary theoretical physics. Could you say something about how you came to realise the great potential for the application of Leibnizian metaphysics to contemporary physics, how your interpretation of Leibnizian ideas relates to your central notion of 'Platonia' as 'the relative configuration space of the universe', and about the key differences between your approach to quantum gravity and quantum cosmology and those of Smolin and Rovelli?

JB: In fact, most of my key ideas were developed and presented in my first paper in *Nature* in 1974 before I read any of Leibniz's writings, which happened in 1976-77. My long journey of conceptual exploration began in 1963 with the chance reading of a newspaper article about Dirac's attempts to quantize gravity. This led me to ask myself seriously: What is time? Soon after that I read Mach's great *Mechanics* and this led me to add the question: What is motion? By 1972 I had worked out the framework of a Machian theory of time and motion in classical physics. This has since been elaborated but not fundamentally changed. The notion of relative configuration space (RCS) of the universe that I published in 1974 is Platonia. What I found exciting in Leibniz was a deeper intellectual under-pinning of my scheme. Above all, Leibniz insisted that real things must have distinguishing attributes, which was not the case for Newton's identical points of space.

What underlies Leibniz's ontology is the conviction that there is no reality without variety. Indeed, reality *is* variety. Leibniz also has this wonderful conjecture that the actually realized universe is more varied than any other conceivable universe. Stimulated by my enthusiasm for Leibniz, Lee Smolin managed to find a way to express this idea mathematically and we together developed a theory of Maximal Variety.[31] I do think it manages to capture the kind of scheme for which Leibniz was striving. It has generated a fair amount of interest, but as of now does not seem to have any obvious applications in physics.

As regards differences between my approach to quantum gravity and the present approach of Smolin and Rovelli, they concern the antithesis of the discrete and the continuous. When Lee met me, he was already convinced that at the deep microscopic level space must be discrete. As I recall, he had come to this view from his early exposure to the problems of infinities in quantum field theory, which he felt could only be cured by an underlying discrete theory. This was a formative experience to which I had not been exposed. I was initially sympathetic to the idea that the continuum of experience should emerge from a discrete foundation, but rather soon came to the conclusion that the problems to be overcome were great and probably insurmountable. In this respect, Lee and I continue to differ, but we are each inspired by relational examples drawn from Leibniz: a discrete genealogical tree in Lee's case, the continuous distances between bodies (as discussed by Leibniz in the Leibniz–Clarke Correspondence) in my case.

---

31. Julian Barbour & Lee Smolin, 'Extremal variety as the foundation of a cosmological quantum theory' (arXiv: hep-th/9203041). This paper can be accessed via Barbour's website, platonia.com.

C: In *The End of Time* you admitted that the idea that time does not exist is still 'only a prospect on the horizon', albeit one which might well ultimately turn out to comprise the next great revolution in our understanding of the universe.[32] Since the publication of your book almost a decade ago, 'the small but growing number of physicists' who 'have begun to take the idea that time truly does not exist'[33] seems to have increased considerably. There seems to be a general feeling abroad amongst those searching for that veritable Holy Grail of contemporary physics – that is, a workable theory of quantum gravity – that something fundamental is missing, a common erroneous assumption which needs to be rooted out, and that this erroneous assumption very likely concerns the nature of time.[34] Carlo Rovelli has compared the situation which has existed in fundamental physics over the past century to the 150-year period between Copernicus and Newton – that is, a period of an 'unfinished revolution' – predicting that the next great synthesis, this time bringing together general relativity and quantum mechanics, will require us to learn how to think of the world 'in completely nontemporal terms'.[35] Similarly, Lee Smolin has suggested that the problem of time in quantum cosmology forces

---

32. *The End of Time*, op. cit., 14.

33. *The End of Time*, op. cit., 39.

34. Cf. Lee Smolin, *The Trouble With Physics* (Boston & New York: Houghton Mifflin Company, 2006), 256.

35. Carlo Rovelli, 'Halfway Through the Woods: Contemporary Research on Space and Time' in J. Earman & J. Norton (eds), *The Cosmos of Science* (Pittsburgh: University of Pittsburgh Press, 1997), 180-223; 'The Century of the Incomplete Revolution: Searching for General Relativistic Quantum Field Theory', *Journal of Mathematical Physics*, Special Issue, 2000 (arXiv: hep-th/9910131v1); and 'Anaximander's Legacy', this volume.

one 'to confront the possibility that time and change are illusions', and that we may ultimately 'have to come to terms with a world which, at the most fundamental level, must be described in a language in that includes no words for time'.[36] And indeed even the most aggressive champions of string theory seem now to have come round to the idea – an idea which you have been insisting upon for decades – that any feasible theory of quantum gravity will have to be formulated in background-independent terms[37] and that this might well require the complete elimination of the notion of space and time as a basis for our description of reality.[38] In light of this, are you now more optimistic than you were ten years ago that something like the picture you have developed over the past four and a half decades will ultimately triumph? How do you envisage the next fifty years of development in fundamental physics panning out,

---

36. *The Life of The Cosmos* (Oxford: Oxford University Press, 1997), 286.

37. See for example Brian Greene, *The Fabric of The Cosmos* (London and New York: Penguin Books, 2004), 485-491.

38. Thus David Gross, described by Smolin as 'one of the most aggressive and formidable champions of string theory' (*The Trouble With Physics*, op. cit., xv), in a recent interview: 'In string theory I think we're in sort of a pre-revolutionary stage [...] we still haven't made a very radical break with conventional physics. We've replaced particles with strings – that in a sense is the most revolutionary aspect of the theory. But all of the other concepts of physics have been left untouched [...] at some point, a much more drastic revolution or discontinuity in our system of beliefs will be required. And this revolution will likely change the way we think about space and time, maybe even eliminate them completely as a basis for our description of reality – that is, leave us regarding them rather as emergent approximate concepts that are useful under certain circumstances. That is an extraordinarily difficult change to imagine, especially if we somehow change what we mean by time, and is probably one of the reasons why we're still so far from a true understanding of what string theory is. [...] Something is missing that is most likely not just another technical development, another improvement here or there, but something that truly breaks with the past. And all the indications are that it has to do with the nature of space and time.' (David Gross, 'Viewpoints on String Theory', at http://www.pbs.org/wgbh/nova/elegant/view-gross.html).

and what do you expect to be the chief obstacles in the way of completing the 'unfinished revolution' of the past century?

JB: It is certainly encouraging that more and more people seem to be taking my ideas seriously. I am currently in the process of writing up everything I have learned in a monograph with the provisional title *Mach's Principle, General Relativity, and Gauge Theory*. Thanks to a generous grant from the Foundational Questions Institute,[39] I am now able to collaborate with more young researchers. However, I am not too optimistic that the Holy Grail will be grasped in my lifetime. I suspect that the main difficulty may well be technical complexity or absence of experimental data that can act as a useful guide. However, major conceptual developments are also probably needed. I see two places where conceptual breakthroughs might occur. One concerns the role of complex numbers in quantum gravity. In the quantum mechanics discovered in the 1920s, they entered through the time-dependent Schrödinger equation; it is a fundamentally complex equation. However, there is neither time nor the imaginary i in the Wheeler–DeWitt equation, which founds quantum gravity. Numerous papers have proposed essentially the same way to get the i back into laboratory physics but I believe that they are all seriously flawed. The other possibility is the one that I already mentioned relating to the failure of general relativity to be scale invariant, so that size is absolute.

---

39. See www.fqxi.org.

C: In his recent book *The Trouble With Physics*, Smolin argues that the lack of progress in physics over the past three decades – in stark contrast to the preceding two hundred years of explosive growth in the field – can in large part be attributed to a certain style of doing science which, while it was well-suited to the problems which physics faced in the middle part of the twentieth century, is ill-suited to the kinds of problems it faces now. Smolin characterises this style as 'pragmatic and hard-nosed', favouring 'virtuosity in calculating over reflection on hard conceptual problems' and contrasts this with the profoundly different way in which Einstein, Bohr, Heisenberg, Schrödinger and the other early-twentieth-century revolutionaries did science, whose work 'arose from deep thought on the most basic questions surrounding space, time, and matter' and who saw themselves as 'part of a broader philosophical tradition, in which they were at home'.[40]

These are sentiments which would certainly have been endorsed by Mach, who put Newton's inability to recognise the equivalence of all inertial frames down to the fact that he lived in 'an age deficient in epistemological critique'[41] and who was the first occupant of the first academic chair explicitly devoted to the philosophy of science. Einstein himself would likewise often extol the virtues of a background in critical epistemology and the history and philosophy of science as providing 'that independence from prejudices of his generation from which most scientists are suffering', holding this 'independence created by

---

40. *The Trouble With Physics*, op. cit., xxii-xxiii.

41. *The Science of Mechanics*, op. cit., 571.

philosophical insight' to be 'the mark of distinction between a mere artisan or specialist and a real seeker after truth'.[42] While letting the philosopher do the philosophizing 'might be the right thing to do when the physicist believes he has at his disposal a rigid system of fundamental concepts and fundamental laws which are so well established that waves of doubt can not reach them [...] it can not be right at a time when the very foundations of physics itself have become problematic'. At such times, insisted Einstein, 'the physicist cannot simply surrender to the philosopher the critical contemplation of the theoretical foundations; for, he himself knows best, and feels more surely where the shoe pinches. In looking for a new foundation, he must try to make clear in his own mind just how far the concepts which he uses are justified, and are necessities.'[43]

In your own intellectual formation, was it your extensive background in the history and epistemology of physics that enabled you, unlike the vast majority of your contemporaries in theoretical physics, to break genuinely new ground? Like yourself, Mach and Poincaré were not only physicists, but also distinguished historians of science, who drew upon the full extent of that history in order to develop their epistemological insights. To what extent do you agree with Smolin and Einstein that the cultivation of such a deep philosophical and historical background is necessary in periods of scientific revolution?

42. Quoted in Don Howard, 'Einstein as a Philosopher of Science', *Physics Today* 58 (12), 2005: 34-40.

43. Ibid.

JB: In the present period, I am sure that Lee and Einstein are right. I love Einstein's comment that, in crisis periods, the task of philosophizing must fall to the physicist, who feels 'where the shoe pinches'. That is surely correct. In my experience, the philosophers tend to try to clarify existing concepts, often ones that the physicists introduced quite some time ago. But the history of science shows that virtually all great breakthroughs have been made by researchers working intensively at the cutting edge. Mostly they can work within an existing paradigm, but at crisis points that fails them. In this case, something new must be tried. It is always the case that revolutions retain much of the old framework and replace parts that have become suspect with genuinely new proposals. In such circumstances a thorough knowledge of the historical development is a huge help.

One sees this especially clearly in the discovery by Kepler of his first two laws of planetary motion; it has been a major inspiration for me. Kepler knew the great work of Hipparchos and Ptolemy intimately, but could see that Copernicus's daring proposal to put the earth in motion forced us 'to philosophize about these things differently'. Kepler combined the new and the old in his struggle to explain the wonderful observational data that Tycho Brahe had made. Brahe's 'destruction' of the crystal spheres previously believed to carry the planets make an immense impression on Kepler and prompted him to a remark that is very apposite in the present search for a background-independent formulation of quantum gravity. He said: 'From now on the planets must find their way through the void like the birds through the air'. Einstein's abolition of absolute space and time puts us in a similar position. I like to put it this way: We must understand how the universe can 'swim in nothing'. It is perhaps here that I may be able to make a useful contribution to current research, in which it has become a commonplace to say that quantum gravity must be 'background-independent' because general relativity has that property. What I think is not adequately appreciated is the precise dynamical structure that does make general relativity background-independent. People do not check out the detailed way in which the theory 'swims in nothing'. Nearly all of my work has been devoted to that project.

C: Do you think that you would have been able to make the kind of profound contribution you have made to the foundations of physics had you, all those years ago, and like just about every other theoretical physicist, taken a position in an academic physics department?

JB: I think I definitely made the right decision to stay out of academia. Every now and then, young researchers do ask me for advice about the possibility of going independent. I emphasize that I was lucky but also that I did make one key decision correctly: to earn my living by a well-paid but boring job (translating). This ensured that I never got hooked by the money-earning job and was always longing to get back to the physics. But the most important thing in my case was simply a gift of fortune: the joint problems of time and motion 'took hold of me'. I could never stop thinking about them and little by little accumulated results and insights that to me at least seem to have promise. If young researchers do not have such a burning desire within them, they probably will not succeed either inside or outside academia.

C: Finally, what advice might you offer to young theoretical physicists and philosophers of science today embarking on the dauntless task of perhaps some day helping to bring to a close the 'unfinished revolution' of twentieth-century physics?

JB: I would say that there is an urgent need for clear independent thinking. Both 'clear' and 'independent' are vital. Far too many papers that are published today by young researchers desperate to build up a long publication list that will look impressive on a CV (and ensure at least short listing in a more or less automated process) lack clarity and take important things on trust just because leaders in the field have made certain pronouncements. Several PhD students I know were given computational problems in string theory and told not to ask why they should be done. I am glad to say that two at least promptly got out of the field in protest. I am not saying that string theory is wrong, only that such practice does not advance science. I do feel very sorry for young researchers struggling with today's conditions – but then perhaps it has always been like that. Only those with deep inner conviction and application have ever made it through to great discoveries.

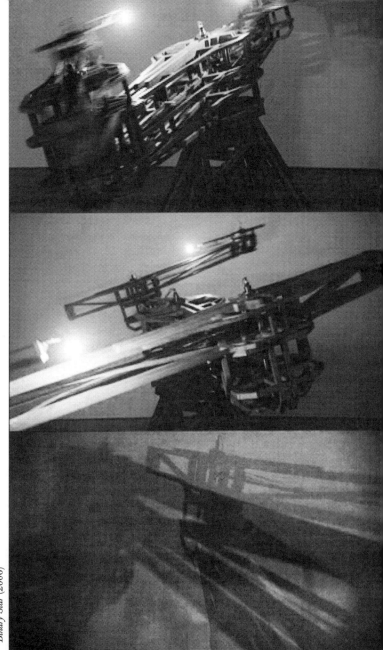

Shadows of Copernicanism

Conrad Shawcross and Robin Mackay

For the best part of five centuries the Copernican revolution has served as a virtually inexhaustible source of philosophical and existential disquiet. Undoubtedly, we have yet to fully adjust our spontaneous image of reality to accord with our displacement from its centre. Yet Copernicus and Kepler retained the Sun as the unique centre. If later developments showed the Sun to be only one of trillions of stars, recent observations even show that singular stars are the exception rather than the rule: The unicity of our Sun is mere cosmic happenstance, in a universe where binary star systems are more common, many capable of supporting Earth-like planets.[1] Considering the overwhelmingly heliotropic tendency of the philosophical imaginary, from Plato to Heidegger,[2] how might our image of thought be disrupted by the loss of the unicity of the Sun, of the object's shadow, of tomorrow's sunrise ...? These are some of the questions posed by Conrad Shawcross's

---

1. E.V. Quintana & J.J. Lissauer, 'Terrestrial Planet Formation in Binary Star Systems', 2007, at http://arxiv.org/abs/0705.3444v1.

2. 'Insofar as it structures the metaphorical space of philosophy, the Sun represents what is natural in philosophical language [...] There is only one Sun in the system [...] the unique, irreplaceable, natural referent, around which everything must turn, toward which everything must turn' – J. Derrida, 'White Mythology', in *Margins of Philosophy* (Evanston, IL: Northwestern University Press, 1988), 243, 251.

motion sculpture *Binary Star* (2006), a faithful cosmological model whose two 'suns' rise on a world in which there is 'No Such Thing as One'.[3] As the massive, wooden beams of the mechanical contraption rotate in their simulated gravitational dance, its two light sources, in their complex paths, cast double shadows whose shifting superpositions are baffling and unfathomable to the eye.

Philosophical tradition has often metaphorically anchored thought to apparently fixed and permanent characteristics of the physical world. Such models are inevitably burdened with an inability to absolve themselves of their metaphorical investment in the very reality they claim to conceptually underwrite. When we select features from a contemporary image of reality to stand for the task of thought, we always run the risk of becoming a hostage to the fortunes of scientific inquiry, whose progress seems eventually to disabuse us of every illusion of fixity and permanence. In Shawcross's work the physical realisation of such emblematic epistemological models exacerbates the problem of this 'bleeding' of the empirical into the philosophical. Through an intriguing lateral shift, *Binary Star* demonstrates how the epistemological trope of 'Copernicanism', in its naïve acceptation as a simple reversal of perspective between two heavenly bodies, remains tied to 'terrestrial' tropes of thought: above all, the notion that an orbiting multiplicity always pays homage to a central unity. It seems that, even confronted by a radical shift in thinking, we always risk attaching importance to the deepseated

---

3. The name of the show at Victoria Miro Gallery in London in which *Binary Star* was first exhibited.

Binary Star (2006)

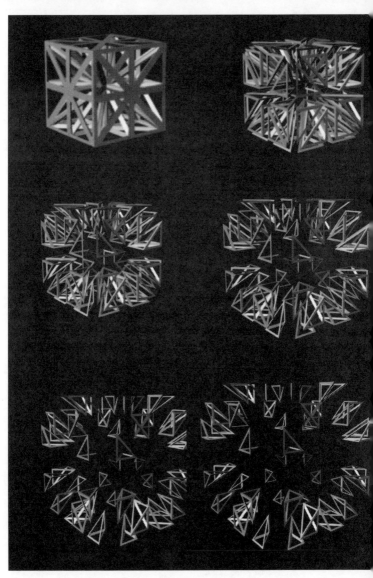

Schematic of *Lattice Cube Sequence* (2008)

prejudices it foregrounds but leaves intact, rather than to its real consequences.

Does philosophy's thirst for such precarious models of thought indicate that a surreptitious exploitation of the all-too-human world is a veritable *condition* for philosophical discourse – at least insofar as the latter seeks to preserve its proper domain from purely mathematico-scientific accounts of reality? The more profound epistemological lesson to be drawn from Copernicanism, of course, is not that of a simple role-reversal. It is that of a gap opened up between a mathematical model freed from the contingencies of human visibility, and the efforts of intuition and imagination – conditioned by those very contingencies – to 'make sense' of such absolutes. Much of Shawcross's work seeks to locate the thinking of the artist and of the philosopher on this fractured terrain, and to inquire after the compromise involved.

In recent work, the artist confronts mathematical models of space with those of an art movement that defined itself in terms of conceptual interrogation. Artists such as Sol Lewitt and Donald Judd, pioneering a research programme into space as the fundamental element of artistic practice, selected the cube as a kind of fundamental particle of aesthetic experience; representing, apparently in the most elementary manner, the three-dimensional Cartesian grid, the plastic degree-zero which these artists would seek to organise in optimally simple and modular fashion. In Shawcross's *Lattice Cube Sequence* (2008) a 'barycentric subdivision' (the cube is sliced by planes connecting the 'barycenters' which divide each of its faces into two) allows the cube to retain maximal simplicity and symmetry, whilst breaking it down into a set of tetrahedrons. With this mathematical procedure of simplification into more basic constituent entities – the same 'simplicial approximation' used to build up from simple forms the complex computer graphics models used in movies – Shawcross questions the claim of Lewitt's 1960s cubes to be the fundamental 'simplex' of three dimensional space ('Space [...] thought of as [...] cubic area'),[4] and reconsiders the nature of a conceptual art practice that avowedly 'doesn't really have much to do with mathematics, philosophy, or any other mental discipline'.[5]

Lattice Cube Sequence (2008)

What Shawcross explodes here is the bond between aesthetic elegance and conceptual simplicity which the sixties conceptualists had tried to push to the limit. He has often tested this fundamental unity of human aesthetic perception and mathematical elegance, confirming

4. S. Lewitt, *Sol Lewitt* (NY: Museum of Modern Art, 1978), 167.

5. Ibid., 166.

it, for instance, in his *Loop System Quintet* (2006), a mechanised visualisation of musical harmony. But contemporary science yields substructures of 'basic elements' whose configuration cedes nothing to our spontaneous image of the world, unbinding us from the Greek heritage of mathematico-aesthetic intuitions (Pythagorean harmony, Platonic solids ...). Tracking this 'Copernican' vector, *Lattice Cube Sequence* sees the serene perpendicularity of the cube giving way to an inner structure whose complexity renders it opaque to the eye. As the simplices explode outward, the form of the cube itself evaporates, and with it the cubic grid system, as if it had never been more than an optical illusion, an anthropological artifact. The rotational 'grammar' of the cube, of which Lewitt was the virtuoso, seems in retrospect a parochial dialect.

It would be wrong to imply that Lewitt himself was unconscious of his 'failure' in this respect: Against any theoretical or illustrative relation to science, he argued forthrightly for the artist's need to be 'smart enough to be dumb'.[6] And his intention, for instance, for the very first modular cube 'to be large, but not too large',[7] clearly betrays the anthropocentric nature of his research programme. In this respect Shawcross's piece is as much homage as critique, since the very manufacturing and exhibiting of *Sequence* opens it to the vagaries of embodied perception. In inviting the emotions and associations occasioned by its physical encounter to derail the precision of the scientific model, *Sequence* seems designed as much to disturb as to evoke the self-sufficient serenity of its abstruse prototype.

6. S. Lewitt (quoted by L. R. Lippard) in Lewitt, op.cit.

7. Ibid., 4.

Shawcross's work is characterised by this ambivalence towards its scientific sources. Against the violence done to the imagination by mathematical science, the deliberate, relentless arcs of *Binary Star*'s hefty oaken beams sing the glory of the creative vigour of the mad inventor, the gentleman-amateur. With scientists' models of reality increasingly inimical to any grounding in metaphors drawn from the everyday lifeworld, Shawcross's diligent physical renderings mimic the efforts that philosophy must make to incorporate them into the grain of language without ceding the latter entirely to mathematical abstraction. The artist himself has consequently qualified his machines as 'tragic' or 'misguided'; but the most profound content of the work seems to lie precisely in the vacillation between object and model that indexes its 'failure'.

From the same group of work as *Lattice Cube Sequence*, *Slow Arc Inside a Cube* (2007) redeploys the mechanism of *Binary Star* at a more abstract level. The 'slow arc' is described by a brilliant, omnidirectional halogen bulb moving inside a cube whose barred walls it projects onto the walls of the installation space, in a ceaselessly shifting mapping of object onto environment. Rather than a separate source of light illuminating worldly objects and casting shadows, the blinding core of the object brands the environment with the continuous phases of its own projected image.

Shorn of *Binary Star*'s literal reference to astronomical Copernicanism, *Slow Arc* exerts all the more profound pressure on philosophical (Kantian) Copernicanism, for which the transcendental ego has become the point-source of objectivity. Its proposed object-model scrambles the Platonic heritage of Kantianism, and releases a cloud of philosophical associations. In transforming the environment into a continuously-shifting image, *Slow Arc* already seems to move through Husserlian phenomenology towards Gabriel Catren's quantum model of objecthood. In Catren's account, the unification of multiple phenomenal aspects into a single object ('eidetic variation') is no longer the work of a synthesising subject. Instead, the object itself is 'a kind of "projector" of phases, aspects or profiles', a hallucinatory 'dream machine' with its own inner Sun.[8]

For Shawcross, *Slow Arc* bears a broader reference to the process of scientific experimentation and discovery. The piece was directly inspired by x-ray crystallographer Dorothy Hodgkin's discovery of the molecular structure of insulin, and in particular by the scientist's comparison of the exhaustive process of extrapolating the dense protein 'cloud' from reams of chromatographic grids with 'trying to work out the structure of a tree purely from looking at its shadow'. Like Plato's Sun, the blinding core of the object cannot be confronted directly, but must be speculatively inferred as the origin of the projections thrown onto the inner surface of a phenomenal *camera obscura*.

Finally, however, the source of light itself is a moving target. It is the cage – that through which the light is thrown to create the shifting projections – that is the only constant. So an alternative interpretation might take up Alberto Gualandi's post-Copernican anthropocentrism:[9]

8. See G. Catren 'A Throw of the Quantum Dice Will Never Abolish the Copernican Revolution', this volume.

9. See A. Gualandi, 'French Philosophies of Nature and the Overturning of the Copernican Revolution', this volume.

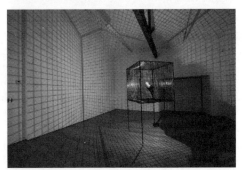

Slow Arc Inside a Cube (2007)

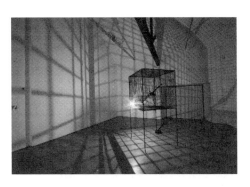

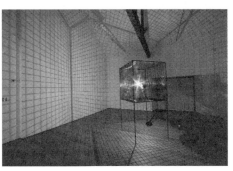

The structure that locks us out of the object's core, imprisoning us in the phenomenal realm, is also the only constant by which we can measure that which exceeds it.

In this case, both artists and philosophers should be wary of falling victim to another superficial reading of the 'Copernican imperative', indicating a peremptory jettisoning of the evidence of the senses and of inherited language. 'Smart enough to be dumb' and 'misguided', a part of their task will consist instead in probing the discontinuities and the slippages between those blinding mathematical abstractions forever closed to intuition, the shadows they cast in experience, and the imaginary heritage with which we struggle to make sense of them.

Fittingly for what has been read here as an extended meditation on philosophical heliotropism, Shawcross's latest 'irrational machine', to be unveiled in summer 2009, returns to the depths of the Earth. But *Chord* does

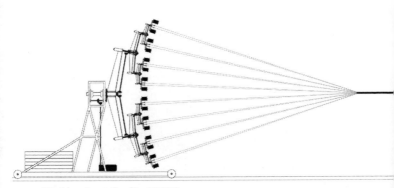

Working sketch for *Chord* (2009)

not presume, like the philosopher, to drag benighted cave-dwellers up into the light; instead it excavates and brings to light a forgotten underground space. A descendent of Shawcross's (2001) spinning-machine *Yarn*, the piece will elaborate on that work's automated weaving of hundreds of coloured threads into a single rope. But in *Chord* this process will be co-ordinated by the two halves of a gigantic 'twin machine' to be installed in London's disused Kingsway tram tunnel. Laying down their own tracks as they proceed, the two machines will illuminate the expanding space between them as their multiply-articulated tri-arms fabricate a line of communication across it. According to Shawcross's latest yarn (narrative, creation myth, epistemological model?), therefore, the emergence of a linear simplicity is contemporaneous with the clearing of the space in which it is knitted together, by intricate machinations on the edge of darkness.

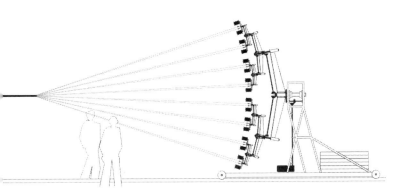

Who's Afraid of Scientism?

Interview with James Ladyman

In 2007 James Ladyman and Don Ross published Every Thing Must Go: Metaphysics Naturalized,[1] *an attempt to synthesize Ladyman's 'Ontic Structural Realism' and Ross's 'Rainforest Realism' into a unified metaphysics applicable to science from physics to economics. Beginning with a blistering polemic against what they call 'neo-scholastic metaphysics', Ladyman and Ross argue for an approach to metaphysics which goes far beyond the vague science-friendliness characteristic of so much of contemporary soi-disant naturalism in favour of an unabashedly 'scientistic' stance. Dispensing with the habitual ontology of 'little things and microbangings' which continues to hold sway in contemporary 'pseudo-naturalist philosophy',* Every Thing Must Go *provides the case for a radically naturalistic metaphysics capable of taking on board the most counterintuitive findings of modern physics without impugning the epistemic credentials of the special sciences. In our interview, Ladyman discusses the reasons for his exasperation with philosophers who persist in doing metaphysics as if modern science had never happened, provides a robust defence of 'the scientistic stance', and explains how the position developed in* Every Thing Must Go *provides a heuristic framework for the unification of the sciences via a dialectical synthesis of the strengths of both realism and empiricism.*

1. James Ladyman and Don Ross with David Spurrett and John Collier, *Every Thing Must Go: Metaphysics Naturalized* (Oxford: Oxford University Press, 2007).

COLLAPSE: You are known within philosophy of science circles for your defence of a form of scientific realism you call 'ontic structural realism'. The list of names of philosophers and physicists who have subscribed to one or another form of structural realism is an impressive one indeed. Restricting ourselves to the twentieth century we have Henri Poincaré, Ernst Cassirer, Bertrand Russell, Arthur Eddington, Moritz Schlick, Rudolf Carnap, Grover Maxwell and, more recently, John Worrall and Elie Zahar. A landmark paper in the current debate was John Worrall's 1989 'Structural Realism: The Best of Both Worlds',[2] in which structural realism is presented as a kind of synthesis of the insights contained in both the (realist) 'no miracles' argument, on the one hand, and the (anti-realist) 'pessimistic meta-induction', on the other. For those who might not be familiar with recent debates concerning scientific realism, could you briefly describe the nature and import of these two arguments, and how they pull in opposing directions?

JAMES LADYMAN: The no-miracles argument in its crudest form is the claim that if scientific theories were not correctly describing the nature of the unobservable entities and processes that cause what is observable, then the success of science in describing the phenomena would be completely mysterious, so our best scientific theories do indeed describe the hidden workings of the universe. The argument is made more sophisticated by Richard Boyd and others who refer not just to the success of science, but the success of the highly theory-laden methods used by scientists as one

---

2. *Dialectica* 43 (1-2), 1989: 99-124.

generation of new hypotheses become the background theories deployed to design instruments and experiments in the development of the next generation of theories. The pessimistic meta-induction can already be found in crude form among the arguments of the ancient Greek sceptics; it says that we ought not believe in more than the approximate empirical adequacy of our best scientific theories because there have been highly successful theories in the past that by our current lights are false, and that our best contemporary theories are no different in kind and liable to befall the same fate. (In the modern literature this argument is was forwarded by Poincaré, and then its name was coined by Hilary Putnam. It is usually now associated with Larry Laudan, but he never really puts it quite like this.) Clearly, these arguments are in tension. The first would now have us believe in the quantum electrodynamic field because of the predictive success of the relevant theory, but would have had us believe in the ether because of the success of Fresnel's wave optics; and the second says that the quantum electromagnetic field will go the same way as the ether in the end, so we ought not to believe in such things.

C: In 1998 you published 'What is Structural Realism?',[3] a paper which quickly became the focus of debate. Here you argue that structural realism 'gains no advantage over traditional scientific realism if it is understood as merely an *epistemological refinement* of it, and that instead it ought to be developed as a *metaphysical* position'.[4] As already mentioned, the version of structural realism which you subsequently

---

3. *Studies in the History and Philosophy of Science* 29 (3), 1998: 409-28.

4. Ibid.: 411; emphasis added.

elaborate you have called 'ontic structural realism' (OSR), though others have preferred the term 'eliminative structural realism'.[5] The more traditional, epistemological variety, in contrast, has come to be referred to as 'epistemic structural realism' (ESR), which you have also called 'Kantian structural realism'. Could you explain the key difference between these two positions, and which considerations led you to the conclusion that structural realism demanded to be reformulated as an ontological or metaphysical rather than a merely epistemological position?

JL: ESR is the claim that our best scientific theories should be thought of as describing the relations among unknown unobservable entities. That is why I have called it 'Kantian structural realism', since it incorporates the view that the intrinsic natures of the unobservable entities are epistemologically beyond reach, i.e., noumenal. Rae Langton's 'Kantian humility', for example, is very similar to ESR.[6] OSR is the claim that the world does not consist of a set of entities with intrinsic natures at all, but rather the world has a relational structure which is described by our best scientific theories. Fundamentally, OSR seeks to deny ontological priority to individual objects, and to upgrade the ontological status of relational structure. Exactly what form OSR should take is a matter of current debate. ESR is an ontologically conservative thesis that proposes a purely epistemological revision of scientific realism – hence the name. OSR is motivated by

---

5. Stathis Psillos, 'Is Structural Realism Possible?' in *Philosophy of Science* 68 (Proceedings), 2001: S13-S24.

6. Rae Langton, *Kantian Humility: Our Ignorance of Things in Themselves* (Oxford: Oxford University Press, 1998).

reflection on quantum mechanics and general relativity, as well as the problem of accommodating theory change in the history of science. I was led to OSR in part by my interest in the ontology of contemporary physics (and Steven French's work on identity and individuality in quantum mechanics),[7] and in part by the thought that the problem of theory change is an ontological one. By this latter claim I mean that the problem is to understand how there can be continuity between theories such as Newtonian mechanics and general relativity, or Maxwell's electromagnetism and quantum electrodynamics. This is an ontological problem because the natures of the entities postulated by the theories are so different. However, there is much continuity in the structure they attribute to the world via their mathematical form.

C: Your 1998 paper contains as an epigram a quotation from Max Planck which reads as follows: '[T]he structure of this physical world consistently moved farther and farther away from the world of sense and lost its former anthropomorphic character [...] Thus the physical world has become progressively more and more abstract; purely formal mathematical operations play a growing part.'[8] The quotation does not receive any discussion in the

7. Steven French has also contributed much to the development of OSR. A comprehensive guide to the literature on both OSR and ESR can be found in the entry 'Structural Realism' by James Ladyman in *The Stanford Encyclopaedia of Philosophy*, http://plato.stanford.edu/entries/structural-realism/.

8. Max Planck, 'The Universe in the Light of Modern Physics' in W. Shirmacher (ed.), *German Essays on Science in the 20th Century* (New York: Continuum, 1996), 38-57; cited by Ladyman, 'What is Structural Realism?', op. cit., 409.

paper itself. Could you explain why you chose this as an epigram, and what light you think it sheds on the debate over scientific realism?

JL: I happened to have a book called *German Essays on Science in the Twentieth Century* and read the Planck paper.[9] At that time I think I was attracted by his claim that mathematics has become more and more central to scientific representation. The quote seemed to encapsulate what I wanted to say in the paper, namely that we should stop trying to interpret physics in terms of objects of some kind and take the mathematics to be describing relational structure directly. When I look back upon it, I'm very glad I chose that epigram since I have more recently come to despair of many philosophers' inability to escape the manifest image, and their insistence on trying to do metaphysics with categories like object and intrinsic property, which I now see as anthropomorphic in the sense that they are a projection of how the everyday world of our experience is conceptualized. Scientists, especially physicists, have moved on, and it is time that metaphysicians tried at least to catch up.

C: Many philosophers will of course strongly protest your suggestion of their 'inability to escape the manifest image', not because they regard themselves as having already escaped it, but rather because they will insist that such an escape is neither possible nor desirable. For many such philosophers, the progressive deanthropomorphisation of the world exhibited by the history of the natural

9. Ibid.

sciences, far from being a cause for celebration, or even for revising our commonsense ontology in accordance with it, is rather something to be fiercely guarded against or 'critically' circumscribed. So long as natural science can be 'kept in its proper place, as a rigorous inquiry internal to the disengaged stance', it does not pose too much of a threat, but to base one's ontological commitments solely on the deliverances of the natural sciences is to be 'uncritical', 'naïve', and 'scientistic'. A crucial part of the philosophers task, on this view, is that of 'stopping natural science from overstepping its proper boundaries' and thereby 'forcing due humility on it'.[10] How would you respond?

JL: Escape from the manifest image is clearly possible for science. The scientific image of the physical world is remote from the common sense one. Let me mention just two of many examples that could be given. Firstly, if you walk in bare feet from a carpet onto ceramic tiles, the latter feel cold. According to the manifest image the tiles are colder than the carpet. Science tells us that this is an illusion. The tiles are at the same temperature as the carpet but they are better conductors of heat and so the heat from one's feet is whisked away by them making them feel cold. Secondly, according to the manifest image motion is observable and so we ought to feel it if the Earth was in motion, but according to the Galilean principle of relativity only relative motion is observable.

The manifest image is not itself fixed or necessary but is a product of the contingencies of our evolution, and of

10. Mark Sacks, *Objectivity and Insight* (Oxford: Oxford University Press, 2000), 323.

course there is some variation in it since the acuity of the senses varies between musicians, artists, surveyors and so on. I see no reason why philosophers should find escape from the manifest image impossible if it is possible for scientists. To those who maintain that science should stay in its proper place I reply that the predictions that science makes are ultimately tested by their observable consequences for the behaviour of things in the manifest image. So it is wrong to suggest that science should not impinge on the manifest image because it just does, as a matter of fact.

Another couple of examples: Firstly, contrary to what one would expect, when a helium balloon is held by a passenger in the cabin of an airplane as it accelerates down the runway, the balloon will spontaneously move forward in the direction of motion rather than backwards. This is predicted by Einstein's Equivalence Principle, according to which it is impossible to locally tell whether one is accelerating in one direction or subject to a uniform gravitational attraction from the opposite direction. Returning to the example above, Galilean relativity is also a feature of the manifest image since, as Galileo pointed out, insects flying around in the cabin of a steadily moving ship on a calm sea move just as if the ship was at rest and behave no differently, and one is able to sit at a desk and write oblivious to the motion of the vessel. Partial and total solar eclipses or the passage of comets are predicted by science but manifest to all.

Of course, scientific knowledge affects the manifest image profoundly in a way that we must celebrate, by extending people's lives through medical intervention. The scientific understanding of the causes and effects of cholera directly motivates the treatment of continual administration of saline solution which is estimated to have saved around three million lives to date. Philosophers may insist that science should keep out the manifest image but they doubtless write their arguments to this effect on computers, arrange to meet their colleagues to criticize science on mobile phones and so on. Does anyone with a seriously ill child really want science to keep out their manifest image?

I regard all such talk of keeping science in its proper place as the expression of either bad faith (because they can't really mean it when push comes to shove), conservatism (because they want to defend the doctrines of some old religion), or intellectual laziness (because science is vast, complicated and hard to learn). The charge that basing one's ontological commitments on science is naïve and uncritical is ironic in the extreme given that it is likely to be made by people who wish to defend the uncritical acceptance of intuition against the hugely complex and constantly evolving refinements engendered by science. The scientific image is ever subtle and never simple. In the end the epistemic authority of science is based on its astonishing novel predictive success and its role in the development of technologies or extraordinary power. Deference to science in respect of how the world is seems eminently sensible, but that science is supreme does not entail that it should be regarded as perfect or uncritically accepted. Scientific knowledge is provisional, incomplete and approximate. One might think that science is very far from ideal and hence that (to paraphrase the well-known saying) science is the worst source of metaphysical beliefs, apart from all the others.

C: While few philosophers would disagree with you regarding the various ways in which science and technology 'impinge upon' the manifest image, many would nevertheless insist that it simply doesn't follow from this that one ought to let the tail of natural science, as it were, wag the dog of our general worldview. Indeed, many philosophers who insist upon the methodological and ontological priority of the manifest image explicitly foreground the ways in which science and technology have radically transformed the 'everyday life-world' in their critiques of what they call the 'technological' or 'instrumental rationality' of late-capitalist post-industrial society. By privileging natural-scientific knowledge over all other forms of human experience and taking technical-scientific rationality as the paradigm of rationality in general, positivist and naturalist philosophers are accused by such critics of espousing a pernicious ideological conservatism which serves to perpetuate the politico-economic status quo and stifle creative thought.

Similarly, while few philosophers would deny the extraordinary success of science in making novel predictions, in improving the general quality and length of human life, and in providing explanations for the behaviour of observable events, many would insist that none of this obliges one to embrace ontological naturalism. Thus, for example, Edmund Husserl famously argued that the ontological posits of natural science comprise 'nothing more than a garb of ideas thrown over the world of immediate intuition and experience, the life-world',[11] amounting to 'the surreptitious substitution of the mathematically substructed world of idealities for the only real world, the one that is

11. Edmund Husserl, *Experience and Judgment* (Evanston: Northwestern University Press, 1973), 44-5.

actually given through perception, that is ever experienced and experienceable – our everyday life-world'.[12] Maurice Merleau-Ponty goes even further, claiming not only that '[s]cientific points of view are always both naïve and at the same time dishonest' on account of their refusal to acknowledge the ontological anteriority of the manifest image, but that it ought to be the task of the phenomenologist 'to re-establish a direct and primitive contact with the world [...] that world which *precedes* knowledge, of which knowledge always *speaks*, and in relation to which every scientific schematization is an abstract and derivative sign-language, as is geography in relation to the countryside in which we have learnt beforehand what a forest, a prairie or a river is.'[13]

Such strongly instrumentalist views of science are by no means restricted to phenomenology, of course, and Husserl's comments have been enthusiastically endorsed by a good number of prominent philosophers in the 'analytic' tradition, including Bas van Fraassen and Hilary Putnam. Thus Putnam, for example, citing the authority of both Husserl and Wittgenstein, argues that since natural science is 'a product of the same interests that underlie our conceptual construction of our *Lebenswelt*' it should no more be considered 'a description of reality "itself" than is our everyday talk of colours or of meanings or of desires or of values or of anything else'.[14]

---

12. Edmund Husserl, *The Crisis of European Sciences and Transcendental Philosophy* (Evanston: Northwestern University Press, 1970), 48-49.

13. Maurice Merleau-Ponty, *The Phenomenology of Perception* (London: Routledge, 1962), vii, ix.

14. Hilary Putnam, *Words and Life* (Cambridge, Mass.: Harvard University Press, 1994), 489.

For all such philosophers, the suggestion that it is possible even for scientists to 'escape the manifest image' would thus amount to failing to take account of the way in which the 'everyday *Lebenswelt*' furnishes the quasi-transcendental 'conditions of possibility' for scientific practice, and that it is only by disavowing the reality of such necessary conditions that it is possible for the scientific realist to reify the 'mathematically substructed world of idealities' of natural science as the only 'real' world. While, as you suggest, such views may indeed often be motivated ultimately by little more than bad faith, conservatism, or what have you, they are undoubtedly widespread in contemporary philosophy, and so if we are to avoid the tiresome spectacle of philosophers slinging *ad hominem* accusations and counter-accusations of 'naïveté' and 'conservativeness' at one another, it would seem that such arguments must be squarely confronted. How, then, would you go about attempting to persuade such philosophers of the erroneousness of their reasoning, or to convince them that they ought instead to embrace what in your recent book you call a 'radically naturalistic metaphysics'?[15]

JL: I see absolutely no evidence for the claim that scientific rationality is ideologically conservative or gives any support to the politico-economic status quo. Of course Lenin was hugely enthusiastic about scientific rationality and empiricism. More recently, note that the enemies of science in the USA are the members of the Christian right, who deny that humans evolved and have highly conservative views about the role of women and the civil rights of

15. *Every Thing Must Go*, op. cit., 1.

homosexual people. Moreover, of course, the existence of human-caused global warming has been advocated for years by independent scientists who have struggled to overcome the opposition of vested interests among the politico-economic elite. Those who are most enamoured of science are often also those who are most critical of prejudices of class, race and gender. On the other hand, cultures that antedate modern science have been capable of slavery and horrendous barbarism.

More generally, I am not even sure that there is such a thing as 'the status quo' in the contemporary world, since it seems to be changing rapidly and quite unstable; but technology is ultimately essential to all human life, given that we have been unable to survive without tools for all of our recent evolutionary history. Most people who live outside of industrialized societies are fairly keen to have their life-worlds transformed by science and technology. (For example, while the medicalization of child-birth may have been overdone in some societies, it should not be forgotten that infant and maternal mortality without modern medicine is extremely high.) Of course, lamentably, what usually goes with that transformation is a degree of exploitation, pollution and so on, but the selfish disregard for the wellbeing of others and of the environment is not a product of the Enlightenment.

I once reviewed a book by Mary Midgley in which she claimed that deforestation was in part caused by Cartesian dualism, as if vast reaches of Western Europe had not been deforested by our ancient ancestors. Frankly, I find the easy association that many intellectuals make between bad things about industrial and post-industrial capitalism and scientism in metaphysics completely naïve. The tragedy of the commons, which may well lead to the extinction of many species of fish due to over-fishing, is just a familiar feature of social life writ-large, and if it is prevented it will be because science has identified the problem and because we rationally decide to collectively deal with it. Science and technology certainly amplify the effects of human greed and our tendency to discount the future in favour of making a fast buck today, but the latter traits are perennial features of our species.

I am completely at a loss about who advocates privileging scientific knowledge 'over all other forms of human experience'. This would be like arguing that listening to music is better than walking in the countryside. I don't know of anyone who argues that scientific reasoning is better than the aesthetic appreciation of music or making love. However, if what is being claimed is that scientific knowledge is superior to folk wisdom or whatever, then I think that this is largely true. Science is the best source of knowledge about disease and how to treat it for example, and exorcism simply doesn't do the trick. If we are to respect people's feelings about the nature and causes of disease then presumably we must respect the feelings of religious fundamentalists who believe that homosexuality is a disease. Similarly, should the views of people whose intuitions tell them that people of a particular race are unlike them and not to be trusted be respected because to not do so is to deny the reality of their experience? While the academic critics of scientific rationality may be expecting it to be replaced by some kind of new age spirituality that will re-enchant nature, de-alienate us and inaugurate some kind of postmodern arcadia, the actual alternatives to science are the ideologies of bigotry and superstition.

As for stifling creative thought, again I see no evidence that taking science to be our best source of knowledge about how things are does this. Nobody is suggesting that artists and musicians must learn scientific theories and use them as sources of inspiration. Lived human experience and the study of great art fuels the imagination and creativity, and will do so regardless of the source from which the individual acquires their metaphysical beliefs. Science is continually renewed by human creativity and in no way conflicts with it. You mention the engaged stance, and here I agree that scientific rationality cannot tell us upon what values to base our lives. However, I am not suggesting it should, just that it be our guide with respect to our metaphysics. Furthermore, let me repeat that as a guide it should be considered to be fallible and liable to revision.

The quote from Husserl is very interesting and makes a very different point from the one about ideological conservativism. In a sense I agree with him that the mathematical idealities are all we have to substitute in metaphysics for the manifest image, since the scientific picture of the world is painted with mathematics. However, I do not think the everyday world is fixed and independent of theory. Note also that it is susceptible to appearances that must be challenged independently of science, for example, mirages and other illusions. Even in the manifest image, a rainbow will be seen to be an illusion since it looks to be in different places to different people. So from my perspective, we have either the manifest image, which we have good reason to believe is full of illusion and not our best picture of the nature of reality, or we have the scientific image. I have plenty of time for philosophers like van Fraassen who say we must embrace agnosticism about all matters metaphysical. However, it is important to note that van Fraassen does not advocate some kind of non-scientific metaphysics but rather recommends not doing metaphysics at all. Again, there is no connection between van Fraassen's and Husserl's claims on the one hand, and the ideological critique of scientific rationality on the other.

I do not think what Merleau-Ponty says about dishonesty is correct, since it is perfectly possible to acknowledge that our experience of the world is the ultimate source of all scientific knowledge while retaining a scientific outlook. Furthermore, to say that our experience is *epistemologically* prior is not to say that it is *ontologically* prior. If by the latter he means to deny that there was lots of stuff going on in the world prior to humans arriving on the scene then I see no reason to believe that. On the contrary, it is the idea that we might restore some mythical purely 'direct and primitive contact with the world' that is naïve. Babies perhaps have it, but they spend their time using their contact with the world to make their subsequent contact with it less direct and primitive, and for good reason since the world unconcep-tualized is much less forgiving to those seeking to survive in it. Of course, there is always an element of direct and primitive contact with the world in our experience, par-ticularly noticeable through intense sensation perhaps. But then it can hardly be the job of the philosopher to restore this in us since it is always present. Anyone who feels a deficit of direct contact with the world is best advised to go for a good walk, as their ailment is not liable to be cured by reading phenomenology.

Against Putnam I argue that the whole point about the scientific image is that it is what you get when you collectively refine the *Lebenswelt* in the light of theoretical reasoning and vast ranges and quantities of empirical data, so of course it is a better description than that with which we started. On the other hand, it would be a fool who argued that the manifest image is not part of the real world. The fact of our experience is itself an empirical phenomenon and, whether or not science can explain it, it would be absurd to deny its reality.

C: You have recently published *Every Thing Must Go: Metaphysics Naturalized*, co-authored with Don Ross and containing contributions from David Spurrett and John Collier.[16] While the first part of the book's title expresses your eliminativism with regard to individual objects – that is, your ontic structural realism (OSR), mentioned above – the second announces a project for a metaphysics that would, as you put it, 'escape from the manifest image'. Such a 'radically naturalistic metaphysics' is 'motivated exclusively by attempts to unify hypotheses and theories that are taken seriously by contemporary science', and you argue that 'no alternative kind of metaphysics can be regarded as a legitimate part of our collective attempt to model the structure of objective reality'.[17]

Given all this, one might be somewhat surprised to hear you say that you 'have plenty of time for philosophers like van Fraassen who say we must embrace agnosticism about

---

16. *Every Thing Must Go*, op. cit.

17. Ibid., 2.

all matters metaphysical'. As far as we understand it, van Fraassen's advocacy of agnosticism regarding metaphysics is to a significant extent motivated by his concern to delimit the scope of what he calls the 'Copernican spirit' or 'objectifying inquiry' characteristic of science in order to make the world safe for the cognitive aspirations of 'non-objectifying' modes of discourse, those of religion in particular.[18] Like many philosophers over the past few centuries, one of van Fraassen's driving concerns is that if we take the scientific world picture to be 'our entire world picture' then 'we ourselves don't seem to fit into our own world picture'[19] – in other words, that there seems to be little room to accommodate our conception of ourselves as *persons* (this being of special concern for van Fraassen 'because that topic covers the, for religion, all-important subject of personal encounter with the divine').[20]

But whether or not the motivating concern is the explicitly fideistic one of safeguarding religion from the supposed perils of a 'materialist worldview', the idea that it is either possible or desirable to base one's entire *Weltanschauung* on the deliverances of the sciences is one which has always been strongly resisted by the vast majority of philosophers, and is nowadays often blithely dismissed with little more than an invocation of the (pejoratively-intended) term 'scientism'. However, while you are happy to assume the latter epithet, you argue that the explicitly 'scientistic stance' you advocate does not 'impugn the everyday status

18. See Bas van Fraassen, *The Empirical Stance* (Yale University Press, 2002), esp. 153ff.

19. Ibid., 189.

20. Ibid., 190.

of objects like tables and baseballs',[21] nor does it entail a narrowly physicalist world-picture suited only for those who share a Quinean 'taste for desert landscapes' (what van Fraassen disparagingly calls 'the spiritually anemic tastes of scientism').[22] While what you call 'fundamental physics' retains an irreducible position of ontological priority inasmuch it is taken to impose definite asymmetrical constraints upon the permissible ontological commitments of the special sciences, your project of unification, guided as it is by the idea of consilience rather than reduction, results in an ontology 'of lush and leafy spaces rather than deserts' for which Don Ross coined the term 'Rainforest Realism'.[23]

Obviously, this is not a simple thing to explain in a few words, but could you say something about how you reconcile your physics-motivated eliminativism with regard to individual objects with an ontology which neither impugns the everyday status of objects nor has recourse to any notion of 'emergence'?

JL: The reason why I have time for van Fraassen's agnosticism about the metaphysical content of scientific theories is because it is an expression of empiricism that is itself scientific. As we discussed earlier, the history of science itself motivates a degree of scepticism about science and especially about any claim to finality or completeness made on behalf of particular parts of contemporary science.

21. Ibid., 5.

22. *The Empirical Stance*, op cit.: 3.

23. *Every Thing Must Go*, op cit., 234.

Van Fraassen's constructive empiricism is defensible on such grounds, and on the grounds that, in the end, what matters in science is making empirical predictions and that hence empirical adequacy is the aim of science. It is true that he has recently advocated his empiricism as a way of placing a limit on the claims of objectifying inquiry and a way of making the world safe for religion, but I am not sympathetic to constructive empiricism for that reason. Indeed, in so far as religions centrally involve doctrines concerning the nature of gods, messiahs and the special place of certain ethical and cultural groups in the history of the world, then they just *are* attempts at metaphysical theorizing. Presumably, furthermore, claims about, say, the unique corporeal manifestation of the divine a couple of millennia ago, are supposed to be objectively true, and so I don't understand the equation of 'the Copernican spirit' with the idea of objectification. Religion seems to me to be replete with objectifying discourse.

As for 'non-objectifying' modes of discourse, we say in the book, and I have implied as much in what I've said, that we do not see our attempts at naturalized metaphysics as rivalling or threatening the articulation of human subjectivity in art, literature, music or even in philosophical anthropology. Of course, the scientific worldview does incorporate us and it tells us about ourselves. Fundamentally, according to science, we are continuous in anatomy and physiology and to an extent in psychology with other animals. We find out many unpleasant things about ourselves from experimental psychology concerning our propensity to identify and persecute those not of our 'group', where the latter may be completely arbitrarily circumscribed. I think it is important that in our attempts to promote social justice and peaceful social living we be informed by the evidence concerning what we are actually like, not by idealized conceptions of personhood derived from our self-image which, like the manifest image, is replete with illusions. Of course, there is something to the claim that the first-person perspective per se cannot be objectively described; however, this does nothing to undermine the importance of using the most realistic models we can when deploying the third-person perspective. Again, as I have said above, naturalized metaphysics and science cannot tell us what to value, indeed the valuing of reason in itself is an extrinsic commitment to science, but that is no argument for adopting an anthropocentric or religious worldview.

Our repudiation of individual objects makes sense only in the context of how many philosophers think about them – it is the individuals of analytic metaphysics that we eliminate from our ontology, not the individuals of everyday life. Furthermore, once we have abandoned the false ideals of a privileged set of fundamental individuals, there is no reason to claim that macroscopic objects are less real or not real – hence our denial of physicalism. As for 'the spiritually anemic tastes of scientism', I think this phrase refers again to objectification, and again I say that naturalists are as capable of appreciating the value of life as anyone else.

You ask that I explain our positive ontology and so I will try to do so. In essence it amounts to seeing what follows once one accepts the idea that there is nothing more to the existence of an object than the necessity of incorporating it into any adequate and efficient predictive and explanatory theory of the world. Such theories are always applied to the world at certain scales of time and space, and often only in special locations, so we advocate what we call 'the scale relativity of ontology'. Tables, for example, are indispensable components of everyday ontology but would deliver no predictive or explanatory power to a theory designed to describe the world over scales of light years and eons, or over scales of nanoseconds and nanometers. The basic idea here is that of Daniel Dennett's 'real patterns'.[24] Don Ross developed Dennett's paper, which was about the philosophy of mind, into a defence of a kind of realism about all the special sciences.[25] We then developed the idea of synthesizing this with OSR. Our claim is that the view that things are scale-dependent patterns best accommodates both the repudiation of self-standing individuals in quantum and relativistic physics, and the ontological variety of the sciences as a whole.

C: In the first chapter of *Every Thing Must Go*, fittingly entitled 'In Defence of Scientism', you mount a strongly polemical attack upon contemporary analytic metaphysics, which you charge with 'sowing systematic confusion about the nature of the world, and how to find out about it'.[26] Analytic or 'neo-scholastic' metaphysics, you suggest, 'contributes nothing to human knowledge and, where it has any impact at all, systematically misrepresents the relative significance

24. Daniel Dennett, 'Real Patterns', *The Journal of Philosophy* 88, 1991: 27-51.

25. Don Ross, 'Rainforest realism: a Dennettian theory of existence' in D. Ross, A. Brook, and D. Thompson (eds), *Dennett's Philosophy: A Comprehensive Assessment* (Cambridge, Mass.: MIT Press, 2000), 147-168.

26. *Every Thing Must Go*, op. cit., vii.

of what we do know on the basis of science'.[27] While often paying lip-service to science (and, for obvious reasons, to physics in particular), or else rhetorically emulating it, such philosophers typically rely upon commonsensical notions of classical physics according to which the physical world is essentially 'made of' myriad 'little things' and 'micro-bangings' – a conception of the physical world which, you argue, has long-since been rendered obsolete within physics itself. Essentially, what contemporary 'neo-scholastic metaphysics' and 'pseudo-naturalist philosophy' thereby do is attempt to 'domesticate' physics on the basis of an illegitimate extension of the manifest image of the world bequeathed to us by our natural history.

Earlier on you spoke of your despair with regard to many philosophers' insistence on 'trying to do metaphysics with categories like object and intrinsic property', which are 'anthropomorphic in the sense that they are a projection of how the everyday world of our experience is conceptualized'. Similarly, in *Every Thing Must Go*, quoting Ernan McMullin's remark that 'imaginability must not be made the basis for ontology',[28] you criticize the demand for an

---

27. Ibid.

28. The passage deserves quoting at length: 'The denizens of the microworld with their "strangeness" and "charm" can hardly be said to be imaginable in the ordinary sense. At that level, we have lost many of the familiar bearings [...] that allow us to anchor the reference of existence-claims in such macrotheories as geology or astrophysics. But imaginability must not be made the test for ontology. The realist claim is that the scientist is discovering the structures of the world; it is not required in addition that these structures be imaginable in the categories of the macroworld. [...] If the success of the argument at the macrolevel is to be explained by postulating that something like the entities of the theory exist, the same ought to be true of arguments at the microlevel. Are there electrons? Yes, there are, just as there are stars and slowly moving geological plates bearing the continents of earth. What are electrons? Just what the theory of electrons says they are, no more, no less, always

ontology based on individuals on the grounds that it is tantamount to demanding 'that the mind-independent world be imaginable in terms of the categories of the macroworld'.[29] However, you have also just said that your position does not entail the elimination of the individual objects of everyday life or the macroscopic objects of the manifest image from one's ontology. How, then, do you go about squaring these assertions? If the mind-independent world is *not* to be thought of as 'imaginable in terms of the categories of the macroworld', how can the individual objects of the macroworld nonetheless be regarding as 'no less real' than the 'real patterns' uncovered by fundamental physics? Are you really suggesting that it is only the way in which certain philosophers think about objects which is 'anthropomorphic', whereas our everyday or commonsensical notion of individual objects picks out something which really exists 'out there' in the mind-independent world?

JL: Our polemic against analytic metaphysics will doubtless not persuade those already committed to it, but we hope at least to provide some solidarity to those who have their doubts about the direction the subject has taken. There is a debate that epitomizes the problem, as I see it, and that is central to the recent literature in analytic metaphysics, and it concerns the question of the conditions under which objects form composite objects. The options range from nihilism

allowing for the likelihood that the theory is open to further refinement. If we cannot quite imagine what they are, this is due to the distance of the microworld from the world in which our imaginations were formed, not the existential shortcomings of electrons [...].' Ernan McMullin, 'The Case for Scientific Realism', in J. Leplin (ed.), *Scientific Realism* (Berkeley: University of California Press, 1984), 14-15.

29. *Every Thing Must Go*, op. cit., 132.

– there are only simple objects and no composites – to unrestricted composition – all mereological sums of simple objects form composite objects. Restricted composition – the natural position that only some collections of objects form composite objects – is considered difficult to defend because finding a non-arbitrary criterion for distinguishing genuine composites is apparently problematic. The analytic metaphysicians really are trying to decide whether or not tables are real – not because they doubt there is an external world, but because they worry that only table parts are real. At no point in these debates do any of the participants refer to the complex and fascinating science of, say, how molecules form liquids, or how atomic lattices form solids. Rather, the debates are conducted a priori and in exactly the same terms as they would be if modern science had never happened. In particular, they persist in operating as if the world can be visualized as composed of little objects, much as the Greek atomists thought, and they pay scant attention to the utterly bizarre nature of matter revealed by physics. This is especially frustrating because there are fascinating issues about individuation, both in physics and the rest of science, that are being neglected by philosophers. For example, in evolutionary biology there are rich puzzles about how and why individual organisms subsume themselves within cells, colonies, multi-cellular organisms, and social colonies. Metaphysicians have realized that people are beginning to wonder about their subject, so the fashionable issue now is called 'metametaphysics'. Apparently they are worrying about whether or not there is a special metaphysical sense of 'exists'. This all strikes me as evidence that the bandwagon is about to crash and burn – but I may be being optimistic.

According to us, then, those interested in metaphysics must look to science, liberate themselves from the strictures of what can be visualized, and avoid trying to 'domesticate' the theories they find by rendering them in terms of the manifest image. We also think that the notion of an 'object' is fundamentally tied to the practical purposes of prediction and explanation to which theories are put, starting with folk physics and folk biology. Whether or not the species concept will feature in a fully scientific evolutionary biology, human beings have an innate disposition to categorize animals into species – and with very good reason, because over the time scales and to the degrees of accuracy that are relevant to us, there are indeed stable kinds with stable properties, and getting them right mattered a lot to our survival. Similarly, while fundamental physics will never recognize the existence of tables at our time and length scales, tables are an essential part of any adequate and efficient ontology of our world. Real patterns are scale relative, and this is why tables are as real as atoms. Life is short and time is precious, so in general people have learned only to focus successfully on salient features of the world. Ones that stick around for a while are objects. The mistake philosophers make is to start asking questions like 'Is the table the same table if some parts are replaced?', or 'Is a neutrino passing through the table part of it or not?' If one is selling an antique table with a provenance then there may be a genuine need to ask whether it really is the same table that was made by a famous craftsman or whether it is a new table with old legs or whatever. However, there are many questions about tables to which we should expect no answer, because real patterns are necessarily approximate and scale dependent, unlike the hypostasized objects of philosophers.

Finally, note that the table as pattern is no less mind-independent for that. It is precisely because it does what it does independently of our beliefs, intentions and desires that it is a real pattern and not a fictitious one.

C: One of the principal reasons that many people regard 'scientism' as inherently objectionable is that they believe that it necessitates a drastic narrowing-down of the range of permissible ontological commitments such that only that which is quantified over by fundamental physics (on some construal thereof) may be regarded as fully real, everything else being a candidate for either (microphysicalist) reduction or straightforward ontological elimination. The charge, in short, is that a strictly physicalist ontology is a necessarily impoverished one inasmuch as it is by its very nature incapable of doing justice to the manifest image of the world – that world 'which spontaneously appears around me when I open my eyes' invoked by Eddington in his famous discussion of the problem of the relationship between the 'two tables' (i.e. the 'scientific' table of microphysics and the 'manifest' table of commonsense). While Eddington concluded that the scientific table 'is the only one which is really there – whatever "there" may be' and that the manifest table is thus a kind of anthropomorphic illusion (a 'strange compound of external nature, mental imagery and inherited prejudice'),[30] you argue that the everyday table is 'undoubtedly a real pattern', whereas '[s]trictly speaking there is no scientific table at all'.[31]

---

30. Arthur Eddington, *The Nature of the Physical World*, (Cambridge, Cambridge University Press, 1928), xii.

31. *Every Thing Must Go*, op. cit., 253.

While, on the face of it, this latter conclusion might sound like an endorsement of an instrumentalist stance vis-à-vis the 'theoretical posits' of physics, it is in fact motivated rather by a kind of instrumentalism about individual objects (both those of everyday life and the special sciences). Given your rejection of ontological physicalism (due to its incompatibility with naturalism more broadly construed),[32] and the fact that the special sciences (including non-fundamental physics) 'are richly populated with individual objects',[33] it is one of the principal objectives of your project of unification to explain the relationship between fundamental physics and the special sciences, and to do so in consilient rather than reductionist terms. As you have already mentioned, two of the key theoretical innovations which you have introduced for this purpose are the 'scale relativity of ontology', on the one hand, and a certain instrumentalist stance vis-à-vis individual objects, on the other. While, as you have said, it is the former (scale relativity) which is supposed to guarantee the reality of individual objects like tables or organisms or persons, one might nevertheless wonder whether this is not somewhat in tension with the latter instrumentalism regarding individual objects. If the objects of the special sciences are to be regarded as 'pragmatic devices used by agents to orient themselves in regions of spacetime, and to construct approximate representations of the world',[34] 'only epistemological book-keeping devices',[35] 'constructs built

32. Ibid., 40-1.

33. Ibid., 130.

34. Ibid.

35. Ibid., 240.

for second-order tracking of real patterns', or 'community representations',[36] how can they at the same time be regarded as fully (i.e. mind-independently) real? Moreover, if 'to be is to be a real pattern', how can real patterns, as you have just put it, be 'necessarily approximate'? Is there not perhaps a certain equivocation between *representatum* and *representandum* here; that is, between real patterns as representations, on the one hand, and as that which is represented, on the other? Perhaps the distinction you draw in *Every Thing Must Go* between second-order ('representational') real patterns and first-order ('extra-representational') real patterns might shed some light on this?[37]

JL: 'Instrumentalism' is a term subject to many interpretations. Normally it connotes the view that the theoretical posits of science are cognitive tools for predicting the phenomena rather than real entities. However, our instrumentalism is universal and admits of no contrast between real objects and mere posits. According to our view, individuation is always a cognitive tool that is used to predict and explain the world at some scale of resolution. The objects of the special sciences and everyday discourse are 'fully real' just because there is nothing more to being a real object than being a real pattern. When it comes to mind-independence the point is that any observer wanting to track the world at a particular scale with respect to particular features will fail to do so most efficiently if they do not quantify over the real patterns. However, reality

36. Ibid., 242.

37. Ibid., 243.

only coalesces into real patterns at all if one is restricted to a particular level of accuracy. Consider what happens in quantum field theory where all the known theories can only be applied when length-scale cut-offs are imposed to prevent infinities appearing in the equations. Of course, it is hoped that a more fundamental theory will be found that does not have such limitations, but whatever the details of it are I think it is a fairly safe bet that it will not describe the world as being composed of some set of individuals, but rather will describe some sort of structure. In the book we are agnostic about whether there will ever be a final theory in fundamental physics. Either way, we argue that our everyday and special scientific conceptions of objects are cognitive tools for getting a grip on the structure of the world. The scale relativity of ontology and the idea that to be is to be a real pattern are hence not in tension but are rather two-sides of the same metaphysical coin.

The distinction we make between first-order and second-order real patterns is not intended to be a metaphysical one, but to draw attention to the fact that the patterns we find in the world – tables for example – are patterns in phenomena that themselves are already cognitively picked out as real patterns – such as properties like macroscopic shapes, colours and textures. Many of these latter real patterns are discerned and packaged for our cognition by our basic perceptual systems. According to us all individuals are second-order real patterns in this sense. We seem to confuse representations with what is represented for our aim is to undermine the distinction when it comes to individuals. However, since it is possible to bump into tables they cannot be mere representations, so our view seems nonsensical.

I hope not, but it must be very carefully stated. When one describes the phenomena as someone bumping into a table one is representing the world at a certain scale and to a certain degree of accuracy. Fundamental physics could have no use nor attach any meaning to such a description and so in this sense the table is merely a representation; but all objects are like this, and so the table is as real as anything could be. Some real patterns are more representational than others though, insofar as they only exist because of the contingencies of our actual representations and their historical development. Hence, while any observer interested in certain scales of resolution would have to quantify over stars and planets, only someone in our particular cultural milieu needs to quantify over Sherlock Holmes. Fictional characters are real patterns but not universal ones.

C: When you say that a table is a representation inasmuch as fundamental physics does not quantify over such things, and yet that, since this is the case for all objects, 'the table is as real as anything could be', is the implication that while a table is as real as any *thing* could be, *things* as such are nevertheless not ontologically fundamental, but must rather cede their traditional place of metaphysical priority to *structures*? This much, at least, would seem to be required by your OSR, according to which there is nothing but 'structure all the way down'. Yet what exactly is it which OSR affirms to be ontologically fundamental when it insists that 'structure' is all that there is? Is it mathematical structure itself, or is it those 'extra representational real patterns' which mathematical structures are taken to represent? If it is the former, you would of course be committed to a radical form of

165

Platonism or Pythagoreanism akin to Max Tegmark's 'Mathematical Universe Hypothesis';[38] if it is the latter, how are we to understand the relationship between the mathematical theories and the metaphysically-real structures which they supposedly track?

JL: This question gets to the heart of the matter and I must confess that I am not sure what the answer to it is. The idea of structure that I have in mind is that of modal structure – nomological structure – rather than mathematical structure. However, it might be that the necessity of mathematics and the physical necessity of laws coincide, and the history of physics has progressively undermined the distinction between mathematical and physical necessity. We do not advocate Pythagoreanism or Platonism, because they contrast mathematical or formal existence with material being. Our metaphysics is directly motivated, just as we say all metaphysics should be, by the actual content of physics, and our review of the latter significantly undermines the distinction between mathematical and physical-nomological structure. However, if mathematical structure does not coincide with physical structure then the relationship between them is surely that of isomorphism (or something similar but weaker such as homomorphism). As to what makes the difference between concretely instantiated mathematical structure (physical structure) and purely mathematical structure, I think that any attempt to say so would amount to empty words that would in the end add nothing to our understanding of the difference. I have no idea what

---

38. Max Tegmark, 'The Mathematical Universe', *Foundations of Physics* 38, 2008: 101-150.

conceptual resources one could deploy to say more about a distinction that, if it obtains, is so fundamental.

C: According to OSR 'structure is all there is', yet doesn't the very concept of structure require as its complement something which is *not* structure? In this regard, Bas van Fraassen has argued that the very distinction between 'content' and 'structure' is 'painfully context-dependent',[39] and that the continuity of structure upon which structural realism's proposed solution to the history of science induction hinges is identifiable only *retrospectively*, rendering the solution both circular and ad hoc: 'The atoms are still there at some level, so that was structure. The ether is no longer there, at any level, so that was a mistake about content'.[40] Thus, van Fraassen asks: 'Is it not a little embarrassing to start with the thesis that what is preserved through scientific revolutions is the structure attributed to nature, and then to have to identify structure by noticing what has been preserved? Must this philosophy of science [not] ultimately rest on a metaphysics to distinguish intrinsic and extrinsic properties (essences and accidents, substantial form and prime matter, relation and pure quality)?'[41] How do you respond?

JL: I respond by saying that some of the structure of the ether is retained and what is retained is more than the pure

---

39. Bas van Fraassen, 'Structure: Its Shadow and Substance', *British Journal of the Philosophy of Science* 57, 2006: 303.

40. Ibid., 290.

41. Ibid., 303.

empirical content of the ether theory. In every revolution in physics much of the mathematical structure of the old theory is recoverable from the new theory. It is not just a matter of the predictions coinciding. The Galilean transformations and the inverse square law of classical mechanics are reached as approximations from relativity theory. Of course we can only say retrospectively exactly which aspects of current science will be retained in its future form, but we can say prospectively that all the well-confirmed laws, and not just the empirical content of the theories, will be recoverable from the next generation of theories. According to OSR the theoretical content of theories tracks the nomological structure of the world and not just the empirical regularities.

C: Isn't it the case that what, at one stage of the history of science, is taken to be 'extra-representational' is at a later stage found to be 'representational'; in other words, that what is at one time taken to be to describe the fundamental structure of physical reality is at a later time shown to be at best only an approximate limiting case of a more comprehensive theory, holding relative to a certain set of special conditions or domain of application? But if that is the case, how can it be legitimate to suggest that we are now in possession of knowledge of 'extra-representational real patterns' at all? Might it not rather suggest that the very distinction between 'representational' and 'extra-representational' real patterns is an epistemologically suspect one, and that we might be better-off talking instead (in the manner of Ernst Cassirer and, more recently, Michael Friedman)[42] about a

---

42. See, e.g., Ernst Cassirer, *Substance and Function and Einstein's Theory of Relativity* (London: Dover, 1923); Michael Friedman, *Dynamics of Reason* (Stanford: CSLI,

continuously converging series of mathematical structures in which the extra-representational real (the 'thing in itself', if you like) is at best a regulative ideal which science only asymptotically approximates?

JL: I agree that the most serious challenge to OSR comes from empiricism and not from scientific realism or analytic metaphysics. Van Fraassen and Friedman present this challenge in different ways because Friedman's view cedes no ontological priority to the manifest image. The thing that makes me disagree with Friedman is that I am confident that the causal and nomological structure of reality as revealed by our best science (and as approximated to a fairly good degree by common sense ontology) amounts to knowledge of real patterns that will be retained in the future. However, the idea of a real pattern is not the idea of a thing in itself, which I agree is at best a regulative ideal.

C: Perhaps the most widespread and persistent objection to OSR is that it makes no sense to talk about *relations* without *relata*; or, in other words, that the very notion of a relation presupposes *objects* which *stand in* the relations. It is on the basis of this assumption that many philosophers, while admitting that physics only tells us about the 'relational properties' of things, nevertheless insist that there must also be 'intrinsic properties' upon which the former supervene, thus motivating only an 'epistemic' or 'Kantian' structural realism (ESR) rather than the strong metaphysical or 'ontic'

2001); and Michael Friedman, 'Ernst Cassirer and Contemporary Philosophy of Science' in D. Veal (ed.) *Continental Philosophy and the Sciences: The German Tradition*, Special Issue of *Angelaki* 10 (1), 2005: 119-28.

variant (OSR) which you endorse. What is your response to this criticism? Is it only an especially stubborn metaphysical article of faith that there must be unknowable intrinsic properties (analogous to Kant's 'thing in themselves') upon which the relational properties revealed by fundamental physics must supervene? Why is it that you insist upon adopting an eliminativist rather than an agnostic stance with regard to the existence of 'intrinsic properties'?

JL: The notion of an intrinsic property is usually defined as a property which an individual possesses or not regardless of what else exists. In the philosophy of physics it has become extremely dubious to suppose that individuals exist independently of other individuals. Once the idea of classical atoms as paradigmatic of individuals is abandoned, although one can make sense of saying that all properties are intrinsic properties of the universe, the pragmatic point of saying that is obscure, to put it mildly. Note, however, that the question of whether everything supervenes on intrinsic properties is different from whether there are any intrinsic properties at all. Many philosophers would concede that there may be some relational properties that do not supervene on the intrinsic properties but insist that the latter must also exist.

C: If OSR was proposed solely as a solution to the pessimistic meta-induction, it would be open to the charge that it is ad hoc, but as you have already said, it is also motivated by reflection on quantum mechanics and general relativity. In particular, you argue that the ubiquity of quantum entanglement provides us with an empirically underdetermined choice between either individuating each particle with respect to some transcendent metaphysical haecceity or else jettisoning the notion of individuality altogether in favour of a structuralist ontology, and that the latter option is preferable on grounds of ontological parsimony. Yet as Paul Dicken has argued in his review of your book, all of this is a debate over the *interpretation* of quantum mechanics, and it is therefore hard to see how a naturalistic injunction to reject any hypothesis that 'conflicts with fundamental physics' (as your 'Primacy of Physics Constraint' demands) could decide the matter either way.[43] After all, as Dicken points out, '[i]f primitive this-ness *conflicted* with fundamental physics, it would never have been a potential *interpretation* of fundamental physics in the first place'.[44] You say in your book that 'we can cite instances of leading physicists who motivate our metaphysical approach from strictly physical considerations';[45] yet, given the problem of metaphysical underdetermination, is it not the case that one could equally cite other physicists, with very different interpretations, and thus come up with a list of constraints that would be incompatible with those which you have picked out? In other words, isn't the criterion according to which something might be taken to conflict or not to conflict with fundamental physics itself somewhat hopelessly underdetermined?

43. *Studies in History and Philosophy of Science* 39 (2), 2008: 290-3, at 292.

44. Ibid.

45. *Every Thing Must Go*, op. cit., 61.

JL: The Primacy of Physics Constraint is not meant to decide the matter. Rather it is supposed to capture the correct insights of the physicalism and reductionism that we otherwise reject. Our argument for eliminativism about self-subsistent individuals is based in part on the ad hoc manoeuvres that have to be made to make fundamental physics compatible with them, and in part on the consilience of our overall metaphysics which does not include them, but we do not take conflict to mean outright inconsistency. I think everyone will agree that there is at least a prima facie conflict between the metaphysical commitment to a world made of some set of fundamental individuals, and quantum mechanics and general relativity. Whether that conflict is there on further consideration is a matter for people's judgement and not a matter of logic. However, we claim to have given reasons to think that the right judgement, in the round, is to break the underdetermination of metaphysics by physics and the rest of science in favour of structuralism. The point about OSR and our overall metaphysics is that our naturalism requires us to abandon it if it does not express a unifying picture of the world that is both compatible with and motivates successful science.

C: The central component of your scientism is your verificationism. While the latter term is nowadays still habitually associated with the failures of the logical positivist demarcationist programme – a failure which, you suggest, paved the way for the subsequent recrudescence of neo-scholastic metaphysics – your own verificationism is not based upon any a priori philosophical criteria of meaning-satisfaction but rather upon the institutionally-selected epistemic reliability of science itself. To cite a relevant passage:

> We admire science to the point of frank scientism [...] what most impresses us about science is not its results – marvellous though these have been – but the way in which its institutional organization selects for rationality and collective epistemic progress in the activities of a species that seems, in its more natural institutional settings, strongly disposed to superstition and fearful conservatism. Our verificationism, like all versions of that, is promoted as a bar against seeking explanation where we have good reasons to doubt that it promises anything but temporary psychological satisfaction at the expense of truth. In particular, we deny that there is value to be had in philosophers postulating explanantia, without empirical constraint, on the grounds that these would make various putative explananda feel less mysterious if they prevailed.[46]

That the institutional error filters of science indeed rigorously select for optimal rationality in a way that few other institutions may claim to even approximate seems incontrovertible. However, isn't there a risk here that making theoretical research entirely subordinate to internal institutional mechanisms of selection might result in a certain counterproductive conservatism or conformism, even a severe diminution in the range and diversity of active research programmes? After all, when talking about such institutional filters here we are not only talking about an ongoing intersubjective process of rational and self-correcting inquiry but also about the power-politics of hiring committees, funding agencies and government institutions. In this regard Lee Smolin has argued in his recent book

---

46. *Every Thing Must Go*, op. cit., 61-2.

The Trouble With Physics that comparatively little progress has been made in fundamental physics over the past three decades precisely because of the way in which certain firmly entrenched institutional filters have served to perpetuate not only a particularly narrow approach to scientific problem-solving but also a particular research programme – namely, string theory – at the expense of its rivals.[47] According to Smolin, string theory 'now has such a dominant position in the academy that it is practically career suicide for young theoretical physicists not to join the field', since 'theorists who pursue approaches to fundamental physics other than string theory have almost no career opportunities'.[48]

It is well known that string theory hardly even qualifies as a candidate physical theory at all, given that nobody seems to have the slightest idea of how to test it. But given that you tie your verificationism so firmly to the processes of institutional selection rather than empirical confirmation or falsification per se, oughtn't the aforementioned institutional hegemony of string theory commit you to embrace the latter as the currently most promising approach to physical unification, despite the fact that your structuralist metaphysics would seem to be more in line with 'relational' interpretations of quantum mechanics such as those proposed by Rovelli and Smolin? Moreover, isn't it the case that it is not only philosophers but also scientists themselves who postulate explanantia 'on the grounds that

---

47. Lee Smolin, *The Trouble With Physics: The Rise of String Theory, The Fall of Science, and What Comes Next* (Boston and New York: Houghton Mifflin, 2006); see also Peter Woit, *Not Even Wrong: The Failure of String Theory and the Search for Unity in Physical Law* (New York: Basic Books, 2006).

48. Smolin, *The Trouble With Physics*, op. cit., xx, xxii.

these would make various putative explananda feel less mysterious if they prevailed'? One thinks, for example, of the popular idea of the postulation of some kind of multiverse in order to 'explain' the putative 'fine-tuning' of the cosmological constants or else to 'explain' the fact that string theory comes in more versions than all the atoms in the known universe. Thus, isn't it the case that a good deal of (institutionally heavily-funded) research in contemporary quantum gravity and cosmology is in this respect at least as 'empirically unconstrained' as anything which one might find in analytic metaphysics?

JL: String theory became popular largely because the existence of spin-2 massless bosons (gravitons ought to be exactly this kind of particle) dropped out of its formalism without being put in by hand. However, Smolin is right that string theory cannot claim any novel predictive success, and, while it is certainly well-funded, I do not think the majority of experts in fundamental physics would say that string theory has the same claim to truth as quantum mechanics or general relativity or even the standard model. It may well be that the institutional processes of science have not functioned particularly well in this case, and it may also be the case that they are not in general that great. Our book contains no arguments against the claim that there is a pressing need to improve and reform science. However, we do think that there is no other epistemic game in town.

Of course scientists also make explanatory posits, but in the end empirical consequences and predictions are what make or break theories in science. There is a big difference between the established theories in physics and the far-out speculations of contemporary theorists that attract the attention of the layperson. I am extremely sceptical about multiverses, and certainly theories associated with them would have to acquire more empirical success before they would be counted as scientific knowledge. Indeed, the 'fine-tuning' problem may be bogus since its formulation relies upon a modal distinction between laws and boundary conditions that might be spurious.

However, the general point that scientists sometimes engage in metaphysics is well-taken and sometimes they too allow themselves to get carried away. I also think that philosophers can and do carry out work that is continuous with scientific theorizing and of scientific value (for example, within the philosophy of physics or the philosophy of biology), but in recent years the field known as analytic metaphysics has been largely characterized by inquiry that ignores science altogether, or by work which addresses a domesticated and distorted scientific image (we call this the philosophy of A-level chemistry). My view is that metaphysical theorizing should always be based on or at least inspired by scientific knowledge rather than intuitions and conceptual analysis (although the latter obviously has a role to play in promoting clarity of thought generally); and also that, whether metaphysics is being carried out by philosophers or scientists, contact with experience must be considered the supreme court. In this sense I have a view of metaphysics very like that of van Fraassen – namely, that it is of epistemic value only in so far as it contributes to the progress of science.

C: Perhaps you could qualify more precisely what you mean by 'experience' and the relevant sense of 'contact' here, since the idea that 'contact with experience must be considered the supreme court' is of course one which would be endorsed by philosophers representing a wide variety of different approaches, yet you surely do not mean by 'experience' here either the 'sense perception' of traditional positivism, the 'lived experience' of the phenomenologists, nor – in spite of your expression of kinship with van Fraassen – anything which depends upon an anthropocentric distinction between what is and what is not humanly observable. Indeed, as we were saying earlier, many philosophers continue to reject the ontological import of modern physics precisely on the grounds that it seems to make *too little* 'contact with experience' in their preferred sense of the term, substituting a 'mathematically substructed world of idealities for the only real world, the one that is actually given through perception', etc. In this regard, it seems important to point out that your verificationism substitutes for the traditional empiricist criterion of *observability* the broader notion of *informational connectedness*.[49] Could you say a little about what this means, and why you deem this substitution to be necessary?

JL: The idea of 'contact with experience' I have in mind includes the traditional empiricist idea of sense perception but also includes the way we have extended our empirical contact with the world using instruments and measuring devices. All such systems have in common that they have

---

49. *Every Thing Must Go*, op. cit., 303-10.

degrees of freedom that become correlated with (contain information) about states of the world. By 'informational connectedness' we refer to a kind of contact between states of the world and subsystems of it that is very general and so does not commit us to doctrinal empiricism. When we talk about 'information' in the book we always have formal information theory in mind. There is an informational connection wherever there's a system with particular detecting capacities, a set of properties that are transduced, and a channel that explains the covariance between aspects of the transduced properties and some states of the transducer. A person, as one kind of transducer, is informationally connected from spacetime coordinates s to any part of the world w when there exists a channel such that records of properties measurable at w are transmitted to s in a way that a person, equipped with physically possible technology, could recover, and it's physically possible that the person could position themselves at s. This isn't supposed to be an analysis of anything, but a description of an important distinction, namely that between states of affairs one *could* set out to empirically investigate if one had a big enough budget, and states of affairs one could not. If the Big Bang was truly a singularity – and of course it might not be – then no one is informationally connected to the other side of it and our verificationism is then the claim that it's silly to speculate about that because anything one can imagine is as probable (in the Bayesian sense) as all the members of an infinite set of descriptions that no person *would* imagine. As always, the scale relativity of ontology applies here. So, to cite an example we use in the book, we're all informationally connected to the approximate amount of hair

Napoleon had on his head at Waterloo because we have paintings, plus records from his contemporaries that don't say he was bald but some of which would have if he had been. But we living today are informationally unconnected with the precise number of hairs Napoleon had that day and it would be foolish to speculate about whether he had x or $x+1$ or $x-1$. Our verificationism doesn't involve any deep thesis but is a form of being practical that scientists themselves observe.

C: In his classic essay 'Empiricism and the Philosophy of Mind',[50] Wilfred Sellars makes the interesting point that whereas before there was any such subject as 'the philosophy of science' all students of philosophy felt obligated to keep 'at least one eye' on the methods and findings of the sciences, once philosophy of science came to have 'nominal as well as real existence' there arose a temptation 'to leave it to the specialists, and to confuse the sound idea that philosophy is not science with the mistaken idea that philosophy is independent of science'. What this gave rise to, suggests Sellars, was the view according to which 'philosophers of science deal with a mode of discourse which is, so to speak, a peninsular offshoot from the mainland of ordinary discourse. The study of scientific discourse is conceived to be a worthy employment for those who have the background and motivation to keep track of it, but an employment which is fundamentally a hobby divorced from the perplexities of the mainland'. Aided and abetted

---

50. All of the quotations which follow are taken from section IX, 'Science and Ordinary Usage', in Wilfred Sellars, *Science, Perception and Reality* (Atascadero, California: Ridgeview, 1963), 170-74.

by an instrumentalist conception of science according to which the categories of the manifest image have an 'unchallengeable authenticity' and the theoretical apparatus of the sciences is a mere 'auxiliary framework', this in turn ultimately paved the way for a resurgence of the kind of neo-scholastic metaphysics which you rail against in your book. Could this be one of the reasons that you call what you do 'metaphysics' rather than 'philosophy of science'? Given that, as Sellars says, 'nominal causes [...] have real effects', is it time that philosophers of science wrestled the banner of 'metaphysics' from the neo-scholastics and, as it were, reoccupied the mainland of philosophical discourse?

JL: It is certainly true that much work has been done by philosophers of science, on for example, causation, laws of nature, natural kinds and so on, that definitely counts as metaphysics. Perhaps I should explain how we came to write the polemic against analytic metaphysics in the first place. We did not set out to write a book that began by attacking other philosophers, but rather to synthesize ontic structural realism and rainforest realism into a unified metaphysics applicable to science from physics to economics. We then realized that we were writing a book about metaphysics but that we were neither reading nor discussing the work of the most prominent metaphysicians of our time, but were engaging only with the literature in general philosophy of science and the philosophy of the various special sciences. At the same time we were encountering the resurgence of analytic metaphysics within philosophy and finding ourselves frustrated by its insularity and lack of engagement with the sciences. Hence, we decided to write a methodological introduction that explained why a book about metaphysics was ignoring the metaphysical literature. Once we started doing that we warmed to our theme and became convinced that what we were saying needed to be said quite independently of the rest of our project. What we say is deliberately polemical and less nuanced than it might be. Of course, there is no sharp distinction between good naturalized metaphysics and bad analytic metaphysics, or between the people who do these things. However, it is undeniable that one of the most significant developments in analytic philosophy in recent years has been the growth in power, prominence and status of metaphysics, and we stand by the claim that this is generally a bad thing for philosophy since it has led to a concentration on internally-generated philosophical problems and a failure to look outwards. By adopting the subtitle 'Metaphysics Naturalized' for the book we hoped in part to stake a claim for the mainland; however, so far I have seen no evidence that we have been successful.

C: The role which your book assigns to the philosopher vis-à-vis the sciences is very much that of an 'underla-bourer' in which philosophers help to build bridges (that is, to trace networks of consilience) between already-established domains of scientific knowledge. However, one might wonder if the history of science, and that of physics in particular, does not suggest the need for an even more intimate relationship between science and philosophy than this. The historical divorce between science and philosophy is, after all, a very recent one, hard as it often is for us to remember that fact. In this regard, not only philosophers and historians of science such as Lawrence Sklar, Michael Friedman and Thomas Ryckman[51] but also physicists such as Lee Smolin and Carlo Rovelli[52] have emphasized the crucial role of an ongoing dialogue between philosophy and physics, especially in times of revolutionary transition in the latter. What is needed at the time of the present 'unfinished revolution' in physics, they suggest, is radical reflection on the very conceptual foundations of physics, and they urge philosophers to take a more active and constructive role in these discussions; thus Rovelli writes:

> if a new synthesis is to be reached, I believe that philosophical thinking will be once more be one of its ingredients. Due to the conceptual vastness of the problematic involved, the generality and accuracy of philosophical thinking and its capacity to clarify conceptual premises are probably necessary to help physics out of a situation in which we have learned so much about the world, but no longer know what matter, time, space and causality are. As a physicist involved in this effort, I wish that philosophers who are interested in the scientific conception of the world would not confine themselves to commenting [on] and polishing the present fragmentary physical theories, but would take the risk of trying to look *ahead*.[53]

51. See, e.g., Lawrence Sklar, *Space, Time, and Spacetime* (Berkeley: University of California Press, 1974); Thomas Ryckman, *The Reign of Relativity: Philosophy in Physics 1915-1925* (Oxford: Oxford University Press, 2005) ; and the references to Friedman in note 40 above.

52. See, e.g. Lee Smolin, *The Life of the Cosmos* (Oxford: Oxford University Press, 1997); Lee Smolin, *The Trouble with Physics*, op. cit.; Carlo Rovelli, *Quantum Gravity* (Oxford: Clarendon Press, 2003); Dean Rickles, 'Interpreting Quantum Gravity', *Studies in History and Philosophy of Science* 36 (4), 2005: 691-715; and the papers in C. Callender and N. Huggett (eds), *Physics Meets Philosophy at the Planck Scale* (Cambridge: Cambridge University Press, 2001).

53. Carlo Rovelli, 'Halfway Through the Woods: Contemporary Research on Space

Given your own underlabourer conception of the role of the philosopher, is this an invitation which you think philosophers of science ought to turn down?

JL: Some philosophers have the capacity to work at the cutting edge of physics or theoretical biology, and have done so and of course should continue to do so. I see no reason why philosophers should not try and look ahead, but then since so many of them insist on looking backwards, even getting them to catch up with the present seems hard enough. However, let me emphasize that within the subfield I know best, namely the philosophy of physics, there are a great many superb intellects engaged in subtle and deep explorations of the conceptual foundations of the most advanced theories and these people are often engaged in looking ahead to some extent (I am not including myself among their number since my knowledge of quantum field theory and general relativity is not nearly good enough for me to look beyond them).

C: Finally, what advice might you have for those who may be convinced by your arguments for the need for a philosophical naturalism which goes beyond a vague sort of 'science-friendliness', yet who are nevertheless daunted by the prospect of doing metaphysics in the way that you recommend; in other words, those who may be not so much afraid of 'scientism' as intimidated by the kind of interdisciplinary omnicompetence that a project such as

and Time' in J. Earman & J. Norton (eds), *The Cosmos of Science* (Pittsburgh: University of Pittsburgh Press, 1997), 182.

COLLAPSE V

yours would seem to demand? Since you argue that a priori metaphysics 'should be discontinued'[54] and exhort contemporary philosophers to 'come back and rejoin the great epistemic enterprise of modern civilization',[55] what exactly would you advise them to do? Should they simply put aside their philosophy books and start reading up on physics, chemistry, biology, cosmology, neuroscience, economics, linguistics, anthropology ...? You said yourself earlier in the interview that science is 'vast, complicated and hard to learn'. Is there really any hope of scientifically- and mathematically-untrained philosophers being able to contribute to the kind of bridge-building which you claim is the only viable form of metaphysics? Isn't there the risk that such philosophers will only end up perpetuating yet more 'pseudo-naturalist' metaphysics due to their superficial acquaintance with the methods and findings of the sciences?

JL: The worry you raise here is a genuine one and it often concerns me given my own avowed feelings of inferiority with respect to theoretical physics. In short I think the answer is not to put away philosophy books but to make sure that one reads the relevant other subjects too. For example, many of my colleagues at Bristol work in the philosophy of mathematics and logic. They continually educate themselves in set theory, category theory, various logical systems and so on. Similarly, I do think that philosophers of mind ought to be reading about the science of the mind, political philosophers ought to be reading

54. *Every Thing Must Go*, op. cit., vii.

55. Ibid., 310.

about history, politics and economics, and so on (as indeed plenty of them do). The fact that there is a vast amount of learning to be had is no excuse for turning aside from the world and looking inwards. Philosophers in my experience are on the whole incredibly intelligent and astute. When they turn their minds to something they quickly spot ambiguities, conflations, incipient contradictions and so on. There is plenty of confusion and poor reasoning in science which they could help to sort out. Furthermore, there is another obvious solution to the problem you raise, namely: collaboration. Papers in particle physics are often written by a hundred or more people. Science in general is now so vast and highly developed that more and more work is done by teams of people. I see no reason why philosophers and scientific specialists cannot work together to integrate philosophy and science.

Enlightenment 2.0

Interview with Thomas Metzinger

Thomas Metzinger's work is at the forefront of interdisciplinary research between the philosophy of mind and cognitive neuroscience. Marrying an encyclopedic grasp of the philosophical literature on consciousness with a superlative mastery of the latest neurobiological research, his Being No One *is a groundbreaking work that recasts the terms in which the problem of consciousness is formulated. Although advances in cognitive neuroscience over the past twenty years have sparked a notable resurgence of interest in this problem among philosophers, many have argued that consciousness cannot be reductively explained by cognitive neuroscience, while others have gone so far as to insist that consciousness is a mystery that cannot be explained tout court, and that cognitive neuroscience lacks the resources to tackle 'the hard problem' of explaining how first-person subjective consciousness could ever arise from un-conscious neurophysiological processes. In our interview, Metzinger discusses not only how he confronts this philosophical challenge head-on by forging new conceptual resources capable of bridging this allegedly irreducible 'explanatory gap', but also how innovations such as the concept at the heart of his new theoretical framework – the 'phenomenal self-model' – might impact upon the personal and social experience of being human.*

COLLAPSE: At the beginning of *Being No One*[1] you criticize the tendency towards 'arrogant armchair theorizing' in what you call 'analytical scholasticism' in the philosophy of mind, a tradition which you charge with 'ignoring first-person phenomenological as well as third-person empirical constraints in the formation of one's basic conceptual tools'. Rather than taking into account empirical constraints on concept formation, such neo-scholastic 'armchair philosophers' will often explicitly stipulate that it is our commonsense or 'pre-philosophical' intuitions which must 'serve as the benchmark for a satisfactory account'.[2] But while you agree that such intuitions 'have to be taken seriously', you are scornful of the idea that they should serve as the *explanans* rather than the *explanandum* in the philosophy of mind, pointing out that it may well be the case that 'our best theories about our own minds will turn out to be radically counterintuitive', presenting us with 'a new kind of self-knowledge that most of us just cannot believe'. Though you suggest that 'nobody ever said that a fundamental expansion of our knowledge of ourselves has to be *intuitively* plausible', it is unfortunately the case that many philosophers of mind continue to act as if that were precisely the case. As Daniel Dennett has recently characterised the situation, philosophers of mind have typically proceeded 'as if the deliverances of their brute intuitions were not just *axiomatic-for-the-sake-of-the-project* but *true*, and, moreover, somehow inviolable'. Whereas in most sciences

---

1. Thomas Metzinger, *Being No One: The Self-Model Theory of Subjectivity* (Cambridge, Mass.: MIT Press, 2004). The quotations in this paragraph are taken from pages 1-3 of the book.

2. Tim Thornton, *Wittgenstein on Language and Thought* (Edinburgh: Edinburgh University Press, 1998), 1.

'few things are more prized than a counterintuitive result', given that it 'shows us something surprising and forces us to reconsider our often tacit assumptions', in philosophy of mind a counterintuitive result is 'typically taken as tantamount to a refutation'.[3]

In your own work, you are not content with simply reversing this order of priorities by taking the commonsensical intuitions and concepts of the folk and the philosophers as the *explanandum* rather than the *explanans*; you also aim to provide an account of precisely how such deeply ingrained intuitions, and the philosophical conservatism which follows from them, are 'ultimately rooted in the deeper representational structure of conscious minds'. So for you, explaining consciousness and subjectivity is not simply a matter of 'changing the way we talk', but of forging conceptually convincing links between sub-personal and personal levels of description which are *empirically* rather than *intuitively* plausible. Can you say more about what this project of 'interdisciplinary philosophy' involves, and the kinds of 'empirical constraints' which have guided the formation of your own conceptual tool-kit?

THOMAS METZINGER: Daniel Dennett is of course right – there is a certain deflationary Gestus in a lot of good, professional analytical philosophy of mind, and it sometimes blocks progress by simply being conservative without independent argument. There may be deeper evolutionary reasons for this attitude (quite obviously, our brains

3. Daniel Dennett, *Sweet Dreams: Philosophical Obstacles to a Science of Consciousness* (Cambridge, Mass.: MIT Press, 2006), 34.

are 'coherence engines', maximizing the coherence of our internal model of reality at any point, often sacrificing veridicality for short-term functional adequacy, with the 'goodness of fit' then being what determines the degree of intuitiveness of a given thought), as well as reasons based in the history and culture of analytical philosophy – which was itself a revolutionary enterprise in the past, a beautiful rebellion against academic pretentiousness and narcissistic obscurantism. I do not want to speculate about these reasons any further, but obviously, to talk in an unnecessarily 'revolutionary' tone and to cultivate counterintuitive interpretations of empirical results in order to achieve media attention (a strategy sometimes found in neuroscience) is not the solution either. It could be just another kind of corniness.

Our resources are limited. My intuition (!) is that, in these exciting times, we should not waste *too* much time and energy investigating what *exactly* the relationship between philosophy of mind and, say, neuroscience, cognitive science or AI ideally should be. Rather, in this particular historical epoch, I think further epistemic progress can be generated by philosophy becoming partly embedded into interdisciplinary research programs, following a strategy which one of my best critics, Josh Weisberg, has called the 'method of interdisciplinary constraint satisfaction' (MICS).[4] Part of the idea is to first confine ourselves to homing in on the target phenomenon in the actual world, using all sources of information available from every

---

4. See J. Weisberg, 'Consciousness Constrained: A Commentary on *Being No One*', *Psyche* 11 (5), 2005, and Metzinger's 'Reply to Weisberg: No Direction Home – Searching for Neutral Ground' in *Psyche* 12 (4), 2006. These papers, as well as a Symposium on *Being No One* can be found online at http://psyche.cs.monash.edu.au/.

single discipline researching the human mind, in order to compress the space of possible solutions dramatically. Then we can see whether, in the course of this historical phase, empirical results have actually changed some of our deeper, theoretical intuitions. Maybe then we might have a better idea of how intuitions evolved in the first place; what concepts actually are; why exactly certain forms of self-deception were adaptive and became superbly robust, spilling over into the enterprise of philosophy and science itself – or perhaps even what actually rendered unargued conservatism and corniness successful strategies in primate societies and the world of our ancestors. Let's say we are interested in consciousness, or in a specific issue like non-conceptual self-consciousness: instead of kicking the problem upstairs into formal semantics and modal logic (i.e., by making *modal* intuitions explicit; intuitions which themselves have an evolutionary history), and instead of analyzing the sociohistorical accident of how we happen to talk about our own minds today, we should perhaps strive to invent a new form of philosophizing, which would be partly data-driven and conducted by philosophers who do not just *talk* about 'first-person methods', but actually *are* phenomenologically well-travelled.

C: Cultivating counterintuitive interpretations of the results of the empirical sciences in order to grab media attention would be 'corny' indeed. Yet the fact remains that much of modern natural science is really in no *need* of any such deliberate 'cultivation' in order to bring out its 'counterintuitive' nature, quite simply because it explores aspects of reality to which our evolutionary ancestors simply had no access, and in regard to which it would therefore not have been reproductively advantageous for them to develop any 'intuitions'. This is a point, of course, which you develop at length in *Being No One* with regard to the likely evolutionary provenance of what you call our 'naive-realistic self-misunderstanding'. Indeed, the 'self-model theory of subjectivity' which you formulate is not only something which is 'radically counterintuitive' *for the time being*, as it were – the kind of theory which is deeply unsettling at first but is destined ultimately to be absorbed into the culture at large – but is something which you insist will necessarily *always* remain counterintuitive. 'Even if you are intellectually convinced by the current theory', you write, 'it will never be something *you* can believe in'.[5] Thus, you insist that we can never come to intuitively believe, properly digest or internalize the fact that the 'selves' which we take ourselves to be *do not in fact exist*.

But in this regard you have sometimes been accused of having cultivated an unnecessarily 'radical' or 'counterintuitive' interpretation of empirical results yourself. Of course, science frequently discovers that our commonsensical or folk conceptions of things are inadequate and so radically revises them. Our folk conceptions of space and time, for example, have undergone extremely profound revolutions, yet it is rarely claimed that space and time *do not exist* (even if there are certain avant-garde physicists willing to make precisely such a claim).[6] Rather, the claim is more often that they are not what we, and previous science, took them to be. Thus a predictable and somewhat inevitable objection to your thesis would be that, in claiming that 'no such

5. *Being No One*, op. cit., 567.

6. See 'The View from Nowhen: An Interview with Julian Barbour', this volume.

things as selves exist in the world: Nobody ever *was* or *had* a self',[7] you are overstating your case, since your arguments only motivate a much weaker, *revisionist* position regarding the self, rather than the strong *eliminativist* one indicated by the title of your book.

Why, then, do you feel it is necessary to insist that selves *do not exist* rather than that they are *not what we thought they were*? Why can't we think of the project as one of revision and redefinition; of replacing our folk-psychological intuitions with the richer conceptual vocabulary provided by cognitive neuroscience; or of developing new and better-informed intuitions which are grounded in science? Can you say more about the ontological constraints that necessitate eliminating rather than revising the idea of 'the self' and replacing it with the theoretical entity you call the 'phenomenal self-model'?

TM: A lot of very good questions, for many of which I do not have a ready-made, official answer. First, if it makes you feel better (it will), to be a revisionist and come up with some weaker notion of selfhood, fine. The title of the book *Being No One* attempted to allude to many different things at the same time, and certainly wasn't about the rather trivial and unoriginal point that the self is not a substance – Hume said that, Kant said that, Buddhist philosophy of mind had made the point long before, and few people uphold this ontological claim today. Yet, for the purposes of scientific psychology and neuroscience we can certainly do without the ontological commitment to 'a' self.

7. *Being No One*, op. cit., 1.

I do claim that everything we want to understand can be understood at the representational, functional, and dynamicist levels of description – and this really is not too breathtaking a point either, at least in my own view. The concept of 'a' self just is not a necessary ingredient of explanatory theories. We can predict what we want to predict and achieve the growth of knowledge we want to achieve with a more parsimonious conceptual framework. For example, relative to our interests and a given context, 'self' can be substituted by simpler notions like 'PSM' (phenomenal self-model), 'SMT-system' (self-model theory), or 'MPS' (minimal phenomenal selfhood).[8] In other contexts, such as literature, art, or everyday communication, we may continue to use the notion of 'self' in order to drive and shape each other's mental models of reality in a way that we find attractive.

But since selfhood ultimately is a form of phenomenal content, we must take the phenomenology seriously – and the phenomenology *is* Cartesian; it is expressed by what I have called the 'substantiality intuition': We actually *do* experience ourselves as ontologically autonomous, indivisible entities, as something that can 'hold itself in existence' all by itself, and as something that *knows* about its own existence, with certainty, because in some hard to understand way it is 'infinitely close to itself'. If we simply take the deflationary attitude again, or try to be good citizens and not exaggerate things too much by saying that, for example, this is just a straw man fallacy and then proposing some weaker notion of the phenomenal

8. See O. Blanke and T. Metzinger, 'Full-Body Illusions and Minimal Phenomenal Selfhood', forthcoming in the January 2009 issue of *Trends in Cognitive Sciences*.

self, then we overlook the fact that the *phenomenology* itself is deeply substantialist. Of course, the phenomenology of substantial selfhood is not an epistemically justified claim, it is just a naturally evolved form of phenomenal content. But it must be taken seriously, as I have tried to do. Deflationary accounts cannot do that: Phenomenal selves are not particulars, simples, or individual entities, but dynamical processes, creating locally supervening forms of conscious content.

C: Clearly, you are not simply reiterating the now familiar claim that the self is not a substance: as you point out, Hume, Kant, Nietzsche, and even Buddhism had already taught us that. Many philosophers, including critics of your views like Dan Zahavi,[9] are perfectly willing to concede this, but only in order to conclude that the self is a *process* rather than a substance. And it precisely by redefining the self as a process that one avoids the stronger (and rather more interesting) thesis that there are no such things as selves. Yet it seems clear that you cannot be content with such a redefinition. Were *Being No One* merely proposing to redefine phenomenal selves as dynamical processes, this would be just a redescription, not grounds for elimination. Rather, your argument would seem to be that the self experienced at the level of phenomenal content is an *effect* generated by non-phenomenal, sub-personal representational processes. Consequently, the self cannot be identified with these processes themselves, since that would be to conflate content at the level of the *representandum* with its *representatum*. This would be why it is no more legitimate to redefine the self

9. See D. Zahavi, 'Being Someone', in *Psyche* 11 (5), 2005.

as a 'process' than it was to call it a 'substance'. Would you agree that this is what distinguishes your thesis from the more familiar 'self-as-process' thesis favored by many?

TM: My perception is that some who now jump onto the 'self-as-process' reading (which I offered myself in the very first paragraph of *Being No One*) perhaps only do so because this wording has a trendy 'narrative' ring to it – and this, in turn, would set the stage for more of what my excellent British PhD student (who is a bit chaotic, but from whom I learn a lot) has recently termed 'Continental Jazz'. (I now use this new technical term all the time!) But there is no narrator, just selfless dynamical self-organization, and if the self *is* a process, then the least we must admit is that it is a very intermittent, patchy one – it comes to an end every night, in dreamless deep sleep. And waking up is obviously not performed by some transcendental technician of subjec- tivity pushing a magical reboot button in our brain – there is no subpersonal 'narrator' or 'author' piloting the conscious self. But it is also true that we do need good, modern neurophenomenology providing us with new conceptual instruments; a phenomenology that is not driven solely by ideological anti-reductionist resentment, but one that is at once historically and empirically well-informed. This is an extremely demanding challenge.

But I am guilty of having indulged in 'process' talk as well. A process is a chain of events, and, roughly, events are property instantiations in some given domain, at a specific location in space and time. As long as we stay with the representational level of description, we may differentiate between the representational content of such a process (an abstract property), its carrier (concrete neural dynamics), and the phenomenal properties co-instantiated along with it (Shoemaker and others would say phenomenal 'character' here, I mostly say 'phenomenal content' in order to distinguish it from intentional content per se). 'Selfhood' is precisely such a phenomenal property. But please note that even the vehicle/content distinction is not a necessary one, because it depends on your chosen theory of mental representation. More empirically-plausible ones, like the connectionist model of representation, demonstrate how the content can be *directly* realized in the physics of the carrier – for example in the sheer synaptic connection strength between individual units. It is the connectivity itself that does the job, and we have a host of formal tools to pick out the abstract properties we are interested in – partitions of activation vector space, points in weight space, trajectories, and so on. My own position is that introspectively available phenomenal content is just a very small subset of the overall intentional or representational content systems like ourselves generate and use, namely that portion which is locally determined, because it depends on microfunctional properties realized by the NCC (neural correlate of consciousness). Consciousness is in the brain, but a lot of cognition certainly isn't – and if you don't believe that, you should read Andy Clark's new book *Supersizing the Mind*.[10]

In the new TICS paper, Olaf Blanke and myself,[11] based on our own experimental work attempting to create out-of-body experiences in healthy individuals, have

---

10. A. Clark, *Supersizing the Mind: Embodiment, Action and Cognitive Extension* (Oxford: Oxford University Press, 2008).

11. See note 8 above.

presented a framework for the *simplest* form of conscious selfhood. Self-consciousness is in the brain, a lot of self-related cognition certainly isn't. In particular, agency is not a necessary condition for conscious selfhood, but self-location in time (presence), self-location in space (embodiment), and identification (with the transparent content of a body-image) seem to be the three decisive dimensions. So if I speak of a 'process' I envision an intermittent neural dynamics that can sometimes instantiate and functionally integrate phenomenal properties of this kind. The existence of content does not, of course, imply that there is *reference* as well. The subjective aspect of substantiality in this representational process could be entirely misrepresentational, a form whose *character* is entirely phenomenal.

C: The Cartesian 'substantiality intuition' regarding selfhood which you have mentioned – rooted as it is, as you say, deep in the evolutionary past of our species, and forming the very content of our understanding of who we are and our place in the world – is certainly not one which is likely to be abandoned any time soon. Indeed, as we've already mentioned, it is extremely difficult to imagine how the idea that what people pre-reflectively take to be their innermost 'self' is in fact nothing other than a kind of ongoing phenomenal hallucination generated by their brains could ever take root at an intuitive level. Broadly similar ideas which were afloat in the psychophysiology and philosophy of the mid-to-late nineteenth century were compared by Friedrich Albert Lange to the impact of the Copernican revolution in astronomy: Just as it was once amazingly difficult for people to think of this fixed earth on which we stand, 'the prototype of rest and stability', as moving, so it would be all the more difficult for them to recognise their own phenomenal selves, 'the prototype of all reality for them', as 'a mere scheme of representation' generated by what Lange called their 'psycho-physiological organisation'.[12] In this regard, you have written that neuroscience may instigate a revolution in our self-conception more radical than any previous scientific revolution, a revolution which might have 'greater social and cultural ramifications than any previous theoretical upheaval'.[13] Could you explain what kind of upheaval you have in mind here? How do you envisage such a cultural and social upheaval given that, as you also insist, your self-model theory of subjectivity is constitutively indigestible for us at any intuitive level of lived experience, and so necessarily confined to the level of the philosopher's conceptual understanding? What conditions would need to be in place for this 'cultural integration'[14] of your thesis to take place?

TM: Again, a lot of very important questions, and I have tried to address some of them in a forthcoming non-academic book, *The Ego-Tunnel: The Science of the Mind and the Myth of the Self*.[15] To cut a *very* long story short, neuroscience turns into neurotechnology, neurotechnology turns into phenotechnology, and in the course of the next fifty to

12. F. A. Lange, *The History of Materialism* (London: Routledge & Kegan Paul, 1925), Book 2, Section 3, Chapter 4, 206.

13. T. Metzinger (ed.), *Conscious Experience* (Paderborn: Ferdinand Schöningh, 1995), 13.

14. See *Being No One*, op. cit., 2.

15. T. Metzinger, *The Ego Tunnel: The Science of the Mind and the Myth of the Self* (New York: Basic Books, forthcoming 2009).

two hundred years such phenotechnologies will gradually invade our *Lebenswelt*, or 'life-world'. Even given a culture of denial this may then actually have a lot of psychosocial consequences – which, however, are very hard to foresee today. We see the very first, early developments in neuro-technology today – cognitive enhancers such as modafinil,[16] forensic neurotechnologies like brain-fingerprinting, and new types of lie detectors, or the development of new brain-machine interfaces, as in the case of the monkeys at Duke University controlling humanoid robots in Japan via the internet,[17] and so on. A small subset of these new technologies is already used to directly control information flow within the NCC itself, for example by alleviating severe, treatment-resistant depression through direct deep brain stimulation with electrodes and so on.[18] My point is that a small fraction of neurotechnology will slowly turn into consciousness technology and that *this* may have cultural consequences, even if we haven't got the proper, comprehensive theory of the human mind yet. The ethically relevant class of actions could be defined as all those forms of practical intentionality in which the content-specifier consists of satisfaction conditions centrally involving phenomenal contents. Now, more and more actions become technologically available, which directly influence information flow in the NCC and directly determine phenomenal content. I'm sure many people will have heard about the full-body illusion

16. See Henry Greely et al., 'Towards responsible use of cognitive-enhancing drugs by the healthy', published online in *Nature*, 7 Dec. 2008: 702-5.

17. See http://www.sciam.com/article.cfm?id=monkey-think-robot-do.

18. See Helen Mayberg et al., 'Deep Brain Stimulation for Treatment-Resistant Depression' in *Neuron*, Vol. 45, 2005: 651–660.

experiments carried out in Lausanne by Bigna Lenggenhager, Tej Tadi, Olaf Blanke and myself,[19] and perhaps some have heard about Henrik Ehrsson's brand-new variation of his own earlier studies in which you actually have the conscious experience of shaking your own hand in cyberspace.[20] What if it actually became feasible to directly control an artificial body-model in VR with your brain *and* to fully identify with the avatar on the phenomenological level (a possibility the self-model theory predicts)? Many might spontaneously say this would be terribly 'cool' or 'awesome' – but for my part, I am not so sure. If one really tries to think through, in a more sober and critical fashion, some of the consciousness technologies that are now on the horizon, one finds that the challenges they present are not only ethical, but perhaps also challenges to our mental health.

C: It is tempting to say that once such 'consciousness technologies' become possible, it will be very difficult for any ethical agency to prevent or control their deployment. But perhaps part of the motivation for your publishing a book aimed at a wider audience is precisely to pre-emptively open up a public discussion of these possibilities before they become reality. What did prompt you to write a non-academic work like *The Ego Tunnel*, and could you summarize its contents for us?

---

19. O. Blanke, B. Lenggenhager, T. Metzinger and T. Tadi, 'Video Ergo Sum: Manipulating Bodily Self-Consciousness', *Science,* Vol. 317, no. 5841, 2007: 1096-9.

20. See V. Petkova & H. H. Ehrsson, 'If I Were You: Perceptual Illusion of Body Swapping' in *PLoS ONE*, Vol. 3, Issue 12, 2008, 1-9. See http://www.plosone.org/article/info:doi/10.1371/journal.pone.0003832.

TM: I just wanted to try something new. *Being No One* was my third monograph. I had also done service for the scientific community by editing two or three anthologies focused on consciousness and by helping to construct an academic society (the Association for the Scientific Study of Consciousness),[21] setting up an infrastructure for consciousness research. So I thought it could perhaps be interesting to move on from research to teaching and the public understanding of science, at least on the level of books. So I began working on a three-volume text-book called *Grundkurs Philosophie des Geistes* (a basic course in philosophy of mind covering mostly the second half of the twentieth century, which will eventually appear in an English version as well). I am now working on Volume 3, which is on intentionality and mental representation and scheduled for publication in summer 2009. Volume One, on phenomenal consciousness, and Volume Two, on the mind-body problem, already appeared in 2006 and 2007 respectively. *The Ego Tunnel* has the subtitle 'The Science of the Mind and the Myth of the Self'. It is a popular book which will appear in March 2009. It addresses a wider audience, has a playful and experimental character to it, and attempts to explain an entirely idiosyncratic selection of those issues I personally judge to be most important in what I call the ongoing 'consciousness revolution', to the educated layperson. Of course, there is a quite a bit on self-models in there, with many concrete examples, and three interviews with prominent neuroscientists as well. The two final chapters address some of the consequences of these new scientific insights into the nature

---

21. See http://assc.caltech.edu.

of the conscious mind-brain: the ethical challenges they pose and the social and cultural changes they may produce, given the naturalistic turn in the image of humankind. I close by arguing that ultimately we will need a new 'ethics of consciousness'. If we arrive at a comprehensive theory of consciousness, and if we develop ever more sophisticated tools to alter the contents of subjective experience, we will have to think hard about what a *good* state of consciousness is. So yes, as you say, one of the functions of this project could be to draw the attention of a wider public to the relevance of neuroethics and *normative* issues that have been neglected. (Another ethical question with which I am deeply concerned these days is whether or not I should stop writing books now!)

C: In his 'Empiricism and the Philosophy of Mind' Wilfrid Sellars suggests that eliminativist claims such as the claim that 'physical objects are not coloured' ought to be construed not as statements *within* the framework of common sense or the manifest image, but rather as *challenges to the framework itself*.[22] Accordingly, is your claim that selves do not exist meant to be construed as part and parcel of a broader challenge to the manifest image, and if so, what else might need to be eliminated from it? After all, it would seem strange to say that it is only our folk conception of human beings as persons that is false; that beliefs and desires and selves do not exist but that the things about which we say we have beliefs and desires are adequately captured by common sense. So if we envision a future in

22. Wilfred Sellars, *Science, Perception and Reality* (Atascadero, California: Ridgeview, 1963), 172-73.

which we employ the language of cognitive neuroscience rather than folk psychology, wouldn't this have to be part and parcel of a much broader overhauling of all our other folk conceptions such as our intuitive or commonsensical folk physics, folk biology, etc.?

TM: Let me first give a 'Continental Jazz' type of answer to this question: Folk psychology is not only a theory, but also a practice. A lot of things will happen in science and philosophy, but the question of course is how this will actually change the practice, what it will do to everyday social interactions for example. As I pointed out above, although the way we speak about ourselves may only change slowly and gradually, the more likely prediction is that new *technologies* will invade our life-world and have an impact on the way we look at ourselves – because they directly change social interactions. The 'manifest image' is anchored in the phenomenal model of reality that evolved in our brains over millions of years, and it will certainly prove to be quite robust, at least in its transparent sensory and motor partitions. Social emotions and the opaque cognitive layers in our self-model, however, may prove to be more sensitive to a new cultural context. Actually folk psychology – understood as a pre-theoretical set of conceptual assumptions about reality – has already been completely demolished, just like folk physics. What will prove to be more robust is the pre-linguistic phenomenal model of reality anchored in our brains. And, functionally speaking, this is predominantly what drives our behaviour.

There is a deeper aspect to your question, however: it pertains to the 'self-as-epistemic-subject'. What many do not see is that there is also a sort of 'folk epistemology' – a deeply engrained, naturally evolved set of assumptions about what it means to know, what certainty is, how we mentally represent the world. If cognitive neuroscience also dissolves our traditional ideas about what a knowing self – an 'epistemic agent' – is, then this might also eventually have interesting consequences for the theory of science and philosophical epistemology.

C: Do you foresee an increasing resistance to your attempt to integrate philosophy and neuroscience, given philosophy's institutional complicity with servicing socio-cultural interests (morality, religion, liberal-democratic consensus, etc.)? What scope might there be for the kind of radically revisionary philosophical naturalism to which you are committed given how energetically some professional philosophers insist on providing alibis for folk superstition? Is the human race doomed to eternal resistance to such difficult and uncomfortable scientific truths? Or is such 'difficulty' simply based upon a misconception as to what theses like yours entail? What sort of cultural effects might we expect were they to be integrated into our everyday understanding of the world?

TM: A sincere sensitivity to ethical issues, a commitment to liberalism and democracy – if taken seriously – are very radical affairs, not something old-fashioned, and if philosophical conservatism (you may be disappointed to hear) means keeping such sociocultural interest alive then we certainly need good, professional, analytical philosophy to do this. The overall situation on our planet reminds me of one big ocean of irrationality, suffering and confusion – if more conservative philosophy's 'complicity' with certain social institutions can help at least a little bit to improve our situation, then this is a good thing.

I think, taken as a whole, humankind will prove to be absolutely robust in its resistance against the growth of knowledge, against what I sometimes like to call the 'Enlightenment 2.0' introduced by modern philosophy of mind and cognitive neuroscience, AI and AL, etc. There may be some rare individuals or even groups who find an interesting new synthesis of intellectual honesty and spirituality. But on a larger scale I believe two types of reactions are most likely to spread: A primitive form of hedonism, based on vulgar forms of materialism and a cynical, simplistic version of normative neuroanthropology; and the rise of irrationalism and fundamentalism, even in secular societies, supported by all those who desperately seek emotional security and espouse closed worldviews, simply because they cannot bear the naturalistic turn in the image of humankind. Both types of reaction are deeply human, and obviously, both are a danger to the very few stable, open societies we have established on this planet so far.

C: We certainly don't intend to denigrate the value of hard-won civil liberties or the democratic ethos: a sincere sensitivity to ethical issues and a commitment to democracy are indeed very grave and important matters, and certainly in no way 'old-fashioned'. But the question remains whether social institutions shaped by a conception of human beings as maximally rational, self-determining agents –

a conception with deep ties to a philosophical tradition that construes 'selfhood' as the defining feature of properly human being or 'personhood' – will prove adequate to the challenge of improving a human condition characterized by the undeniable surfeit of what you yourself describe as 'irrationality, suffering, and confusion'. Might there not be a fundamental difficulty in reconciling the naturalistic understanding of selfhood as an inevitable 'user-illusion' generated by the human organism with a commitment to the irreducible worth of persons understood as the ultimate loci for the freedom and dignity attributed to the individual? Does the notion of 'selfhood', given its close ties to the concept of 'personhood', not serve to anchor the ethical, political, and juridical norms upheld by those who espouse liberalism and democracy? Can one really retain these norms while denying the existence of the 'selves' that were supposed to feature among the necessary conditions for human personhood and serve as the bearers of freedom and dignity? Can there be persons without selves?

TM: Persons are not something we find out there, in objective reality. Persons are *constituted* in societies – through mutual acts of, say, acknowledging each other as rational and morally sensitive individuals. There can be selfless persons. Selfless individuals could certainly acknowledge each other as rational, and agree on a basic political and moral consensus. The problem is rather that we may turn out to be less rational than we thought, and less self-deter-mining (whatever this might mean exactly) than our own previous anthropological self-idealizations have encouraged us to believe. My point is that (if this unargued empirical speculation turns out to be true) it would be irrational as well as unethical in itself if we didn't take such new empirical insights into account. But will we be rational and ethical enough to let new data about the evolutionary history and the neural underpinnings of rational thought and moral cognition themselves influence decision-making, say, in pedagogy or politics?

I think you make a very good, and relevant, observation in describing why many of our best political theorists assume they *must* resist a naturalization of selfhood: They see the danger of bulldozing the normative dimension of personhood, of losing the 'critical subject'; the dangers associated with an erosion of precisely what you call the 'anchor' of our ethical, political, and juridical norms. You cannot imagine how well I know these worries and anti-reductionist resentments! When I studied philosophy at Frankfurt in the late 1970s, it was not only trendy, but a frequently repeated and politically-correct commonplace move among we students to call the kind of stuff I and others do today 'proto-fascist'. I was part of the more radical wings of the alternative movement of the late 70s, and when I sat in the seminars of Jürgen Habermas and so on all of this was certainly too superficial and not radical enough for me – at that time I thought that if you were really *serious* about getting in touch with political reality then you could do this by smelling some tear-gas, or by *actually* walking through shanty-towns in India. I certainly do respect Habermas and old-school political philosophy, but I have always thought that one has to dig *much* deeper in order to understand not only how the German catastrophe could happen, but why we seem unable to end all this violence and oppression, the constant turmoil on our planet that we call our 'history'. I think it is a kind of intellectual tragedy that most of the best political philosophy is systematically shielding itself off from neuroscience, evolutionary psychology, and so on. It does damage to our discipline.

C: This obdurate refusal on the part of most political philosophers to acknowledge any possible connection between the normative and the neurophysiological is indeed a kind of intellectual tragedy. But tragedy also veers into farce, as when the veritable phobia towards 'scientism' and 'reductionism' exhibited by Frankfurt School Critical Theory leads its adherents to issue moralistic denunciations of science and technology which are virtually indistinguishable from those of institutions like the Catholic Church. But critical theorists are certainly not alone in this regard. Returning to your earlier comments about analytic philosophy: We share your admiration for the analytic tradition's commitment to intellectual sobriety, responsibility, and rigour. However, despite these virtues, it cannot be wholly absolved from responsibility for the kind of neo-scholastic 'intuition-mongering' critically invoked at the beginning of this interview. Thus we are less convinced that this tradition is entirely innocent when it comes to promulgating the kind of 'closed worldviews' which actively obstruct the growth of natural-scientific knowledge. While twentieth-century analytic philosophy may have started out in part, as you put it, as 'a beautiful rebellion against academic pretentiousness and narcissist obscurantism', once should not forget that it was also in many cases an avowedly *anti-naturalist* rebellion bent on preserving the autonomy and 'purity' of philosophy by actively preventing its hybridization with empirical disciplines such as experimental psychology (a story minutely documented in Martin Kusch's *Psychologism: A Case Study in the Sociology of Philosophical Knowledge*).[23] Indeed, one might argue that the active resistance on the part of many academic philosophers to any miscegenation of philosophy with the empirical sciences ultimately has the unfortunate effect of helping to make the world safe for the irrationalism and fundamentalism of those who, as you put it, 'cannot bear the naturalistic turn in the image of humankind'. In this regard, your use of the expression 'Enlightenment 2.0' is particularly suggestive: could you elaborate? Are you referring to the way in which the techniques and methods of the natural sciences are now being used to explore those phenomena which we take to constitute the core of our humanity, i.e. mind and consciousness? The emergence of a 'science of cognition' would seem to represent science's attempt to understand itself by investigating the structure of the mind engaged in investigating reality. Is this the ultimate twist in the trajectory of Enlightenment: the twist whereby the explanatory strategies hitherto used to disenchant 'outer nature' are now being deployed to disenchant our own 'inner nature'?

TM: Well, first, anti-naturalism could be true. We have to take one philosopher and one argument at a time. I certainly do understand your point – academic disciplines are self-modeling entities too, and they tend to preserve their boundaries. There will always be individuals who

23. New York and London: Routledge, 1995.

profit from isolationism, from keeping the boundaries hard and the methods 'pure'. There is this conservative social movement within analytical philosophy, yes. But let us not commit a psychologistic fallacy or indulge in paranoia – I do not know any anti-naturalists who *intend* to make the world safe for the irrationalism and fundamentalism. The question is simply who is right here.

Enlightenment 2.0 will tell us more about what the conditions of possibility for knowledge are. We will use our intelligence not only in order to understand its own evolution, but also to begin to optimize it. We will use scientific rationality to gradually understand the fine-grained, microfunctional properties realized by our brains that *enabled* scientific rationality in the first place. If one takes a closer look, it is unclear what 'Enlightenment 1.0' actually was, but at least there were certain general *attitudes* increasingly shared and cultivated in Western society – a critical questioning of traditional institutions, customs, morals, and so on. I think that in the decades to come we may be able to elevate this old philosophical project to a new level of precision and generate a sustainable growth of knowledge by connecting it to our new partner disciplines like cognitive neuroscience. In particular, we could free the Enlightenment project of the accusatory, moralizing tone it has tended to exhibit in the past – we may obtain a better understanding of the ways in which in-group behaviour, tribalism, traditionalism, unargued conservativism, higher-order forms of self-deception and cultures of denial actually evolved, what their neural underpinnings are, why they proved to be adaptive in the world of our ancestors and how they now spill over into the process of doing science.

We may also come to understand how this effect could be minimized. In the course of this process we will also see that actual scientific practice is not at all something carried out by philosophical saints pursuing the ideal of self-knowledge, but is often driven by jealousy, ill-will, ostentatious behavior and brute career interest. This could indirectly bring about a great improvement in the process itself; it could serve to foster intellectual honesty. But Enlightenment 2.0 may also have a sobering quality about it, extending Max Weber's 'disenchantment of the world' to the conscious self. We will have to pay an emotional price for it – and what I am interested in is what this may do to the forces of social cohesion, to what Habermas would have called *soziale Bindekräfte*.

C: In *Being No One*, you describe the object which I consciously experience as holding in my hand as 'a dynamic, low-dimensional shadow of the actual physical object in your hand, a dancing shadow in your nervous system'.[24] Does this not also imply that the hands which are holding the book, and indeed, the entire manifest image of the world, turns out to be 'a dancing shadow in my nervous system'? There are several other places in your book where you say that the content of our phenomenal image of the world is 'solely' and 'exclusively' due to our neurophysiology. For example, you write: 'Our conscious model of reality is subterranean in that it is *determined exclusively by the internal properties of our nervous system* [...] phenomenal experience as such unfolds in an *internal* space, in a space quite distinct from the world

24. *Being No One*, op. cit., 549

described by ordinary physics [...] [and] evolves within an individual model of reality, in an individual organism's brain, and its experiential properties are *determined exclusively by properties within this brain*'.[25] Similarly, the cognitive scientist Donald Hoffman has argued that our perceptions of the world no more resemble the world itself than a computer icon resembles the inside of a computer.[26] Would it be fair to say that, for you, representation is more akin to simulation, understood as the process whereby the mind-brain *generates* its own virtual phenomenal reality, than to replication, understood as the process whereby a mirror *reflects* a pre-existing reality? But then what is the ontological status of the reality that is being perceived or simulated? Moreover, how do we get to know about the non-phenomenal objects to which the phenomenal 'shadow-objects' of our experience supposedly correspond in some way, and what is the nature of this correspondence? Does your conception of representation allow for the possibility that our perceptions might resemble aspects of the unperceived world in some sense, at least at a structural level? Or does the world generated by representational processes, the world of commonsense phenomenal experience, screen us from the world in itself? We might be tempted to insist that the only real objects are those quantified over by fundamental physics, but the problem with this is that fundamental physics nowadays doesn't quantify over *any* objects (a point made by James

25. Ibid., 547-8; emphasis added.

26. Donald Hoffman, *Visual Intelligence: How We Create What We See* (New York: W. W. Norton and Co., 1998); cf. 'Conscious Realism and the Mind-Body Problem' in *Mind & Matter*, 6:1, 2008: 87-121.

Ladyman in another interview for this volume),[27] and certainly doesn't provide us with anything like the 'actual physical objects' experienced in phenomenal consciousness. How, then, is science, which would seem to be rooted in the domain of phenomenal experience at some level, able to access reality? Can science dispense with appeals to perceptual consciousness altogether? Where do you stand on these basic epistemological issues?

TM: Well, we should never conflate intentional and phenomenal content. Conscious experience *per se* is how the world *appears* to you – that is all. Epistemology only comes in with intentionality, with semantic properties of representations, such as reference or truth. Unfortunately I don't know Ladyman's work yet, but it seems obvious to me that he has a very good point – we have to assume those entities as existing that our best current theories with the highest predictive success etc. *need* to postulate, and classical objects will not be among them. I like to look at our phenomenal model of reality – including objects, properties, relations, naïve physics and all – as a multimodal interface to navigate our behavioural space, a tool enabling the organism to successfully close certain sensorimotor causal loops on a very coarse-grained level, shielding it from the underlying causal complexity. Consciousness is autoregulation in a system that has become much too complex to understand itself. The phenomenal model of reality is a naturally evolved virtual organ, and segmented scenes, sets

---

27. See 'Who's Afraid of Scientism? Interview with James Ladyman' (this volume), and James Ladyman and Don Ross with David Spurrett and John Collier, *Every Thing Must Go: Metaphysics Naturalized* (Oxford: Oxford University Press, 2007).

of properties bound into robust objects, and so on, were functionally adequate fictions – just as selves were. But the majority of these fictions *must* have picked out at least some of the relevant causal regularities governing 'middle-sized' physical phenomena in our space of interaction, or else they would not have helped us to copy genes more efficiently. Other virtual models may have been adaptive precisely *because* they created functionally adequate forms of self-deception. But given the evolutionary history of nervous systems as a background assumption, it is hard to see how the majority of relational/structural assumptions about our ecological niche could have been outright false – our ancestors would not have survived.

You may remember that in *Being No One* I explicitly and deliberately decided not to develop a theory of mental representation, and to ignore epistemological issues in favor of fine-grained neurophenomenology. But I did – very vaguely and perhaps inconsistently – endorse connectionism, embodied dynamicist cognitive science and Johnson-Laird's theory of mental models as working background assumptions. For a mental model, the key phrase you are looking for could be 'partial relational homomorphy' – perhaps it is like a child's colouring-book: an extremely selective set of outlines is given, but all the colours are self-made. The extremely small and selective set of spatiotemporal relations and causal regularities faithfully carried over into our perceptual model of reality might then be something that is strongly relative to our bodies and the actions beings like us can perform in the world – a world without objects or selves, but one that can be known through the right combination of science and philosophy.

Thinker Dejecta

Nigel Cooke

All works oil on paper, 76 x 57.5cm, 2008.

Courtesy of Stuart Shave/Modern Art, London, and Andrea Rosen Gallery, New York

Alien Science

Interview with Jack Cohen and Ian Stewart

One of the most fertile collaborations in contemporary popular science writing began with a biologist and a mathematician meeting for lunch at a Coventry pub in 1990. Combining their prodigious knowledge of contemporary science, the unique partnership between Jack Cohen and Ian Stewart has spawned a series of popular science books remarkable in their scope, epistemological subtlety and conceptual innovativeness. To read 'Jack&Ian' is to embark upon an exhilarating and intellectually enriching ride through the thickets of contemporary scientific thinking and emerge with a profound sense of how it all interconnects. Their combined critical perspective brings much-needed clarity to popular science memes such as 'emergence', 'chaos' and 'complex systems', and they can be relied upon never to neglect the 'big picture'. In our interview, Cohen and Stewart recount the history of their 'complicit' collaboration, discuss the significance of the novel ideas proposed in their co-authored works, explain their criticisms of reductionism, anthropic reasoning and astrobiology, and tell us about the aliens who helped them to write their books.

COLLAPSE: Perhaps a good place to begin would be with one of the key conceptual innovations of your work together, namely 'complicity', which you define in the opening pages of your first major co-authored work, *The Collapse of Chaos*,[1] as 'the tendency of interacting systems to co-evolve in a manner that changes both, leading to a growth of complexity from simple beginnings – complexity that is unpredictable in detail, but whose general course is comprehensible and foreseeable'. The same concept is introduced more succinctly in *What Does a Martian Look Like?*[2] as referring to 'any process by which two different systems recursively complicate each other by repeated interaction'. Perhaps you could say a few words about the simple beginnings and co-evolution of what you have described as 'the collective entity [...] Jack&Ian'?[3] When and how did this unique collaboration come about, and what are some of the ways you have 'recursively complicated' each other over the years of your repeated interaction?

IAN STEWART: Jack and I met in 1990. He had read my book *Does God Play Dice?*,[4] and some of my SF stories, and sensed a fellow spirit. He phoned me, we met in a pub for lunch, and we were still there at about half past five, discussing various areas of science. We continued to meet about once

---

1. Jack Cohen & Ian Stewart, *The Collapse of Chaos: Discovering Simplicity in a Complex World* (London: Penguin Books, 1994).

2. Jack Cohen & Ian Stewart, *What Does a Martian Look Like? The Science of Extraterrestrial Life* (London: Ebury Press, 2002).

3. *What Does a Martian look Like?*, op. cit., xii.

4. Ian Stewart, *Does God Play Dice? The Mathematics of Chaos* (Oxford: Blackwell, 1989).

a week for several years, and out of those discussions emerged the plan for a book: *The Collapse of Chaos*. One of the first questions Jack asked was 'what's a good word for two processes interacting but modifying each other recursively, so that they end up being completely different from anything you'd expect just by putting them together?'. At the time, I had no idea.

JACK COHEN: I'd been very caught-up in this issue, looking for a vocabulary for interaction with change in both sides, having in mind nature/nurture etc., specifically for embryology (a book on reproduction was in preparation); asking actors (e.g. Ken Campbell – recently deceased alas) what words they used for audience relations: when actor comes on stage, audience changes; seeing that change, actor reacts. 'Well, yes', they said, 'that's so of course – but we don't have words for it … !'. I was also doing the 'Cell Biology' chapter for a great tome in *Obstetrics & Gynaecology* and, having done a drawing of a lot of the reactions in 'the cell', had come to the conclusion that it would all knot up, there was no way that these reactions could 'proceed'. There was something in *Does God Play Dice?*, which I'd just read, that suggested that Ian could be of help, so I rang him. We arranged to have lunch in the Coventry Cross pub the next day.

IS: During the writing of *The Collapse of Chaos*, I was playing word-games with 'simplicity' and 'complexity', as part of an attempt to characterise how simple large-scale structures and behaviours can emerge from the interaction of large numbers of simple components, and the words 'simplexity' and 'complicity' presented themselves. Of course 'complicity' is a standard word, but what it means has strong echoes of Jack's question about recursive interactions between two systems. So we decided to give it a more technical meaning, in the context of complex systems.

By the time we wrote *What Does a Martian Look Like?* we had become used to employing the word, so we explained it in the simplest terms we could think of to avoid importing too much baggage from complex systems.

Jack&Ian is itself an example of complicity. We have similar attitudes in many ways, but very different backgrounds. In particular Jack is a biologist and I'm a mathematician, and in those days the two subjects tended to see eyeball to eyeball rather than eye to eye. But we discovered that most of the generic questions (such as 'how do you stop PhD students spending their time on tedious routine work and get them to start thinking about the problems?') were common to both subjects. As we explored the common issues, we found that the combination of viewpoints often led us in directions that neither of us would have thought of on our own. The concept of 'complicity' was one example. It very much felt as though there was a combined entity which somehow knew more than both of us did put together. To distinguish our individual ideas from the joint ones, we referred to 'Jack&Ian'.

JC: The Jack&Ian viewpoint(s) was a curious mix: Ian was very divergent (consistent with the chaotic viewpoint: the space between the piano-keys increases, and you get more keys etc.) and I was very convergent (the egg splits, but you don't get two half-embryos – each 'heals' and becomes a complete embryo!). The first paper we did together, which was called 'Chaos, Contingency and Convergence',[5] exposed this difference amusingly, and laid the foundation for *The Collapse of Chaos*, in many ways.

C: One of the most striking aspects of your collaborative works is the impression one receives of a genuinely creative symbiosis of ideas originating from widely disparate fields of inquiry. While one can of course at times identify certain concepts and themes as bearing the signature of either 'JC' or 'IS', the way in which they then come together and re-emerge, reciprocally transformed as it were, in your co-authored writings, is something remarkable indeed. Would you care to comment upon the collaborative process which goes into writing your books?

IS: We even make such identifications ourselves, on occasions when one of us has a particular viewpoint and the other isn't sure. So we kind of sense when we are in JC and IS mode, and when it's Jack&Ian.

How we work depends on the book. *The Collapse of Chaos* and *Figments of Reality*[6] were both written the same way. We talked a lot, about whatever came to mind. We took rather scrappy notes. As the ideas came together, Jack would put together a plan.

5. *Nonlinear Science Today*, 1991: 9-13.

6. Jack Cohen & Ian Stewart, *Figments of Reality: The Evolution of the Curious Mind* (Cambridge: Cambridge University Press, 1997).

JC: Only about a sentence or two for each chapter ...

IS: After I'd commented on the plan, he fleshed each chapter heading out into about four pages of notes. Then I expanded them to chapter length, usually rewriting heavily, putting in anything related that seemed to fit, marking gaps for later repair ('Jack: tell me more about ampulla of Lorenzini'), making suggestions ('Would it be worth referring to Schrödinger's cat here?'). Jack would return the manuscript covered in pencilled responses and comments, and we'd go round the same procedure several times. On the whole we did this chapter by chapter, so I might be polishing one while Jack was tearing another to bits. As it began to converge, we took a broader view, did an editorial job on each other's contributions, chucked stuff out, replaced it with something we thought was better.

JC: A lot of this involved quite deep argument. I think there were times when the question 'How could I ever have thought that we could work together?' occurred to both of us. But then we just had to get Jack&Ian to sort out the problem, or – occasionally – we'd just leave both views in.

IS: Some stuff was self-indulgent – notably the Zarathus-trans, a race of aliens with a group mind – but they were there for a reason. Their role was to jog us, and our readers, out of the safe, familiar, parochial way of thinking. Sometimes the Zarathustrans illuminated things for us, too. I'd write a sentence, look at it, and ask myself 'now what would the Zarathustrans say about that?' And sometimes they'd say it was rubbish, and I'd work out what their viewpoint would lead to, and occasionally that made more sense than what I'd written. I think many authors find that their characters sometimes take over the book – not in reality, they're inventions, but in imposing a kind of consistency. 'Would my character do/say that?' And sometimes the answer changes your mind.

Our science fiction novels *Wheelers*[7] and *Heaven*[8] followed a very different pattern. We plotted *Wheelers* on a boring car journey from Coventry to Plymouth, and then I scrambled to write it all down on hotel stationery. Then Jack's agent sold it. Then we wrote it. Jack invented most of the characters, ideas, background, and plot. I wrote virtually every word. We did much the same for *Heaven* (not our choice of title and possibly a mistake) except for the original plot, which we assembled over several weeks. We plotted out a prequel, *Oracle*, during a very uneventful book-signing (the shop hadn't advertised it until the morning of the event). We're still looking for a publisher, though.

The *Science of Discworld*[9] series with Terry Pratchett was written differently again, as befits a three-person collaboration, but I won't go into details.

C: *The Collapse of Chaos: Discovering Simplicity in a Complex World* was published in 1994, and was followed in 1997 by

7. Ian Stewart & Jack Cohen, *Wheelers* (New York: Warner Aspect, 2000).

8. Ian Stewart & Jack Cohen, *Heaven* (New York: Warner Aspect, 2004).

9. Terry Pratchett, Ian Stewart & Jack Cohen, *The Science of Discworld* (London: Ebury Press, 1999); *The Science of Discworld II: The Globe* (London: Ebury, 2003); *The Science of Discworld III: Darwin's Watch* (London: Ebury Press, 2005).

Figments of Reality: The Evolution of the Curious Mind. For those of our readers who may not be familiar with your work, could you briefly explain a little more about what you set out to do in these books?

IS: *The Collapse of Chaos* was an attempt to tackle one of the big questions Jack asked as a result of reading *Does God Play Dice?*, which is about the mathematics of 'chaos' – which, by the way, isn't just another word for 'random'. The full term is 'deterministic chaos', and it reflects what I would argue is one of the most fundamental discoveries of the late twentieth century. Namely: rigid mathematical rules, in which the entire future of a system is determined by its present state, still permit behaviour so complex that it can be unpredictable, and certain features are genuinely random – that is, they can be modelled with complete rigour as stochastic processes.

Anyway, Jack wanted to know how a complicated system like a biological organism could exist as a coherent working structure when 'everything is chaotic'. Part of the answer is that the mathematics tells us chaos is possible, indeed common, but that it is not ubiquitous. Non-chaotic deterministic systems also exist. But the deeper issue is how chaotic systems can have robust features, as if the chaos somehow 'collapses' – hence our title. In retrospect it may not have been a good choice: people sometimes think the book is an argument against 'chaos theory', which it absolutely is not.

What we concluded – and I'm not claiming this is either correct or the last word – is that robust patterns not only can, but typically do, emerge from complex interacting systems. Down on the level of fine detail, nothing makes sense.

JC: This was my stuff with cell processes again. 'Nothing makes sense', says Ian, but it works, so far as we can tell, totally reliably. So, at the level of the cell, we're not in a 'soup' of chemicals dissolved in water; we have proteins all hooked up to each other, systems of membranes all interleaved, an immensely complicated network of causality that simply isn't a watery solution. I've done a lot of EM (electron microscopy) of cells, and quite a lot of time-lapse photography. The two views – EM revealing a series of 'rigid' membranes, time-lapse photography showing fluid movement – don't make any sense with each other. The pictures you get are incommensurate, 'wave' and 'particle' – so the cell 'is' something else again, with Ian's view and mine wrapped up in it. But this is quite common – think of nerves and 'mind'!

IS: Observe a local region of neurons firing in a brain, and you won't be able to tell what it's thinking – or even *that* it's thinking. But on a higher level, there may well be coherent structure. And (I'm basically a determinist) it is a *consequence* of the underlying small-scale structures and rules; it doesn't transcend them in any causal way. However, there is no mathematical scheme that can derive the large-scale structure from the small-scale rules, except by simulating the entire system step by step. There are no short cuts to the patterns. Basically, this is how I like to define 'emergence' as a mathematical concept.

So *The Collapse of Chaos* was mainly about physical science and evolutionary and developmental biology. *Figments of Reality* was a kind of sequel, concentrating on the mind/brain problem. From our point of view it seemed plausible that mind is an emergent property of a brain – under suitable conditions. Separating the two and making them essentially independent, as Descartes did, misses the crucial feature of emergence: that it is *caused* by the fine-scale structure and rules, but is not something that can be *derived* from them (by an argument short enough for humans to follow). So mind is a consequence of brain structure, but it cannot be *reduced* to brain structure by any rigorous logical scheme. Our chapter on free will is an attempt to reconcile the small-scale determinism of neurons with the apparent lack of determinism in the brain's decisions. We ignored quantum indeterminacy for two reasons: it may not be as random as physicists think – it might well be deterministic chaos – and if it is genuinely random, then it doesn't explain free will anyway, because that is a directed choice, not a coin-toss. What we ended up with is very close to (and anticipated) what Daniel Dennett argues in *Freedom Evolves*.[10]

C: This is the chapter in *Figments* amusingly entitled 'We Wanted to Have a Chapter on Free Will, but We Decided not to, so Here It Is'. The conclusion you reach on the problem of free will, as pithily summarised in the final sentence of the chapter, is that while freedom is indeed an illusion of sorts, it's 'not "just" an illusion: it is a *figment*

---

10. Daniel Dennett, *Freedom Evolves* (London: Penguin, 2004).

rendered real by the evolutionary complicity of mind and culture'.[11] Could you say a little about what this means, and how it anticipates Dennett's conclusions?

IS: We think that the brain makes *decisions* rather than *choices*. That is, when faced with various courses of action, the brain decides on one of them by some process which depends on our past history, personality, and so on. We feel as though we could make either choice, but that feeling may be just the 'quale' of deciding – just as the vivid impression of red is the quale of whatever in the physical world makes us perceive the colour red. This resolves the apparent conflict between physical laws that are either deterministic (Newtonian) or random (quantum). Neither fits the simple 'free will' model in which under identical circumstances the human brain is free to behave in several different ways. It *feels* as though it could do that, but what it actually does is constrained by the physics. However, because the brain is a complex system, it may in practice be unpredictable even if it behaves deterministically.

We don't really think others have free will. When they do unexpected things, we always wonder 'Why did they do that?' and seek excuses. Once we realise 'Oh, she's had a row with her boyfriend' we feel we understand the reason for the choice. With true free will, there doesn't *have* to be a reason.

Dennett argues his way to a very similar view, with 'free will' as the *quale* of decision-making.

---

11. *Figments of Reality*, op. cit., 241.

JC: Dennett takes the first three chapters to show that we can't 'decide' if the universe is determinate because, essentially, of levels with causality between them – which is essentially what in *Figments* we called 'Ant Country'.

C: For those unfamiliar with your writings, what do you mean by 'Ant Country'?

JC: The Ant Country side of things refers to all the turmoil of micro-causality that underlies history, while the 'figments' level is not just aggregates but rather 'things' with emergent properties, that (seem to) react to each other on the higher level; this separates the causality into different provenances, so that 'determinism' can't be determined! Dennett, finding this essential a-causality, leaves the question of freedom of will aside; he goes on to say that the only use of this notional 'freedom' is to make the inevitable evitable. From the same indeterminacy we go for the joke in our chapter title.

IS: Ant Country is our term for the way that many localised parts of complex systems tend to be indistinguishable from each other as far as significant differences go. Rather like being somewhere randomly chosen in a big UK city: There will be a main road with shops, an Indian restaurant, a pub, a Chinese takeaway, a betting shop, a church, some side streets, ordinary houses ... a bus stop, a set of traffic lights ... the locality will have much the same stuff as any other 'non-special' locality.

The prevalence of Ant Country means that it is virtually impossible to understand what a complex system is doing by looking at the details. A computer program, for instance, will always look like 0011011011100101 ... no matter whether it is a word processor, a spreadsheet, or the computer's own operating system. So Ant Country represents a particular kind of barrier to reductionism, when considering complex systems.

JC: We called it 'Ant Country' for essentially three reasons: Firstly, Aunt Hillary in *Gödel, Escher, Bach*,[12] the anthill whose recognition of her friend the anteater works by the ants panicking; secondly, Langton's Ant game, which demonstrates that even knowing all the rules you can't predict what'll happen; and thirdly, by envisioning a kind of suburbia, an Ant Country in which all paths are equal, some leading up and some down but without any scheme. Like suburbia, the location of the odd pub and post office doesn't imply a general geography. When trying to argue across this Ant Country to explain chemistry by physics one can use the odd by-way, but there are no general rules! This is what Ian means when he says that mind is a consequence of brain, but can't be reduced to brain. Ant Country doesn't have any general rules.

C: Apart from anticipating Dennett on freedom, what you say in *Figments* about the illusory nature of selfhood and the evolutionary provenance of that illusion also strongly gestures towards ideas subsequently worked out at considerable length by Thomas Metzinger in his recent tome

12. Douglas R. Hofstadter, *Gödel, Escher, Bach: An Eternal Golden Braid* (London & New York: Penguin, 1979), 311-336.

Being No One.[13] For example, you write about the difficulty of trying to explain how the brain creates the illusion of an internal observer 'to a person who has the strongest feeling that they *are* an internal observer, sitting inside their own head, *experiencing* that self-same illusion.'[14] In this respect, Metzinger describes us as self-modelling systems permanently ensconced within an evolutionarily bestowed 'naïve-realistic self-misunderstanding', a naïve realism in terms of which we constantly *confuse ourselves* with the content of our own self-models. Pushing this idea to what would seem to be its logical conclusion, Metzinger even goes on to insist that inasmuch as there is an illusion in operation here, it is quite literally *no-one's* illusion, since there is no-one there to be the *subject* of the illusion. As with the case of free will, however, I suspect that you would want to insist that the illusion of selfhood is not 'just' an illusion.

IS: I think 'illusion' is a loaded and overworked term. For example, physicists often say that the solidity of matter is an illusion because matter is mostly empty space. I'd prefer to say that the space, far from being empty, is full of inter-atomic forces, and it is this that creates the impression of solidity. Far from being an illusion, that's what 'solid' means on the atomic level.

So our *feeling* of 'self' is not illusory – we really do feel that way. But this of course doesn't imply that our naïve interpretation of what we feel is the literal truth. 'Self' is

---

13. Thomas Metzinger, *Being No One: The Self-Model Theory of Subjectivity.* MIT Press: Cambridge, Massachusetts, 2003. See also 'Enlightenment 2.0. Interview with Thomas Metzinger', this volume.

14. *Figments of Reality*, op. cit., 205.

whatever causes us to feel that we *have* a self. And it must be real (whatever that means) or it wouldn't happen.

JC: Metzinger clearly has gone further than we did; we're clear about 'self-hood', but only in the context of the Zarathustrans, as a model for our multibrains.

C: Metzinger describes *Being No One* as 'an experiment in *interdisciplinary* philosophy',[15] and it seems to us that this could equally well serve as a description of your work together. In the Preface to *The Collapse of Chaos* you forewarn the reader that while, for the first, more orthodox and conventional half of the book, you are able to 'provide plenty of roadmaps to tell you in advance just where we want to take you', you are unable to do this for the second, more experimental and speculative part of the book, since 'where we wish to travel, there are not only no road maps, but no roads'.[16] It is perhaps in part this sense of embarking on a real intellectual adventure, a genuine experiment in thinking, which makes your work so attractive to a growing philosophical readership who find themselves becoming increasingly disillusioned with the self-enclosed and narrowly specialised nature of much of contemporary academic philosophy. Your books tackle ontological and epistemological issues by directly drawing upon the full extent of contemporary science rather than from the point of view of a priori conceptual analysis or textual hermeneutics. To those of us who have relinquished the conceit that one ought to be able to do epistemology and

---

15. *Being No One*, op. cit., 2.

16. *The Collapse of Chaos*, op. cit., 2.

metaphysics without actually *knowing* anything – that is, without drawing upon the immense labours of the empirical sciences – and yet who remain dissatisfied for one reason or another with most versions of contemporary philosophical naturalism, your work thus provides a real breath of fresh air. Would you care to comment on this? How do you see your work in relation to traditional and contemporary philosophy? While your books are in no sense works of philosophy in the traditional sense, and although you rarely cite or discuss any of the great philosophers, you do speak of 'invading their spaces and reinventing their wheels'.[17] What precisely did you have in mind here?

IS: I think Jack and I both realised we were impinging on philosophical territory, and that we were very much amateurs (though Jack was quite widely read in philosophy – another of his roles in the collaboration). So we tried to tread a fine line in which we put forward our own ideas without explicitly relating them to mainstream philosophy, yet also without claiming that everything we said was new. We've been gratified by the way the philosophical community has responded.

The 'road-map' remark was motivated by Terry Pratchett, who read the book in manuscript form, and commented that in the first half he felt he was being pushed to the top of a roller-coaster, and was awaiting a wild ride – but the rails disappeared. We did our best to fix this problem, but we didn't want to do the usual academic trick of giving the main point away before we got to it. Sometimes suspense is better than foreknowledge.

17. Ibid., 5.

I think that what we're doing is tossing out various ideas, mostly with a sound scientific pedigree, that might stimulate a few philosophers and set them thinking along fresh lines.

Contemporary philosophy is pretty much a mystery to me, except that some of it seems to embrace a rather extreme form of social relativism – that science is whatever scientists agree on, for example. Now, there is a sense in which that is true, but there is a definite mechanism involved in coming to agreement, and it involves cross-checking with the external world. Even if every scientist in the world decided that gravity pushes things up, they still wouldn't want to stand underneath a piano when someone pushed it out of a window. Someone once said that when postmodernists come into a room they always use the door. Isn't it strange that they don't just get together and agree they can walk through the walls? A lot of this stuff strikes me as pretentious and silly. It certainly misrepresents science.

I also think that there is an ever-present danger, when thinking about 'philosophy of science', to put forward rather simplistic models of how scientists work – simplistic in the sense of being too rigid and broad – and then when it turns out scientists don't do that, to argue that they are doing it wrong because they're not doing what the model says they should. (I'm pleased to see that philosophers are generally avoiding this pitfall nowadays).

Now, I'm prepared to be put right on some of this, and I'm risking letting my hair down because I think I'm among friends. And I get the impression – in part from talking to colleagues in the Philosophy Department at Warwick – that many of today's philosophers have the same misgivings.

Though I'm sure they would phrase them differently.

As for the comment about invading the spaces of the philosophers, that was partly a get-out clause, acknowledging that our ideas have all sorts of relations to things that philosophers have been saying for ages, while sidestepping the obligation to give chapter and verse. Because I, for one, wouldn't be able to give chapter and verse. Jack might do better, and maybe he can come up with a good example. Within science, a similar problem arises. Some of what we say can be seen as 'systems theory', so we ought to pay homage to Ludwig von Bertalanffy. But the books cover a huge amount of ground, and the whole area has been so widely trampled that picking our way through the undergrowth would probably create more injustices than it removed – and it would make the book pretty much unreadable. In an academic work, we'd have to sort out sources like that, but this is popular science, and the most important thing is to tell a story. However, we did say when we consciously got ideas from some specific source.

JC: I'm as annoyed by philosophical relativism as Ian is, but this is complicated by my philosophical allegiances. I started off to be a rabbi, but read Spinoza's *Ethics* at the age of sixteen or seventeen, so became a biologist instead. But I still have Jewish associations (my rabbi says I'm the best atheist in her congregation ...) and read Spinoza, very conscious of how much has been done to build on the original – and to edit lots of it out. The quasi-religious bits of *Collapse* and *Figments* – not to say anything about *Heaven* – are very naïve (though not so naïve as other scientists 'looking into the Mind of God': ouch!); but I do read *Nature* every week – all of it. Ian reads *Science* and *New Scientist*, too. So we have a very useful body of knowledge from which to extract ideas, and against which to ring our own new thoughts.

So as you say, I think this is the main difference between our work and that of most philosophers: we do have much of modern science available to us; we do actually know quite a lot! But what we know isn't (just ...) the fashionable stuff, mostly quantum physics, that 'real' philosophers of science play with; we discuss between ourselves all kinds of stuff, from geology/palaeontology and embryology/ *in-vitro* fertilization to quantum experiments (the philosophers don't 'get' the experiments, just the thinking!). For example, in my own field, there has been almost no 'professional' notice taken of the Waddington symposia which, from the mid-fifties up to the nineties, began to sort out the real (philosophical) problems of development-and-evolution – what's in general being ducked now under the heading of 'evo-devo'. Professional philosophers took no real notice of those symposia, or of the (admittedly rather difficult) philosophies expounded therein – even though these symposia dealt with such issues as the thalidomide disaster, and began to deal with issues like what the genome was and what it did. This stuff is coming in now under the heading of 'epigenetics', and philosophers (with the notable exception of Evelyn Fox-Keller) are still bemused by it. It's desperately important stuff, but it's not physics, so isn't dragged into discussion!

C: Well, you're certainly right when you say that many philosophers share your misgivings about relativism, and in fact I think you'll find that the few prominent philosophers who espouse something like the kinds of views you mention tend to enjoy far more popularity outside philosophy than in it. The idea that science is 'just another narrative', for example, has an air of superficial plausibility about it when not examined too closely, and it's undoubtedly a comforting thing for many people in the humanities to be told by a sophisticated philosopher like Richard Rorty; but then Rorty's pragmatism has always received a far more severe critical treatment within philosophy than in, e.g., literary criticism or cultural studies departments.

But getting back to your comment about 'infringing upon philosophical territory', one area in which your work strongly overlaps with contemporary debates in philosophy concerns something you've already touched upon, namely: emergence. You mentioned that you endorse a kind of 'emergent monism' rather than any variety of Cartesian dualism – and this perhaps relates to the impact of Spinoza's *Ethics* on the teenage Jack – but unlike many contemporary philosophers, you do not restrict your interest in emergence to specifically human or mental features such as consciousness. Rather, you argue that emergent phenomena are ubiquitous in nature: 'emergence', as you put it in *Collapse*, 'is the rule rather than the exception'.[18] The many examples of apparently emergent phenomena which you provide in both *Collapse* and *Figments* indeed make a compelling case for this thesis, but you also do not shy away from the properly philosophical task of clarifying precisely in what sense your claim that many natural systems are 'emergent'

---

18. *The Collapse of Chaos*, op cit., 436.

is to be understood. Given the plethora of widely divergent notions of 'emergence' one can find in the literature – and we're talking about a truly vast literature here, stretching across fields as diverse as complexity theory, artificial life, biology, physics, psychology, cognitive science, sociology, philosophy, etc. – this is of course a crucially important task. Ian has already mentioned a couple of times that which just about everyone agrees constitutes the distinguishing feature of emergent phenomena: namely, that they are 'macro' phenomena (properties, entities, systems, laws ...) which are both *causally dependent on* and yet in some sense *irreducible to* or *autonomous with regard to* their 'micro' causal bases. The real philosophical difficulties arise, of course, as soon as one attempts to clarify the precise sense in which such phenomena are said to be thus 'irreducible' or 'autonomous', and in this regard philosophers typically distinguish between *metaphysical* or *ontological* notions of emergence, on the one hand, and *epistemological* ones on the other. To quote Paul Humphreys, whereas advocates of ontological emergence 'consider emergent phenomena to be objective features of the world, their emergent status being independent of our own existence and knowledge', advocates of epistemological emergence 'consider emergent properties to be a result of our limited abilities to predict, to calculate, to observe, and to explain'.[19] However, as with any such broad distinctions, there is of course plenty of room for manoeuvre, and one can indeed find a whole

19. Paul Humphreys, 'Emergence' in Donald Borchert (ed.), *The Encyclopedia of Philosophy*, Second Edition (New York: MacMillan, 2006), x. In this article Humphreys also mentions 'conceptual emergence' as a sub-category of epistemological emergence, advocates of which 'consider emergent features to be a product of our theoretical and linguistic representations of the world' (ibid.).

spectrum of views stretching between the 'metaphysical' and 'epistemological' poles on this issue.

So the question is, where does your own notion of emergence sit along this spectrum? From what Ian has already said, it seems that your conception is one which combines explanatory autonomy (irreducibility) with ontological and causal dependence (reducibility). Would that be a fair way to characterise it?

JC: Yes, that's more or less fair. Bear in mind that I have an easy time by saying that emergence is simply the difference between the sum of the parts and the whole, thus eliding the question of whether it's an idea or an objective natural phenomenon – perhaps the word can serve either interpretation! Emergence is, indeed, a very difficult issue. If one establishes a set of levels of understanding in the old familiar way, with God at the top and a Theory of Everything at the bottom, one can read upwards through physics, chemistry, biology, sociology and psychology, politics or whatever ... There is clearly a sense in which chemistry is dependent upon the working out of physical principles, in which biology is dependent upon chemistry (and much else ...), and so on. But there is no way in which we can argue from physics to chemistry, and not only because we don't know 'all of' physics. Take any chemical item, and its explanation rests upon many physical principles; there are many explanatory roads – 'Ant Country' again.

IS: My approach to emergence views all emergent phenomena as causal consequences of underlying rules.

Emergent phenomena often *appear* to 'transcend' the underlying causality of the system, by being very different from anything we expect the rules to lead to. But this may be just our lack of imagination. It's amazing what complex things very simple rules can generate.

If the detailed deduction of the phenomenon from the rules is too long and detailed for the human mind to grasp, I consider the phenomenon to be emergent. If there is some shortcut, some structure that allows a logical deduction, I call it a theorem.

For example, from the simple 'bouncing ball' model of the gas laws, mathematicians can now prove certain technical properties ('ergodicity') which imply that, say, the system almost always distributes the pressure evenly everywhere. So this feature is *not* emergent – there is a deduction short enough to be understood. Where every atom in the room will be in ten seconds' time is emergent – but not significant. The significant emergent properties are ones that really do inform us about the capabilities and behaviour of the system. The fact that the Lorentz equations have a strange attractor is now a theorem, but it relies on a gigantic computer calculation so I'm inclined to view it as effectively being emergent. So here chaos is pretty much an emergent property according to my definition of emergence.

C: It sounds very much as though, then, for Ian at least, emergence is to be regarded as an epistemological rather than an ontological or metaphysical notion. In his recent book *What's Wrong With Microphysicalism*, Andreas Hüttemann has argued that if we take emergence to be an ontological notion, candidates for emergence that depend on the epistemological inaccessibility of explanations to human beings (as opposed to, say, a Laplacian supercalculator or what the early twentieth-century theorist of emergence C. D. Broad called a 'mathematical archangel') cannot be accepted as genuine examples of systems exhibiting emergent behaviour.[20] In this respect, if we were to adhere to an ontological concept of emergence, deterministic chaos would *not* count as a genuine example of emergent behaviour.

Yet I wonder whether things are quite so simple. Earlier on you characterised the crucial feature of emergent phenomena as being that while they are caused by the fine-scale structure and rules, they are not something that can be derived from them 'by an argument short enough for humans to follow'. Similarly, you have just said that a phenomenon ought to be regarded as emergent if the deduction of the phenomenon from the rules is 'too long and detailed for the human mind to grasp'. But I wonder if this emphasis upon the cognitive limitations of finite observers such as human beings might not be somewhat misleading, inasmuch as it would seem to suggest that all apparently emergent phenomena are merely 'in the eye of the beholder', as if the simple large-scale patterns we discern in nature are somehow illusory ('*mere* appearance'), being merely an artefact of the way in which human beings are constrained to represent the world rather than something

20. Andrea Hüttemann, *What's Wrong with Microphysicalism?* (London: Routledge, 2004), 56; for Broad's 'mathematical archangel' see C. D. Broad, *The Mind and Its Place in Nature* (London: Routledge and Kegan Paul, 1925), 70.

belonging to the objective structure of reality itself. But were that the case, your conception of emergence as being 'the rule rather than the exception' for natural systems would seem to open you to the charge of anthropomorphism with regard to your conception of nature itself.

However, I take it that when you say above that 'there is no mathematical scheme that can derive the large-scale structures from the small scale rules' and that 'there are no shortcuts to the patterns', you are not making a point about the *de facto* limitations upon the computational power which happens to be available to human beings, but rather about the formal limitations upon any possible mathematical derivation in principle. In other words, the underivability which you are talking about is the kind which would prove computationally intractable for even a Laplacean supercalculator, short of a step by step simulation of the entire system. But if that is the case, does this not imply that your notion of emergence is, after all, an ontological one, and that emergence as you understand it applies directly to natural systems as objective patterns in nature, regardless of whether anyone constructs a model or simulation of them or not? In other words, emergent phenomena are not simply the product of what you have aptly described as the 'quick-and-dirty feature-recognition-systems'[21] that the human brain has evolved in order to perceptually filter the underlying complexity of nature and so survive in a hostile world; rather, the latter is just one example of the way in which the emergent patterns and structures of nature itself 'collapse' the underlying sea of chaos via the complicit interaction of the phase spaces of

21. *The Collapse of Chaos*, op. cit., 433.

complex rule-based systems. As you put it in *Collapse*, it is not only the human mind which sees the word in terms of simple high-level features; rather, 'the universe itself often functions by operating upon a high-level structure *as* a high-level structure'.[22]

Would it be right to say, then, that your critique of microphysicalist reductionism and your attempt to develop a 'contextualist' approach to science is not a matter of bestowing some kind of ontological privilege upon those high-level, macroscopic patterns and structures of the world which happen to be perceptually available to human beings – in which case you would be open to the charge of anthropomorphism or anthropocentrism just mentioned – but rather of complementing and completing the reductionist picture of nature by developing a scientific approach which would be able to do justice to those objective high-level features of nature by treating them, as it were, 'in their own terms' or 'on their own level'?

IS: I don't think we can ever apply a mathematical concept directly to reality. If I say that some real-world feature is emergent, what I mean is that, relative to a specific mathematical model, it satisfies (or at least I think it satisfies) my definition of emergence. The real world just *does* whatever it does. The main issues are about how our attempts to understand it relate to what it does.

I would say that your summary above – your last paragraph – is a very good statement of what I think is going on. There do exist mathematical theories in which

22. Ibid., 430.

the 'higher level' structures get manipulated in their own right, as concepts on their own level. For logical rigour they must be derived from the underlying mathematical rules. An example is the idea of a strange attractor in chaotic dynamics. Mathematicians had actually proved a lot of interesting things about how attractors behave before anyone could prove they existed in a specific differential equation with any link to models of real physics. So there was a 'calculus of attractors'. Now we have effective methods to prove that some systems (such as the Lorentz equations) do have strange attractors. This completes the picture.

Our understanding here, however, is much better informed by the 'attractor' concept than by the vast calculations needed to prove that one exists.

JC: Treating them on their own level resonates with me. Think of a goat and some grass. The goat is emergent, in all kinds of ways, from goat embryo (*ex* goat egg, etc …). The grass has photosynthetic cells making up most of its leaves (under the silica cuticle), and it has stolons running over the ground, etc. The reductionist's goat is a physiology in lots of detail, a genome, a pelt, a grass-eater (they're really browsers, but reductionists don't care about such details); now, I'm tempted to say that the goat is emergent from the physiology, from the embryo, even from the pelt … all the ways in which the goat is a 'whole' where they are 'parts', so that the emergent properties are those that 'fill in the space' between the parts and the whole. But when the goat 'sees' the grass, it sees the high-level grass, not the cells, not the stolons. Even when it grinds it up, it doesn't relate to the cells but to the leaves – it's important that they have a silica coat, so the goats teeth get more *worn* than if it were browsing (on softer leaves-and-twigs). There's no way that the goat embryo is causally connected to this eating: It's 'goats' and 'grass', no substructure interpolated (the goat embryo just *isn't* fundamental to the goat that's eating!). The silica erodes the teeth. The goat's eyes 'see' the leaves of the grass. We see the goat; when we handle it, it's the whole goat we relate to. That's what I mean by 'at the same level'. Yes, I can take out some goat blood and get antibodies from it, investigating the way that the goat interacts with potential bacterial parasites. But there's a strong sense in which the antibodies are part of the goat: its 'defense' against bacteria (not some lower-level, 'more fundamental' structure). The cellular level seems subservient to 'goatiness' too, in a kind of top-down way – some of the emergent properties can turn around on themselves and organize the suite of emergents into goat! (There is room here for a whole argument about the recursiveness of emergents; as in, for example, Jaegwon Kim's essay, 'Making Sense of Emergence', in Bedau and Humphreys' nice book, *Emergence*.)[23]

So I don't think that this is just a matter of the way *we think about* goats and grass; I think that goats and grass interact directly, at the level of 'goats' and 'grass' – and, moreover, *that they did so before there were people!* So for dinosaurs, too, and for seaweeds and fishes – not interacting at more basic (or fundamental) levels but *as* seaweeds and fishes, with all their (emergent and other) properties intact. The fishes 'see' the seaweed. As the rock rolls down the hill, bouncing and splashing a bit here and there, I don't think it's doing

---

23. Mark Bedau and Paul Humphreys (eds), *Emergence: Contemporary Readings in Philosophy and Science* (Cambridge, Mass.: MIT Press, 2007).

very clever mathematics; I think its emergent properties (and possibly others) are interacting directly and simply – at the level of 'bounce' and the properties of mud(s), to result in the path taken. The cryptic structure of the rock doesn't affect the trajectory, just as my appendix doesn't affect the goat. That's what we mean when we say that we find emergence in the chemical and physical world as well as in the world of people.

C: You've already mentioned 'the Zarathustrans' a couple of times – a fictional race of aliens with a 'group mind' who make numerous guest appearances in both *Collapse* and *Figments* in the form of necessarily imperfect (because anthropomorphic) 'translations' of their dialogues. As you've said, this was not just a matter of self indulgence on your part: they were there not simply to add an extra populist SF edge to your work, but rather 'to jog us, and our readers, out of the safe, familiar, parochial way of thinking' and 'to push our minds in new directions, to stimulate lateral thinking'.[24] In your most recent co-authored book, *What Does a Martian Look Like?*, you mount a strongly polemical attack upon what you regard as the lamentable lack of such 'lateral thinking' in contemporary astrobiology. Indeed, you argue that the very name 'astrobiology' is an unfortunate one, betraying 'an unimaginative approach to a subject that absolutely cries out for imagination'. Instead of 'opening up new worlds, new habitats, new types of lifelike organisation', you charge that astrobiology 'narrows everything down to two existing areas of science [...]

24. *The Collapse of Chaos*, op. cit., 51.

[o]ne of which has its feet firmly set on Mother Earth, while the other is mostly looking for duplicates of Mother Earth'.[25] While most current work on the science of extraterrestrials is carried out by astrophysicists relying upon out-dated folk biology, you argue for the need for 'a much wider form of thinking', a properly interdisciplinary approach to alien life which you call 'xenoscience'.[26] Could you say more about this?

IS: *What Does a Martian Look Like?* has a lot of Jack&Ian. The topic of alien life is one of Jack's long-term interests, and he has a lot of expertise, having advised major science fiction writers, and lectured hundreds of times to schools. My interest was more casual: as an SF fan, I'd often thought about the topic. We both felt that 'astrobiology' was too unimaginative – good, solid science for the most part, but much too happy to close down possibilities on spurious grounds. One symptom of this lack of imagination is the tired concept of 'habitable zone', which still tends to be trotted out on every possible occasion as if it tells us anything useful. A star's habitable zone is usually defined as the region around it in which liquid water can exist, and this is identified with the range of distances at which a planet supporting life can orbit.

Unfortunately this is such a simplistic concept that it obscures rather than illuminates. It is often stated that Venus, Earth, and Mars are within the Sun's habitable zone, and this is not too far wrong in terms of incident radiation

25. *What Does a Martian Look Like?*, op. cit., 6.

26. Ibid.

from the Sun. But Venus is far too hot for liquid water to exist, and Mars is too cold. Why? Sure, Venus is closer than Earth, Mars further out, but that's not the whole story. An important reason is that Venus has huge amounts of carbon dioxide in its atmosphere, and Mars lost most of its atmosphere long ago, possibly when its core solidified, its magnetic field vanished, and the solar wind blew the atmosphere away – or perhaps not, it's controversial.

The point here is that what counts for having liquid water is not how far the planet is from the star, and how hot the star is, but how the planet's atmosphere modifies the amount of radiation that the planet receives. If Mars had Venus's atmosphere and Venus had Mars's, they'd both be a lot closer to being able to support liquid water. The Earth, in fact, is probably outside the Sun's habitable zone, strictly interpreted. That's why we have ice at the poles. It's our atmosphere that keeps us warm enough for water. Agreed, if you get *too* close to the star, or *too* far away, no amount of atmospheric tinkering can keep water liquid. But that leaves a much bigger region for water than the traditional 'habitable zone'.

But that's just the first reason why 'habitable zone' is such lamentably silly thing to bang on about. At the same time the astrobiologists were promoting the concept, NASA (and its astrobiologists) were getting excited about the possibility of life on Europa, one of Jupiter's moons. Europa is *way* outside the 'habitable zone', even interpreted more generously. But it almost certainly has liquid water. There is very strong evidence of an ocean under Europa's ice. So the imaginative question is not 'what's the most simple-minded way to rule out liquid water?', but 'what other conditions would allow liquid water to exist?' And there are lots. A planet very close to the Sun, but tidally locked, would be enormously hot on one side, very cold on the other, with a ring of moderate temperatures in between. And so on.

Up to this point, I've been accepting the view that water is essential for life. But that's not clear either. In fact there was a high-level conference on that topic at the Royal Society, and the conclusion was that waterless life is very likely to be feasible.

Now, a common response to such criticisms is to ask for evidence of the existence of tidally locked planets with a ring of water, and evidence of life that does not involve water. And of course we don't have any such evidence. But that's not as strong a rebuttal as a lot of people think, because what's under discussion here, at this stage, is the *logic* of the arguments. Is it logically correct to claim that life cannot *possibly* exist except inside the 'habitable zone'? And the answer is 'no, the logic is full of holes you could drive a truck through'. It is not necessary to find actual examples to show that the logic is faulty. As a mathematician I am constantly surprised by how poorly people appreciate this point. When exposing a logical error, it is not necessary to demonstrate which alternative argument is right. Here's a simple example. Suppose someone argues that $2+2 = 22 = 2x2 = 4$. Is the logic correct? Of course not: the intermediate step $2+2 = 22$ is wrong, and so is $22 = 2x2$. I don't need to know what $2x2$ *is* to spot these errors. As it happens the argument even gets the right answer, but that doesn't mean it is logically correct!

Astrobiologists of the 'habitable zone' variety claim to rule out water-based life except on planets that are within specific limits. That argument is wrong. It may well be true most of the time, but we don't *know* that. I think there's a bit more justification for the assumption that water-based life may be more common than other kinds – but nothing *rules out* other kinds, not yet. And basing our concept of 'life' on just one sample – one planet – is hopelessly parochial. It would be like an Inuit arguing that the only habitable part of the Earth must be the polar regions, because there's no ice anywhere else, so you can't hunt seals or make igloos to live in.

Surely the most interesting thing about alien life is that it may, just possibly, *be* alien. By all means let's put most effort into locating life like our own, because we know that definitely works and maybe the same trick has worked elsewhere. But we shouldn't rule out alternatives just because they wouldn't work here.

JC: Ian has taken quite a lot of space to sort out a major way in which our *Evolving the Alien* (a more stylish title than *What does a Martian look Like?*, for the same book) differs from standard astrobiology, and from the 'habitable zone' idea – which turns out to be mistaken. In the book we introduce each chapter with an anecdote about two (very different) aliens that are cooperating on a popular 'Visits to Earth' enterprise (from a three-bedroom house in St Albans). This was intended primarily to introduce the reader to a variety of the Earth's ecosystems, but it also exposes many Terran-centred assumptions, like the Zarathustrans in our other books. But all of the ideas that postulate aliens like Terran life forms are mistaken too; so much so that I don't know whether Terran universal/ parochial ideas can work off Earth; we try to establish rules by setting out the Europa story, but we genuinely *don't know*! There are many super ideas in that book, but all of them are highly relative, not quite applicable to 'real' science. As a work of the (disciplined) imagination, it's great – and was great fun to write. But I'm not sure that you should use it as an exemplar of 'serious' science! Certainly it's scientific, in that Ian and I took the arguments very seriously (but not too solemnly), but nearly all of the arguments are relative to the possibilities that we'll find aliens some time, to test them (except, perhaps, for the bits about Ray's Tierra, computer viruses, Conway's Game of Life, and possibly sun-spots, that certainly look as if they're based in some kind of life!). It's a useful exercise for throwing out anthropic arguments, but the latter are themselves only rather silly justifications of physical constants, varied in not nearly enough dimensions. The contrast we set up in *Figments*, between the way that we introduced the Big Bang origin at the beginning of the book, and the way that a Zarathustran sees it at the end of the book (as a series of semi-realised potentialities), says a lot about anthropics: different creatures abstract different rules; which are the anthropic ones? And it also says that there isn't one way of interpreting the universe: different creatures, different interpretations; but we could so easily be simply wrong about that: many very clever people think we are – and not only Catholics!

C: Regarding so-called 'anthropic reasoning', there's no doubt that there have indeed been a plethora of very silly arguments put forward under that rubric, especially in popular pseudo-science literature. But as I understand it, your argument is not so much against anthropic reasoning per se – at least, if we understand that in its originally intended sense as merely a type of observation selection effect – but rather with the problem to which it has been typically evoked to explain: namely, that of the supposed 'fine-tuning' of the physical constants of the universe. After all, if there were ultimately a way of proving that the physical constants were indeed exquisitely 'fine-tuned', it would seem that the multiverse scenario would indeed be just about our only reasonable option, and an anthropic selection effect would then have to be invoked in order to explain why we observe the kind of universe we do. But your argument attempts to nip the whole problem in the bud from the get-go, as it were, by showing that the kind of thinking involved in the very idea that our universe is fine-tuned is not only 'misleading' and 'wrong', but even 'downright silly', being based on nothing more than 'bad logic'. One might be surprised to learn that so many eminent scientists – including the likes of Steven Weinberg, Stephen Hawking, Martin Rees, Roger Penrose, Andrei Linde, Alexander Vilenkin, Lee Smolin, Leonard Susskind, Richard Dawkins, Max Tegmark, John Gribbin, et al. – have all been guilty of such flagrant 'bad logic'. Could you explain what this charge amounts to?

JC: The business of anthropic reasoning comes under three heads, for me: Firstly, there is the 'fine-tuning' issue, which physicists resolve either by invoking a Designer who does the fine-tuning of the laws and constants, or by postulating that this one universe out of quintillions is the one which has the tuning 'just right'; it is assumed that the 'crystalline' properties of, especially, that carbon chemistry that makes physicists possible, has no flexibility whatsoever (or that it can only be moved one dimension at a time). There is no choice – it's *our* physicists or none!

Secondly, there is the 'Earth hasn't moved out of the habitable zone throughout its history' story, making control of this temperature etc. one of God's many miracles – choosing this one out of hundreds of millions of possible histories, nearly all of which failed to keep temperate! Apart from several feedback mechanisms, and that we had several Snowball earths, as well as continents of volcanoes and a few asteroid hits, can we claim that this Earth was the only one that 'made it'?

Thirdly, there is the ('Rare Earth'-type) argument from evolution: in order to get creatures that can describe what happened here, so can find it remarkable, we had to have eukaryotes/cellular life forms/echinoderms then chordates/vertebrates (or, presumably, equivalents, whatever that can mean), amphibians coming out from Devonian fishes ... Dinosaurs and the K-T meteorite had to be supplanted by mammals, and primates then apes had to do the goods. Any break or stop along the line, and we wouldn't have creatures who find the whole business so unlikely that they need to argue anthropically ... Unless we agree that 'higher' life forms will arise, sooner or later, on almost any aqueous planet, so that on any planet with extelligence it must look as if the evolutionary history was both necessary and spectacularly unlikely!

Whatever happened, happened; agreed, if the sun had gone nova we wouldn't be here; and it's quite likely that only one in a quintillion planets comes to have physicists. But a hell of a lot of the others might have creatures that remark on their own unlikelihoods!

Basically, it's the old chestnut about how unlikely *you* are to have been born: that your parents met, that your grandparents met and mated, that *that very sperm* fertilized ...; or that you live in a house which was not destroyed by the war ... wow, you just can't exist!

Start with the idea that, however unlikely, you *do* exist! Then argue away from unlikelihoods into the common elements of existence. There must be plenty of flexibility about laws, about constants (not changing them one-dimensionally, perhaps; but if we change Planck's constant by ten percent and *then compensate* by changing the ratio of electron to proton ...), about paths. There must surely be a vast phase space of possibilities, not just one particular universe whose unique solution allowed history to happen! And as soon as you allow that there are many paths, we can surely not be too surprised at existence, in almost any form! If you like, wonder at how long it took to get to physicists from fizzy clays, how long it took to get to physicists from australopithecines, why the Antikythera mechanism didn't bring the Greeks into modern physics; but then think: what happened, happened! And the alternate paths didn't (unless you think they did, in all dimensions and whenever there was a choice ... in which case, you have *more* possibilities, not less!). So the 'real' history sits among a plethora of possibilities, and is not in any sense unique. And to attempt to argue for its uniqueness by constraining the rules until it appears unique, then arguing that it had to be like that – either because God pruned all the other possibilities, or because all the other paths ran into impossibilities (such as extinction …) – is simply mad!

IS: This is a huge area so let me focus on so-called 'fine-tuning' arguments. This is about the 'fundamental constants' in the physical equations for universes – speed of light, Planck's constant, and so on. These are numbers, with no special pattern to them, and it is assumed that any choice of these numbers is in some sense just as likely as any other. The claim, widely publicised, is that our universe is virtually unique in its choice of constants: these are almost the only values that make life possible.

The argument involves the effect of changing the values a little bit. Make the gravitational constant smaller, and stars blow up, galaxies disappear. Make it larger, and everything collapses into a single gigantic black hole. If you change any one of those constants by more than a very tiny amount, it is said, then the resulting universe will be unable to support the organised complexity of life. Having lots of constants compounds this – it is like winning the lottery many times in a row. Since our universe is so improbably 'tuned for life', we then run into mystical anthropic territory: Basically, 'it must have been made specially for us'.

This claim is a wild exaggeration. One source of error is that the effect of each constant is considered in isolation, with everything else unchanged. But a change to one constant may compensate for a change to a different one – if you allow such changes. If not, you are in effect standing near Centrepoint in London, wandering a few yards along Oxford Street and Tottenham Court Road, and then claiming that there are no museums in London because you haven't found any in that limited locality.

In a recent paper in the *Journal of Cosmology and Astroparticle Physics*, Fred C. Adams[27] looked at what happens when you vary just three of the constants, those that are particularly significant for the formation of stars: the gravitational constant, the fine structure constant, and a constant that governs nuclear reaction rates. Crucially, he allowed *all three* to vary independently. He defines 'star' to mean a stable self-gravitating object that generates energy by nuclear reactions. His calculations reveal no sign of fine-tuning. Instead, stars exist for a huge range of constants: in fact, the probability of getting a universe that can make stars is about 25 percent. If you count more exotic objects as effectively being 'stars', such as black holes generating energy by quantum processes, the figure increases to around 50 percent. So, as far as stars go, our universe is not improbably finely tuned, battling odds of billions to one against. It just called 'heads', and the cosmic coin landed that way up.

This is just one flaw in the usual 'fine-tuning' claims. There are many others – including the unstated assumption that the only way to make a universe is to keep the standard equations but change the constants. In *The Collapse of Chaos* we use an analogy with cars. If you take, say, a Ford Mondeo and change the diameters of all the bolts by just a tiny amount (or indeed by a large one) then the car won't work. Either all the nuts fall off, or they don't fit on to the bolts at all. But this does not imply that the Ford Mondeo

27. F. C. Adams, 'Stars in Other Universes: Stellar Structure with Different Fundamental Constants', *Journal of Cosmology and Astroparticle Physics*, 08, 2008: 010.

is the only possible design for a car, uniquely fine-tuned for nuts and bolts to exist. All it means is that when you change the size of the bolt, you must also change the *nuts* so that they still fit. There are tens of thousands of ways to design a working car.

Another staple of fine-tuning, the 'triple-alpha' process in Red Giant stars that makes carbon, falls to bits because of an even simpler mistake. The claim of fine-tuning involves a remarkable coincidence of energy levels in various atomic nuclei, which allows the nuclear reaction that makes carbon to happen rapidly enough to make a lot of it. But the coincidence is not actually very remarkable, because stars have 'thermostats' which affect their temperature. Coal fires burn at exactly the right temperature to burn coal, because the nature of the chemical reaction affects the temperature. If the temperature is too low, the coal burns faster and the fire heats up. If the temperature is too high, the coal burns slower and the fire cools down. So it sits neatly in between, and the reaction works beautifully. There is nothing mysterious about this: it is merely a matter of negative feedback, which automatically stabilises the reaction and homes in on a temperature that works. It is the same with Red Giant stars.

A common metaphor in fine-tuning arguments is that our universe is 'balanced on a knife-edge'. This sounds dramatic, but it is misleading. To see why, take a steel ruler and a carving knife. First, try to balance the ruler on the edge of the knife. It will tilt, slide, and fall to the ground. This is the 'fine-tuning' metaphor made real. Now try to balance the ruler on your arm. It will obligingly tilt, wobble a little, and settle down to rest in perfect balance. The reason is feedback. Because your arm is rounded, gravity automatically pulls the ruler towards a suitable balance point. It doesn't have to 'aim for' some specific balance point – the correct angle emerges from the natural dynamics. Most natural systems are 'nonlinear' – like the arm, not the knife-edge.

C: Clearly, those who argue that the universe is 'fine-tuned for life' have things the wrong way around – as Victor Stenger has nicely put it: the universe is not fine-tuned for humanity; rather, humanity is fine-tuned for the universe.[28] However, it perhaps ought to be emphasized that the scientists I mentioned in my last question – all of whom seem to agree that the so-called 'fine-tuning coincidences' do indeed cry out for explanation – are in no way guilty of drawing such patently unwarranted teleological conclusions; nor, indeed, are the vast majority of scientists and philosophers who take fine-tuning and anthropic reasoning seriously.[29] Creationists and their ilk will of course always seize upon what is happening in science in order to furnish putative

---

28. Victor Stenger, 'Is the Universe Fine-Tuned for Us?' in *Why Intelligent Design Fails: A Scientific Critique of the New Creationism*, (eds) M. Young and T. Edis (New Brunswick: Rutgers University Press, 2004), 184.

29. For sophisticated treatments of anthropic reasoning see, e.g., Nick Bostrom, *Anthropic Bias: Observation Selection Effects in Science and Philosophy* (London & New York: Routledge, 2002); G.F.R. Ellis, U. Kirchner & W.R. Stoeger, 'Multiverses and Physical Cosmology', *Monthly Notices of the Royal Astronomical Society* 347, 2004: 921-936; Milan Ćirković, 'The Thermodynamical Arrow of Time: Reinterpreting the Boltzmann-Schuetz Argument', *Foundations of Physics* 33, 2003: 467-490; Mark Walker & Milan Ćirković, 'Anthropic Reasoning, Naturalism and the Contemporary Design Argument', *International Studies in the Philosophy of Science* 20, 2006: 285-307; Milan Ćirković, 'Too Early? On the Apparent Conflict of Astrobiology and Cosmology', *Biology and Philosophy* 21, 2006: 369-379; and Milan Ćirković, 'Sailing the Archipelago', this volume.

vindications of theological and teleological metaphysics – and, unfortunately, this of course sometimes includes 'believing' scientists.[30] But the fact that, for example, some such people spuriously claim that the Big Bang furnishes evidence for creation of course does nothing to invalidate modern cosmology.

IS: Yes, but my view is that not only is the 'fine-tuning' argument the wrong way round: basically, it's bogus. Many wildly different kinds of universe would be suitable for (wildly different) kinds of 'life', by which I mean systems as complex as living ones in our universe, with similar features (reproduction, autonomy, and so on). Stuart Kauffman employs that sort of concept of 'life' in his *Investigations*.[31] My point is that the so-called fine-tuning *doesn't* cry out for explanation. As coincidences go, they are no more rare than rolling a die and getting a 6. The 'explanation' required is not to explain why our universe is so terribly, terribly special. It is to realise that it's *not* special at all. Moreover, it's not the conclusions I'm objecting to: it's the hypotheses. The claim that, in effect, our universe is the only kind capable of supporting 'life' is simply wrong. Where that claim leads is another matter. I don't think it leads anywhere.

C: Your complaint about the practice of varying only one cosmological parameter at a time – thus assuming that they are all independent and failing to explore more than one

30. For an notable recent example, see Simon Conway Morris, *Life's Solution: Inevitable Humans in a Lonely Universe* (Cambridge: Cambridge University Press, 2003).

31. S. Kauffman, *Investigations* (Oxford: Oxford University Press, 2002).

or two axes of the whole phase space – is of course very well-taken, and is a point which others have also raised.[32] However, as Milan Ćirković argues in his contribution to the present volume,[33] this has far more has to do with the numerical intractability of *ab initio* variations of multiple parameters rather than any kind of insidious teleological or theological agenda on the part of the scientists doing the research. Moreover, the fact that such computational limitations exist is surely not a reason to give up exploring these things, but rather simply suggests that one must exercise extreme caution in assigning probabilities (if indeed it makes sense to assign probabilities to an infinite, non-normalisable parameter space at all, which also presents a very significant challenge for proponents of fine-tuning).[34] While, as you point out, several physicists and cosmologists have indeed begun to explore what happens when one varies several constants at a time,[35] and have indeed concluded that the probability of the existence of (e.g.) stellar structures may not be as low as first thought, such models

32. See, e.g., Stenger, op. cit.; Neil Manson, 'There Is No Adequate Definition of 'Fine-Tuned for Life', *Inquiry* 43, 2000: 341-52; Gilbert Fulmer, 'A fatal logical flaw in anthropic principle design arguments', *International Journal for Philosophy of Religion* 49, 2001: 101-110; and Cory Juhl, 'Fine-tuning is not surprising', *Analysis* 66 (4), 2006: 269-275.

33. Milan Ćirković, 'Sailing the Archipelago', this volume.

34. See, e.g. T. McGrew, L. McGrew & Eric Vestrup, 'Probabilities and the Fine-Tuning Argument: a Sceptical View, *Mind* 110, 2001: 1027-1037; Colyvan M. Colyvan, J. Garfield & G. Priest, Problems with the argument from fine tuning', *Synthese* 145, 2005: 325-338; and J. Koperski, 'Should We care about Fine-Tuning?', *British Journal for the Philosophy of Science* 56, 2005: 303-319.

35. See, e.g., Stenger, op. cit.; Adams, op cit.; T. Nakamura, H. Uehara & T. Chiba, 'The Minimum Mass of the First Stars and the Anthropic Principle', *Progress of Theoretical Physics* 97, 1997: 169-171; Anthony Aguirre, 'The Cold Big-Bang Cosmology as a Counter-example to Several Anthropic Arguments', *Physical Review* D64, 2001: 083508; R. Harnik, G. Kribs & G. Perez, 'A universe without weak interactions', *Physical Review* D74, 2006: 035006; and Milan Ćirković, op. cit.

are still based on the same low-entropy initial conditions of 'our' Big Bang, which have been shown, by Roger Penrose among others, to be stupendously improbable themselves (estimated by Penrose to be of the order of about one part in $10^{10^{123}}$ – a number which surely cries out for explanation).[36] Moreover, as Ćirković also argues, it is highly questionable whether such research invalidates anthropic reasoning per se, rather than simply helping to make the problems more tractable and well-defined by providing more useful data to work with.[37]

IS: Agreed, it's difficult to do the sums correctly. So that justifies doing them *wrongly*? The universe is not obliged to behave in ways simple enough for humans to calculate. The difficulty of doing anything beyond 'perturbation' calculations, where a few parameters are changed by very small amounts, doesn't mean that the computable cases are the only ones available. It actually strengthens my point, because the claim that anything else cannot possibly support life falls to bits if you haven't got a clue how other possible universes behave. There is a huge difference between claiming that no other possibility works (which in effect is a claim of complete knowledge of the consequences of alternative laws of nature) and pointing out that since we don't know that, and cannot know that, then we cannot make that claim. What's at stake here is the logic of the argument. I'm not trying to prove that our universe is not special. I'm pointing out gaps in the logic of the claim that it is.

36. Roger Penrose, *The Emperor's New Mind* (Oxford: Oxford University Press, 1999), 445.

37. See Ćirković, 'Sailing the Archipelago', this volume.

If by 'invalidates anthropic reasoning *per se*' you mean 'shows that *any* kind of anthropic reasoning is silly' then of course nothing we've discussed does that. What I'm saying is that the 'classic' examples of anthropic reasoning are all flawed. Carbon in stars, fine-tuning – the logic is bad, the arguments are full of holes. I don't reject all anthropic reasoning. I just ask that it be done carefully and with imagination.

It's the Sherlock Holmes point – or, rather, what Holmes failed to mention. 'Once you have eliminated the impossible, then whatever remains, however improbable, must be true'. What Holmes failed to point out is that this line of thinking is hugely dangerous unless you are very, very careful that the things you claim to be impossible really *are* impossible. My view, and that of most mathematicians, I imagine, is that if what remains is wildly improbable, you probably made a mistake earlier on.

I agree with you on the problem of the application of probabilities: my use of probabilities of 25 percent rather than infinitesimal accepts the fine-tuning way of doing it (which is naïve but qualitatively defensible) to show that it doesn't lead to the claimed conclusions. 'Stars' can exist in a huge chunk of parameter space, not a tiny bit. End of story.

As for the idea of the supposed specialness of 'our' Big Bang, Jack and I argue in *Science of Discworld II: The Globe*[38] that Penrose's calculation is absurd. It assumes a purely

---

38. Terry Pratchett, Ian Stewart & Jack Cohen, *The Science of Discworld II: The Globe*, op. cit., 194-5. A more extensive treatment can be found in Ian Stewart, 'The second law of gravitics and the fourth law of thermodynamics', in (ed.) N. H. Gregsen (ed.), *From Complexity to Life* (Oxford: Oxford University Press, 2003), 114-50.

thermodynamic universe (which is why 'entropy' comes into the story). Here all forces are short-range – acting only at the level of collisions of molecules – and repelling. The result is a long-term trend towards a uniform distribution of matter (disorder). But the real universe has many other forces, notably gravity. This is long-range and attracting – the exact opposite. The result is a long-term trend towards 'ordered', clumpy distributions of matter. If you use a thermodynamic model on a gravitic system, the results won't make much sense.

I don't actually think the use of 'order' and 'disorder' when discussing entropy is very helpful, because those terms are highly ambiguous, but for the sake of simplicity let's say that a high-entropy state is disordered and a low-entropy state is ordered. Then thermodynamic effects turn order into disorder; gravitic ones do the reverse. So any natural 'final' state of a gravitic universe is highly ordered. If you now pretend it's a thermodynamic system, the initial state must have been *even more* ordered (because entropy increases over time). This leads to Penrose's minuscule estimate for the probability of the presumed initial state that would lead (by *thermodynamic* action) to the final one. However, that's not how it happens. Instead, an initially disordered state naturally clumps under gravity. 'Entropy' measured by the clumping decreases over time. It doesn't increase.

C: While the use of anthropic reasoning in astronomy and cosmology has a long history,[39] the term 'anthropic

39. See, e.g., J. D. Barrow and F. J. Tipler, *The Anthropic Cosmological Principle* (Oxford: Oxford University Press, 1986); Milan Ćirković, 'Ancient Origins of a

principle' itself was first introduced by Brandon Carter in the early seventies as a corrective to what he called 'exaggerated subservience to the "Copernican principle"' – that is, the inference from the idea that we are not *special* to the idea that we must therefore be *average* or even *representative*.[40] It was this kind of uncritical acceptance of what has popularly taken to be the chief lesson of the Copernican revolution which in part led many Enlightenment thinkers in the centuries following Copernicus to assume that not only the other planets, but even moons and comets, must be populated by rational beings very similar to ourselves.[41] In *What Does a Martian Look Like*, as already mentioned, you charge much of contemporary astrobiology with a similar kind of (for want of a better word) 'terracentrism', charging it with being 'by its nature too narrow-minded and too unimaginative to tackle the really big questions about aliens'.[42]

IS: That's a fair summary, and it raises a fascinating issue that I've not thought of before. Anthropic reasoning concludes that we are special; Copernican reasoning concludes that we are not special. The cosmological mainstream (or at

Modern Anthropic Cosmological Argument', *Astronomical and Astrophysical Interactions* 22 (6), 2003: 879-886; and Milan Ćirković, 'On the First Anthropic Argument in Astrobiology', *Earth, Moon and Planets* 91, 2002: 243-54.

40. B. Carter, 'Large number coincidences and the anthropic principle in cosmology' in M. S. Longair (ed.), *Confrontation of Cosmological Theories with Observational Data* (Boston: Reidel, 1974), 291; cf. the discussion in 'Dark Matter: Probing the Arche-Fossil. Interview with Roberto Trotta' in COLLAPSE II: 83-169.

41. On this see, for example, Frank Tipler, 'A Brief History of the Extraterrestrial Intelligence Concept', *Journal of the Royal Astronomical Society* Vol. 22, 1981: 133-145.

42. *What Does a Martian Look Like?*, op. cit., 5.

least, many prominent members) tends to believe both of these.

Carter's point is the key. I think that it is probably correct to assume that we are not special – not in general terms. But does this imply that we are *representative*? I'd go with Carter: it does not. The reason, to use the central distinction of *What Does a Martian Look Like?*, is that we can be (and virtually by definition always are) special in *parochials* but not in *universals*.

Intelligence is a universal (we have argued, after a lot of debate, and we acknowledge that we may be wrong here – but let's take that as an example anyway). So by the Copernican view, our intelligence is nothing special. There will be lots of intelligent aliens out there.

However, our particular level of intelligence, our use of a brain as the seat of intelligence, what we do with our intelligence – many features will be parochial. Aliens won't do it the same way as us. Which implies that in these respects we *can't* be representative.

In short: to be representative *is* to be special! As soon as diverse histories can lead to the same universal result, each history will be special, and nothing can be representative. Jack and I hit this problem when writing *What Does a Martian Look Like?*: I kept asking Jack to stop saying 'we can't know what aliens look like', and he kept saying 'but it's true'. We compromised by talking of 'placeholders' – 'as long as you don't take this example literally, they might be like *this* ... but not in any of the details'.

C: Perhaps you could explain what you mean by 'universals' and 'parochials'. This distinction was introduced in *Collapse*,[43] developed in *Figments*,[44] and you put it to work in *What Does a Martian Look Like?* in order to hazard educated guesses regarding which kinds of biological features we might hypothetically expect to find exhibited by extraterrestrial life forms. Could you explain how one sets about trying to distinguish between the 'universal' and the 'parochial' in evolution, and what tentative conclusions you have reached regarding the possibilities of alien life?

JC: It is essentially a very simple idea, and argues the 'likelihoods' of events – innovations – in *our* evolutionary story. If an innovation happened just once, this tells us that it is possible, but not how likely it is to have happened – perhaps the invention of DNA was such an event. On the other hand, eyes evolved in many different clades, apparently independently (although there are some puzzling equivalencies in some of the biochemistries), making it appear likely that eyes will evolve. If we 'ran Earth again', or found another planet on which eukaryotes (or equivalents …) had evolved from prokaryote (bacterial/archaean) progenitors, we would expect to find eyes. But DNA? We would not be able to argue for DNA *in the same way* (but there might be chemical reasons to expect it – or not!). Similarly for photosynthesis: there are five extant methods of photosynthesis. Granted an oxygenated atmosphere, then flight would be expected: insects, birds, bats, pterosaurs, and

43. *The Collapse of Chaos*, op. cit., 404.

44. *Figments of Reality*, op. cit., 109-134.

some fishes all invented flight independently; we would expect flying life forms on a re-run Earth, or on another aqueous planet. I have suggested that we call such multiply-invented innovations 'universals', while those innovations – nearly all of them – that happened but once in our evolutionary story I call 'parochial'. Vertebrates are parochial – we won't find that pattern elsewhere (nor would it occur again on a re-run Earth). So are feathers; and hair (but not 'fur' – bumble bees have it for warmth, as do many plants – mammalian hair is a parochial instance of the universal 'fur').

Now there is the question of whether our universal/parochials are transferable to other planets, and the answer is: We simply don't know. We don't know how different even the most earth-like aqueous planet will be. But we can certainly rely on the negative: We won't get vertebrates! But whether we'll get flight or photosynthesis … ?

IS: We started out with Jack's working definition: a feature is universal if it has evolved independently more than once, and parochial if not. That works fairly well for life on Earth, but if aliens exist that may be too small a sample. So I argued for a more 'mathematical' definition (or characterisation): if some feature or mode of behaviour offers evolutionary advantages for generic reasons, it's a universal. By 'generic' here I meant that the *reasons* should be valid in many diverse contexts. So having a sense of vision ought to be universal, because it helps you detect danger in almost any form.

On Earth, vision evolved many times, so in this case the two approaches to universality coincide. In a way, my definition is a theoretical one and Jack's is the experimental test. But when it comes to aliens, we can't yet do the experiments.

C: According to your book, many proponents of orthodox astrobiology – most of whom are astrophysicists rather than biologists – 'seem not to have realised that there has been a revolution in evolutionary thinking during the 1980s, just as radical as the Newton/Einstein paradigm shift in physics', one consequence of which being that they 'are ruling out various scenarios for alien life, even though those scenarios already occur on this planet'.[45] 'Our own planet', you suggest, 'is far weirder than anything permitted elsewhere by astrobiological orthodoxy'.[46] For those still not 'in the know' on all this, could you describe what this recent revolution in evolutionary thinking amounts to, and provide some examples of the (from the human point of view) weird and wonderful forms of life only recently discovered on our planet?

JC: The evolutionary paradigm is usually taken, by philosophers and physicists – but also by many biologists – to be that of the 1950s: all the organisms of a population have much the same genome (hey, that's why they belong to the same species ...), but a few have mutations that usually make things worse but occasionally make things better (because if you fire bullets randomly at a car engine you'll mostly damage it, rarely improve it!). So most mutations are lost in the first generation ... or so they thought!

45. *What Does a Martian Look Like?*, op. cit., 7.

46. Ibid., 39.

Lewontin's group in the 1970s[47] (and hundreds of others since) discovered that wild animals and plants – and humans – are not like that at all: in a typical individual about 10 percent of the genes are heterozygous (different versions from Pa and Ma) and about a third of genes have different version(s) in the population (say, more than 1/1000 individuals – with rarer mutations, it comes up to about two-thirds or more!). So lots of old mutations are still about, recombining in different assortments in each of the progeny. That's much more like Darwin's picture, incidentally, which he got to by arguing from domestic species (mostly pigeons!). Each of the progeny is different in many genetic respects, and only because of 'genetic assimilation' and other developmental tricks can so many actually develop, the developmental programme is so diverse. Put this against the Malthusian background – so many progeny, so little room. Realise that 1/1000 survival is not unusual, 1/million or even 1/100 million is found in oysters and codfish; 1/8 in songbirds like starling (a female starling lays about sixteen eggs in her life, which 'on average' produce two parents in the next generation – only 'averages' ain't the way to calculate), 1/4 in hippos and rhinos, 1/3 in elephants. Most progeny fail to breed. And because they are all so genetically different from each other, this is mostly because of different programmes; but *because they are all so different* what is being selected is not particular genes, but particular – and very varied – combinations for the next generation. By any number of developmental tricks, these different versions can all develop, but they are not like Ford Model

47. R. C. Lewontin, *The Genetic Basis of Evolutionary Change* (New York: Columbia University Press, 1974).

T's, some with bumps and a few with better headlamps etc; they are like handmade cars, all adjusted differently to give much the same results. Add to the puzzle that the parts that they are using are very various, perhaps from the last ten models (and a few from similar models …), and it is clear that the DNA genome ain't even half of the trick – the RNAi (which were thought to be products of 'junk' DNA) turn lots of genes on and off in different tissues, and there are perhaps thirty other tricks we know about (epigenetic tricks, for example, that carry information to the next generation by modifying DNA …) – as well as the hundreds we don't know about yet.

So the picture we should have of alien genetics is not at all the Lego model: has it got the right genes? So diverse is the developmental/genetic system *here* that we have to suppose that at least equivalent complexity would be needed to 'drive' an alien ecology, even just a bacterial-grade one. To get 'higher' organisms we must invent a whole new slew of *really* complicated/complex biology, that involves selection of *genetic variety of progeny*, not just selection of progeny!

We have, now, hundreds of 'anomalous' species on earth, that don't fit the new paradigm of genetics, let alone the 1950s one. From parthenogones (females only …) in some rotifers, for 100 million years, to a whole slew of genes that have been 'shared' by 'primitive' (bacterial and archaean) genetics, to a variety of genes that have been lifted across from species to very different species by viruses, to cichlid fishes of Lake Victoria with morphologies that are very various, from nearly a metre long to 2cm (a female that is kept in a snail shell by a male, and fed there), we now know of life forms with an enormous variety of life strategies – but with a genetic variety that is only about that of human beings!

C: In both *Collapse* and *Figments* you draw upon the massive evidence for evolutionary convergence to take issue with Stephen Jay Gould's argument that, if one were to re-run evolution on Earth, nothing like human intelligence would evolve a second time around. Intelligence, you argue, is a universal. What, then, do you mean by 'intelligence' here, and what is the evidence of convergence that led you to the conclusion that it is a universal – that is, something one might expect to find on any planet with a comparable biological complexity to that of the Earth? Presumably, unlike Simon Conway Morris in his recent *Life's Solution: Inevitable Humans in a Lonely Universe*[48] – apart from strongly disagreeing with his 'lonely universe' conclusion – you do not suppose that this 'universality' or 'inevitability' of intelligence has any special 'metaphysical' (read: theological) implications!

IS: It's worth noting that Gould himself rather backtracked on his claim. It was a way of dramatising the remarkable diversity of life in the Burgess Shale. (Which may also have been exaggerated, according to more recent studies of the fossils.) We would agree with Gould that *humans* would not evolve the second time round. Not just like us. Too many accidents of history are embedded in our genes. However, that doesn't rule out similarly intelligent creatures evolving by a different route, and we rather think they could – and, given long enough, should.

48. See note 30 above.

What do we mean by 'intelligent' here? I don't want to try for a philosophically waterproof definition (too hard). Informally, intelligence (as we experience it) has a number of striking features. The ability to manipulate mental models of the world, to ask 'what if?' questions, to let future prospects affect the present, and so on. As a universal, 'intelligence' ought to have similar features. You can construct your own list.

If we are right that intelligence is universal then it should evolve many times, either in a single run of this planet or in hypothetical multiple reruns. In effect, Jack's experimental test should work. So we would expect some kind of intelligent creature to turn up, some time. If intelligence is a parochial, limited to us and *our* evolutionary history, then Gould would be right, and intelligence would have lost its chance to evolve on Planet Earth.

JC: The answer to the question of whether intelligence is a parochial or a universal, in our evolutionary scheme, comes out as a resounding 'universal': from mantis shrimps to octopuses, geckoes to owls, dolphins to killer whales, creatures that 'think' have evolved many times - here. But can the same be argued for other planets? I like to think that it can; like Ian, I put it into a theoretical context: like vision, intelligence is a general way of dealing with the world, and will be 'chosen' frequently. So my prejudice is that we'll have (equivalents of …) mantis shrimps and killer whales, owls and octopuses on all those planets that have taken the steps towards the multicellular (or bzqwar … I don't know that multicellular is the *only* way 'upwards'!) – intelligence, in a variety of forms, will be rife, as it is here.

But extelligence? That is a quite different matter. There are steps towards extelligence: chimps, meerkats, wild dogs … so it could be claimed as a universal; but then these are all mammals, so should we count this as one single case (Mammalia), thus making it a parochial? Really, however, there is only one case: us. Only we have more information outside the brain (in other brains, initially …) than inside the individual brain – so that a Make-a-Human-Being kit requires pouring a whole lot of cultural stuff into each of us, as we grow up. How likely is that on another planet? Well, taking Ian's stance on universals, pretty damn likely, given time! It's clearly the best way (so far …) of exploiting intelligence, transforming it into cultural capital that grows down the generations – becoming 'extelligence'.

Simon Conway Morris has an interesting take on this issue. Because he is Christian, he sees the 'highest' form of life on any planet (that's got far enough …) as being effectively, and morphologically, humanoid; essentially, he believes that the form of life 'made in the Image of God' is effectively the top of *any* evolutionary tree. Like Waddington, he believes that our morphology is just about 'right', and uses the (alien) convergences in evolutionary pattern to get there. Well, it may be so. If there actually *is* a real theology, that is to say there actually is a Someone who organized the whole matter, then one would perhaps expect to find that kind of contingency – if the Someone were smaller-minded than I would hope!

C: In *Figments* you introduced the ideas of 'privilege' and 'extelligence' by way of providing an evolutionary account of the origins of the peculiar nature of human intelligence and culture. These are remarkable ideas which one feels really ought to have achieved wider currency than they have so far. Could you briefly explain what you mean by these terms?

IS: I'll let Jack do 'privilege', because it was his idea long ago. 'Extelligence' came from a discussion between us both, but it was my word, so I'll tackle that.

The reason that humans have overrun the planet (and consider themselves Top Dog, or rather Top Species – although there are other contenders, depending on criteria) is *not* that we are intelligent. It helps, but it doesn't go far enough. Purely intelligent mortal creatures have to reinvent the wheel (literally) in each generation. Lessons derived by the exercise of intelligence have to be relearned – they can't be passed on.

But if some sort of cultural memory exists, the next generation can build on the lessons learned by the previous one. The mechanism can be as simple as mother dog teaching the pups where to find water, or as sophisticated as the Internet. But without it, 'civilisation' could never have happened, and as individuals we would be virtually powerless. We'd be back in the caves, battling the monsters, staving off starvation on a day-to-day basis.

Anything that can pass 'cultural capital' or 'know-how' down the generations we call 'extelligence'. It is that part of our intelligence *as a species* that does not reside in all (most) individuals. Until a few thousand years ago each bit of it resided in the brains of specific individuals – the copper-beaters knew all about making things from copper, and so on. It was passed on by word of mouth, often from parent to child.

Our ability to manipulate the planet to our own ends started to take off when we found ways to store this stuff *outside* human brains. We carved it on walls, wrote it in papyrus, whatever. Now the amount of 'extelligence' is limited only by the available space to store it, not by the capacity of one human brain. Its use is limited by our ability to access it, as well.

JC: In my 1977 book *Reproduction*[49] I invented the idea of 'privilege', as that which offspring receive from their parents, to give them a start in life. So yolk, milk, starch, etc., represent food that could have been used by the parent chicken, cow, wheat plant, etc., for its own purposes, but that has been donated to the offspring to help give them a start, to give them privilege. Laying eggs in the right place (e.g., on a paralysed spider, or on a mammalian corpse), counts as privilege – so does sending the child to a special school. So this is a very general concept, emphasizing that the break between generations is not very 'clean'. Equally, of course, teaching/learning is another instance of this passage across the generations, initially in the nest: cats teach their kittens to deal with prey. (This seems to be a solely mammalian trait – other nests, like those of some turtles, crocodilians or even cephalopods seem to have no passage of information – even birds don't seem to 'teach' their young.) From those small beginnings, however, arose languages like those of wild dogs (whose puppies learn the pack's special noises for 'hunt'), leopards, eagles; surprisingly, perhaps, chimps – our closest relatives – don't have

---

49. Jack Cohen, *Reproduction* (London: Butterworth, 1977).

much by way of language-learning, perhaps less than dogs; a few monkeys, especially vervets, have tens of 'words'.

Our trick has been to explode this initial trick into complex language, by which we pass a tremendous amount of information from maternal brain to infant brain, accumulating cultural capital across the generations. Priests, as temporary repositories of the cultural capital, made it much more stable, ubiquitous. Then writing, to produce a more permanent store ... teachers, specialists in passage, then books, libraries, the Internet. Knowledge outside brains, for which Ian invented the happy word 'extelligence'.

C: In *What Does a Martian Look Like* you suggest that the question of whether extelligence is a universal or a parochial is 'the central question of xenoscience'.[50] What conclusions did you reach?

IS: Well, in brief, if it's *not* a universal it surely *ought* to be one! But it's not yet possible to make too strong a claim. With intelligence, we can argue that there is experimental confirmation of universality: it evolved many times – octopus, dolphin, monkey ... But right now we are the only extelligent species on the planet.

Finding aliens (even bacteria) would be fantastic. Complex aliens, at the level of a snail, would be amazing. The level of intelligence of a cat – awe-inspiring. But what we really mean by 'alien intelligence' is actually *alien extelligence*. That's the big one. It's the extelligent aliens who

---

50. *What Does a Martian Look Like?*, op. cit., 277.

would be able to build those massive starships and travel across the Galaxy. The merely intelligent ones would reach dolphin level, and stay in their oceans or methane-pools or crystal forests or whatever, stuck on their home world.

JC: I think there are too many unknowns. We don't know if we can transfer the ideas of universal/parochial to any other planet – though of course I'd like to think that we could! Then there's the whole question of whether extelligence derives naturally from intelligence (does it need a nest, for example? I played with this question in Harrison's *West of Eden* series, inventing an r-strategist extelligence [r-strategists have many offspring, not looked after ...]; and we produced another in *Wheelers*). Too many intelligent creatures on this planet *haven't* developed extelligence (even k-strategists, who look after their few babies)! So I'm not optimistic. But there are hundreds of millions of planets out there. Who knows?

C: When first introducing the topic of 'alien science' in *Collapse*, you did so in the context of raising the question of whether the so-called 'laws of nature' discovered by science are genuinely objective features of reality itself, or only 'brain puns' which happen to appeal to the pattern-seeking human mind, by considering the question of the extent to which we might expect alien sciences to be congruent to our own. An idea which has often been forwarded in this connection is that while it is doubtless the case that much of our science is indeed distinctively 'human' or 'anthropomorphic', reflecting the peculiar nature of our species' physiological make-up and idiosyncratic modes of perceiving and conceiving the world, when it comes to *mathematics* or *mathematical natural science*, at least, we can be far more confident that we are indeed tracking genuinely objective patterns of nature itself – patterns which, therefore, we might expect also to have been discovered by any sufficiently advanced science. A century ago, for example, Max Planck characterised the history of the physical sciences in terms of a progressive unification brought about the liberation of the physical world-picture from 'anthropomorphous elements', ultimately resulting in the discovery of 'universal constants' which, he maintained, 'must necessarily retain their meaning for all times and for all environments, terrestrial and human or otherwise'. It is only if such constants retained the same significance for 'the inhabitants of Mars, and indeed all intelligent beings in our universe', he suggested, that it would be meaningful to say that, for example, 'the principle of the conservation energy was valid in nature, before any man was able to think about it, or that heavenly bodies will still move according to the laws of gravity when our earth, with all its inhabitants, has disintegrated'.[51]

This issue of how peculiarly 'human' our own science may be in relation to the phase space of possible sciences in general is a recurring theme of all your co-authored works. What, then, are some of your own conclusions on this issue? Are there any aspects of modern science and mathematics that one might reasonably expect to find

---

51. 'Max Planck, 'Die Einheit des physikalischen Weltbildes', *Physikalische Zeitschrift* 10, 1909: 62–75; translated as 'The Unity of the Physical World-Picture' in Stephen Toulmin (ed.), *Physical Reality: Philosophical Essays on Twentieth-Century Physics* (London: Harper and Row, 1970), 1-27; also translated as 'The Unity of the Physical Universe' in Max Planck, *A Survey of Physical Theory* (New York: Dover, 1993), 1-26.

represented in any possible science, even that of extrater-restrials with very different modes of perceptual access to the world to our own; or is human science, necessarily and inescapably, only ever going to be *our* science, irremedi-ably marked by the peculiar environment, evolutionary development and modes of access to reality of the human organism and its instrumental extensions? Is mathematics, at least, able to gain traction upon what used to be called the 'primary qualities' of nature, and thus provide knowledge of a reality entirely uncorrelated with peculiarly human modes of access to it; or is mathematics, too, only 'our' mathematics?

IS: We could let our imaginations run riot and invent aliens with virtually any kind of theory of the workings of the universe, including none at all, but I don't think such specu-lations would be very useful. On the one hand, it's not a good idea to assume that an alien view of the universe *must* be similar to ours. On the other hand, mathematics and science developed from questions about the world around us, so we might expect aliens to have come to similar conclusions.

There are merits to both arguments, I think. You may have noticed the phrases I used – 'On the one hand/On the other hand' and 'view of'. These metaphors involve human physiology, and you can make a case that (say) our two-valued true/false logic may have been influenced by various dualities in our daily lives. Working from inside the human mind, as we all do, it may be difficult to determine how strongly (muscle-power ...) our world-view (here we go again ...) is influenced by this limitation.

But equally, the number system (1, 2, 3 ...) or the conservation of energy do seem rather basic, and we might reasonably expect aliens to have related concepts. I wouldn't want to place too much weight on that, though. I do think that if aliens have developed similar ways of thinking to us, so that they have some sort of 'alien maths', say, then it should be consistent with ours. A universe in which Fermat's Last Theorem is true on planet Earth but false on Zarathustra is a bit too wild for my taste.

However, it's not at all clear to me that what we think of as basic maths would necessarily be what an alien would think of as basic maths. I'm not worried about, say, base-10 versus base-12 numerals, or whatever: those are parochials, not universals. But would aliens have a concept of whole numbers – counting – at all? Imagine wispy creatures that float in the turbulent atmosphere of a gas giant like Jupiter, always growing whole, being ripped apart by the winds (this is how they breed ...). They might not have counting numbers because there's very little in their world to *count*. Few discrete structures exist: all is flux. 'One, two ... no, it's gone ...'. But their intuition for turbulent fluid flow (which for us is an almost intractable mathematical problem) would be amazingly advanced compared to ours. Some theoretician might introduce 1, 2, 3, ... as a topological invariant for systems of vortices. For these aliens, $2 + 2 = 4$ would be a major theorem. Even more speculatively, a creature made of gravitons (hypothetical particles that carry the force of gravity) would develop a very different physics from us.

If the two races came into peaceful contact, the synthesis of their 'mathematicses' and 'physicses' would be very powerful, and I'd expect some really extensive complicity to transform everything completely. But it would take a lot of effort, because it would all be cross-paradigm to start with.

Many scientists would simply assert that science is science and being human has nothing to do with it. I think this is too simplistic. The other extreme, the notion that science can be anything we all agree on, is worse – it exaggerates the human element, ignores the way scientists try to disprove their own theories, and is ultimately self-destructive. However, science isn't just about the answers you get, but about the questions you ask. Even today, different cultures often ask different questions and use science for different purposes. Aliens might ask *very* different questions. So while one part of me would be delighted if my chosen subject, mathematics, were the basis of reality, the more cynical part doubts that this could be the case.

Gregory Benford, a top-notch science fiction writer and an excellent physicist, once wrote an essay (in *Analog* magazine somewhere, I think) based on the distinction between two very different ways of looking at the world:

(1) Humanity is the context for the Universe;

(2) The Universe is the context for Humanity.

That is: do you (1) think of humans as what's important, and everything else as some kind of support or resource system for us to exploit? Or do you (2) see humans as one small, local consequence of whatever is going on out there is a gigantic universe, about which we know very little?

I've come to realise that almost all of the world-views with which I have serious disagreements adopt (1), and that almost all of my contrary stances are based on (2).

JC: I believe, as you say, that human science is 'necessarily and inescapably, only ever going to be *our* science, irremediably marked by the peculiar environment, evolutionary development and modes of access to reality of the human organism and its instrumental extensions' – yup, afraid so! Think, if we – Rutherford, I suppose – had started with the proton rather than the electron, we'd have a whole different zoo of particles, and different equations and constants, which would explain the natural world just as well. Or do you think that we would have converged on to electrons, and Planck's constant, because they are actually *there*? I have no such confidence; we had a good, workable system, electrons, protons, mesons; as soon as we went down into quarks I was completely persuaded that there are a million such systems, and that we had found another workable one – or invented one, it doesn't make much difference.

C: Finally, looking back on your many years of collaboration together, what would you each single out as the most important contributions which 'the collective entity Jack&Ian' has made to contemporary debates? Which of the ideas of Jack&Ian do you expect might stand the test of time?

JC: I'd like to think that the deep meaning of complicity will open up thinking in that area – people are still thinking that A affects B, then B affects A … when it is at least A' and B' by then … Extelligence is a wild card – it crept up on us from my idea of cultural capital, accumulating across the generations … The idea that simplicity is the problem, not complexity ... And mostly, the meta-idea that one can be serious – deadly serious – without being solemn!

IS: I have a real difficulty here because I have no idea how much influence any of those books has really had. So I hesitate to claim any credit.

For instance, it is very noticeable that conventional astrobiologists are finally beginning to appreciate just how different alien life might be. Focus is shifting, to some extent, from Earth-like worlds to more diverse settings. But I don't think that has happened because we wrote *What Does a Martian Look Like?* I think we just rode the wave a little bit ahead of the scientists who were doing serious research in that area instead of just writing a pop science book about it.

'Extelligence' is a nice concept. Right or wrong, I think it encapsulates an important point of view. I would also like to think that 'complicity' in our sense will turn out to be useful.

Most of all, I'd be delighted if more people took the attitude of the Zarathustrans' 'Institute for Simple Systems' – in which demolishing a wing of the library, because it has been superseded by greater *understanding*, is an event to be celebrated.

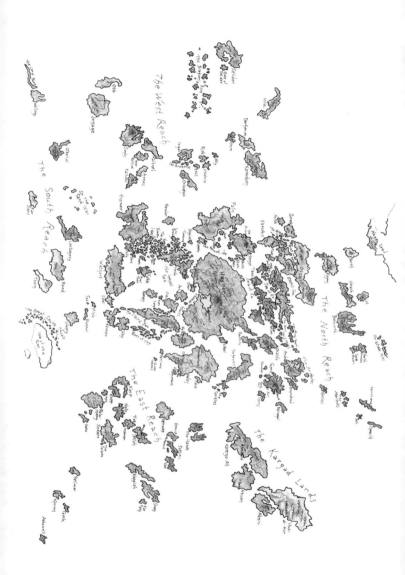

Figure 1. A prototypical archipelago (according to Ursula LeGuin's
A Wizard of Earthsea [Crockett, Cal.: Spectra, 2004]).

Sailing the Archipelago[1]

Milan M. Ćirković

I made it to the forward deck
I blessed our remnant fleet
Leonard Cohen

1. INTRODUCTION: MULTIVERSE AND ARCHIPELAGO

We live on a small island. We have not yet ventured much beyond our immediate locale on this small island; even our own inconspicuous location still holds great mysteries for us. It seems that we find ourselves near the mountain peak on our island, but even that is uncertain. We have only recently discovered that there are other islands besides our home scattered in a vast (possibly infinite) ocean. And the ocean is dead. It is not just devoid of fishes, algae or anything similar – it is empty of any *conceivable* form of life; it epitomizes the absence of life itself. But recently we have made our first attempt at mapping our surroundings and, in particular, sketching the outline of the ocean shores.

1. It is a pleasure to thank Damian Veal for kind encouragement and very helpful comments on the subject matter of this essay. This work has been partially supported by the Ministry of Science and Technological Development of the Republic of Serbia through project ON146012. Useful discussions with Irena Diklić, Richard B. Cathcart, Anders Sandberg, Nick Bostrom, Petar Grujić, Tanja Berić, Robert J. Bradbury, Slobodan Popović, Max Tegmark, Branislav Šimpraga, Ivana Dragićević, Clément Vidal and Robin Hanson are also hereby acknowledged. This is also an opportunity to thank the *KoBSON* Consortium of Serbian libraries, which enabled at least partial overcoming of the gap in obtaining the scientific literature during the tragic 1990s. Aside from the sources cited, some of the biggest inspiration for this study came from various writings of Thomas Pynchon, Stephen Jay Gould, Howard P. Lovecraft, and Charles Stross, as well as the music of Nat King Cole, Nick Cave and the Bad Seeds, and Diana Krall.

In this, some of us bear similarities to the great adventurers of the European Age of Exploration in the fifteenth and sixteenth centuries; only in this case the explorers are not sea-captains and conquistadors, but theoretical physicists, cosmologists and philosophers.

Before I explain the central metaphor of the *Archipelago of Habitability*, I wish to emphasize how difficult and different from our modern experiences cartography once was.[2] Imagine the huge tasks facing the explorers of old – for instance, that of mapping a newly discovered South Seas archipelago with the rather crude geographical and navigational means at their disposal. No *Google Earth* or aerial reconnaissance surveys or photography. On the contrary, the explorers of old had to rely on quite uncertain and imprecise navigational aids – including often very vague time-keeping. It is hardly a wonder that their maps were usually very wrong in their details, and at best imprecise and fanciful. This is a point to keep in mind when we discuss this much vaster and more abstract Archipelago.

Five developments in the physical sciences which have taken place in the last ten to twenty years mark the intellectual convergence necessary for discussing the Archipelago:

(1) The emergence of the 'new standard' cosmological model of the flat universe dominated by dark energy (after 1998),[3] connected with the predominance of the inflationary paradigm; especially chaotic inflation seen today as

---

2. Splendid recent histories of the subject can be found in J.N. Wilford, *The Mapmakers* (New York: Vintage, 2001) and R. E. Ehrenberg, *Mapping the World: An Illustrated History of Cartography* (Des Moines: National Geographic, 2005).

3. E.g., S. Perlmutter et al., 'Measurements of Omega and Lambda from 42 High-Redshift Supernovae', *Astrophysical Journal* 517, 1999: 565-586.

the generic form of the process.[4]

(2) The astrobiological 'revolution' (1995-today), offering a new unified framework for the old set of questions about the place of life and intelligence in the cosmic context.[5]

(3) The rise of string theory as the best candidate for the 'Theory of Everything' and the realization that it implies a huge number of low-energy sectors (or vacua) forming a 'landscape'.[6]

(4) The elucidation of anthropic principle(s) as observation selection effects by Leslie[7] and Bostrom,[8] leading to rejection of the old-fashioned teleological (mis)interpretations.

(5) The rise of an 'information paradigm' in many sciences, from biology to fundamental physics to computer science.[9]

4. A. D. Linde, 'Eternally existing self-reproducing chaotic inflationary universe', *Physical Letters, B* 175, 1986: 395-400.

5. For beautiful reviews of these developments, see D. J. Des Marais and M.R. Walter, 'Astrobiology: Exploring the Origins, Evolution, and Distribution of Life in the Universe', *Annu. Rev. Ecol. Syst,*. 30 (1999), 397-420; D. Darling, *Life Everywhere: The Maverick Science of Astrobiology* (New York: Basic Books, 2001); and D. Grinspoon, *Lonely Planets: The Natural Philosophy of Alien Life* (New York: Harper Collins, 2003).

6. L. Susskind, 'The Anthropic Landscape of String Theory' (2003), preprint at http://arXiv:hep-th/0302219; B. Freivogel & L. Susskind, 'A Framework for the Landscape', Physical Review D 70, 2004, 126007; and L. Susskind, *The Cosmic Landscape: String Theory and the Illusion of Intelligent Design* (New York: Back Bay Books, 2006).

7. J. Leslie, 'The Anthropic Principle Today', in J. Leslie (ed.), *Modern Cosmology & Philosophy* (Amherst: Prometheus Books, 1998), 289-310.

8. N. Bostrom, *Anthropic Bias: Observation Selection Effects in Science and Philosophy* (London and New York: Routledge, 2002).

9. S. Lloyd, 'Ultimate physical limits to computation', *Nature* 406, 2000: 1047–1054; M. W. Coffey, 'Estimates of universal computational capacity to the present', *Physics Letters A* 304, 2002: 8-12; E. Fredkin, 'An Introduction to Digital Philosophy', *International Journal of Theoretical Physics* 42, 2003: 189-247; G. Chaitin, 'From Leibniz to Ω: Epistemology as Information Theory', *Collapse* Vol. I, 2006: 27-51; M. Tegmark, 'The Mathematical Universe', *Foundations of Physics* 38, 2008: 101-150.

All these developments have contributed something to the tremendous increase in work on various theories of the *multiverse* – a term promoted (if not truly invented) in popular culture by the great British novelist Michael Moorcock.[10] In general (though the particulars may vary), a multiverse is a set of large, causally connected cosmological domains – conventional universes. The multiplication – no pun intended – of multiverses has occurred over a wide spectrum of disciplines, from cosmology and mathematics to quantum information theory to philosophy: see Tegmark's review[11] and the popular books of Rees or Vilenkin[12] on the subject. In the rest of this paper, we shall use the anthropic landscape of string theory as the prototype physical realisation of the multiverse, while strongly emphasising that it serves just a placeholder and that no conclusion is crucially dependent on this choice.

The idea of the Archipelago of Habitability was introduced by Max Tegmark in his intriguing paper on the relationship between mathematical and physical worlds.[13]

10. See M. Moorcock, *The Eternal Champion* (Clarkston, Georgia: White Wolf, 1995), esp. the new Introduction.

11. M. Tegmark, 'Parallel Universes', in J. D. Barrow, P.C.W. Davies & C.L. Harper (eds.) *Science and Ultimate Reality: From Quantum to Cosmos* (Cambridge: Cambridge University Press, 2003).

12. M. J. Rees, *Before the Beginning: Our Universe and Others* (Cambridge, MA: Helix, 1997); A. Vilenkin, *Many Worlds in One* (New York: Hill and Wang, 2006).

13. M. Tegmark, 'Is "The Theory of Everything" Merely the Ultimate Ensemble Theory?', *Annals of Physics* 270, 1998: 1-51.

Conceptually:

> **The Archipelago of Habitability**: A set of regions in parameter space describing those parts of the multiverse which are hospitable to life and intelligent observers of any kind.

In the language of physics, the Archipelago is a subset of the anthropic landscape of either string theory or any other overarching 'Theory of Everything' with multiple low-energy solutions ('vacua'). Thus, the Archipelago is part of the abstract space defined by whatever physics determines the structure of the multiverse. It is both logically and physically contingent on the reality of the multiverse; but that is still not saying much, since, as Tegmark emphasizes,[14] simple variants of the multiverse are completely uncontroversial and legitimate consequences of our firmly established cosmological theories. Whether the multiverse is infinite – as in the currently popular cosmological theory of eternal inflation – or finite – as in some construals of the string theory landscape, reflects directly on the structure of the Archipelago as well.

What is an island?[15] It is a set of parameters describing habitable universes which are close in parameter space; whether we can specify the meaning of 'closeness' beyond simple intuition depends crucially on the structure of the multiverse itself. In other words, the multiverse imposes a natural or at least convenient metric upon the Archipelago. By definition, there is at least one island in the Archipelago – our home island. If the multiverse contains arbitrarily

14. M. Tegmark, 'Parallel Universes', op. cit.

15. Cf. M. Houellebecq, *The Possibility of an Island,* trans. G. Bowd (New York: Vintage, 2007).

small variations in the constants of nature or cosmological parameters or even the mathematical shape of physical laws, than it is reasonable to conclude that the Archipelago is as dense as the remainder of the multiverse; for instance, it is clear that the change in the coupling constants of fundamental forces of 1 part in 10^{50} in comparison to those actually existing in our universe (not those actually measured, since we are unable to measure them to such precision yet!) – will not change anything in the habitable status of our universe. If such minuscule variations are actually realized within the multiverse, a universe otherwise described by identical laws and parameters to ours also belongs to our habitable region = our home island. It is easy to see that various constants and parameters of the multiverse play the role of geographical coordinates in maps of terrestrial archipelagos. Thus, if we start on a land point in, say, Sumatra, and continuously (or in sufficiently small steps) change either longitude or latitude along any chosen direction, we are bound to end up in the ocean. Similarly, if we start with a universe like ours and continuously change some parameter – say the strengths of forces, or the baryon-to-photon ratio, or the cosmological constant – we shall inevitably end up in a universe lacking prerequisites for life and observers. However, in the same manner as it is possible to start in Sumatra and, by a non-continuous increase in longitude, to end up in some other island – for example Borneo or New Guinea – it is possible that after a large interval of non-habitability, our parameter again enters an interval which (with appropriate changes in other parameters) enables the existence of life and observers. Thus, even if we did not know anything about possible different habitable universes

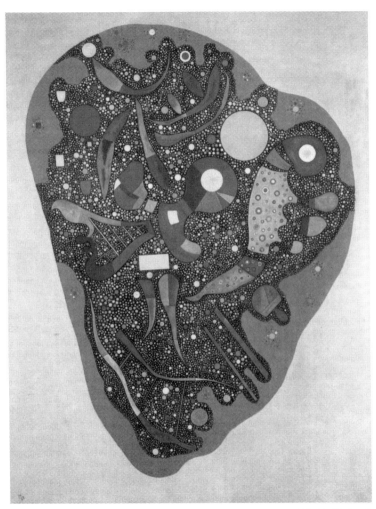

Figure 2. *Colourful Ensemble*, Wassily Kandinsky's 1938 canvas (Musée National d'Art Moderne, Centre Georges Pompidou, Paris), can be regarded as a symbolic representation of the multiverse: no colour is special as long as it is embedded in a wider ensemble.

(see §3), it would still be both rational and prudent to allow for the existence of other islands beyond our home island in the Archipelago.

Copernicanism is inscribed in the Archipelago picture right from the start – we are dealing with the widest conceivable ensemble in which our universe can be embedded, so as to avoid assigning it any special status. From the very beginning of the Copernican revolution, we have witnessed the loss of special status for ever-wider and more encompassing environments. First we concluded that there is nothing special about Earth, then about the Sun or the Solar System. In the 1920s, we finally realized that even our Galaxy, the Milky Way, is just one of billions of galaxies spanning the distance to our cosmological horizon. Now, in the twenty-first century, we should not be surprised to learn that, in spite of the apparent fine-tuning, there is nothing special about the whole of our cosmological domain – our universe – either.[16] Only in that manner will our universe's obvious property of being home to life and intelligent observers be adequately and naturalistically appreciated.

The exposition in the rest of this paper is as follows: After a brief survey of the role of astrobiology in defining the Archipelago (§2), I analyse recent discoveries of other habitable islands in some detail, with an emphasis on their philosophical significance rather than on technical issues and computational procedures (§3). This prepares the ground for putting the recent resurgence of anthropic arguments in cosmology into a new context, as well as for answering some of the common and/or fashionable

16. Cf. G. F. R. Ellis, U. Kirchner, and W. R. Stoeger, 'Multiverses and physical cosmology', *Monthly Notices of the Royal Astronomical Society* 347, 2004: 921-36.

criticisms of anthropic reasoning (§4). Most of the latter are based upon the alleged teleology of anthropic reasoning, a widespread and quite robust meme which has infected large segments of both philosophical and scientific populations, but which is nevertheless misleading and wrong. Finally, some summarized points and prospects for further research are given in the concluding section (§5).

2. ASTROBIOLOGY AS MAPMAKING

We are lucky enough to live in an epoch of great progress in the nascent discipline of astrobiology, a discipline which deals with three canonical questions: How does life begin and develop? Does life exist elsewhere in the universe? And what is the future of life on Earth and in space? A host of important discoveries has been made during the last decade or so, the most important certainly being the discovery of a large number of extrasolar planets whose number increases on almost weekly basis; the existence of many 'extremophile' organisms possibly comprising Thomas Gold's 'deep hot biosphere';[17] the discovery of subsurface water on Mars and the huge ocean on Europa, and possibly also Ganymede and Callisto; the unequivocal discovery of amino-acids and other complex organic compounds in meteorites; the modelling of organic chemistry in the atmosphere of Saturn's moon Titan; the quantitative treatment of the Galactic habitable zone; the development of a new generation of panspermia theories, spurred by experimental verification that even terrestrial microorganisms can easily survive conditions of an asteroidal or a

17. See T. Gold and F. Dyson, *The Deep Hot Biosphere: The Myth of Fossil Fuels* (New York: Springer, 2001).

cometary impact; methodological progress in the Search for ExtraTerrestrial Intelligence (SETI) studies, etc. However, the epistemological and methodological basis of astrobiology and SETI presents us with a hornet's nest of issues which, with a few exceptions, have not been tackled in the literature so far.

One such issue is the role of astrobiology in mapping the Archipelago of Habitability, which, it is worth repeating, is a continuous part of the general parameter landscape – with the sea level defined on the basis of our understanding of habitability. Even more, habitability determines the altitude profile of an island in the Archipelago: how high will it be, will it have steep or shallow slopes, great plains or even depressions inside it, and so on. We all agree that our universe is hospitable to at least some forms of life and there is very strong empirical evidence that significant changes in values of some or all parameters will lead to an inhospitable universe (the subject matter of classical anthropic 'fine-tuning' arguments, to be considered in the next section). Asking about the sea shores of the Archipelago is tantamount to asking Schrödinger's famous question 'What is life?'.[18]

There are many ways of surveying the Archipelago, just as in terrestrial geography one can either do satellite imaging, or search for water, or observe in the infrared, or do mineral prospecting, and so on. It is impossible here to give more than a cartoonishly brief sketch of some of the directions currently being actively pursued (although not always, or even mainly, recognized as belonging to the astrobiological domain; but such is often

18. E. Schrödinger, *What is Life?* (Cambridge: Cambridge University Press, 1944).

the historical pathway of young interdisciplinary fields). Research dealing with the preconditions for life and observership as we know them in a physical, chemical or geological sense is a part of the mapping endeavour; most of the research currently done and published, *inter alia*, in novel journals like *Astrobiology* or *International Journal of Astrobiology*, as well as in the older ones like *The Origin of Life and Evolution of the Biosphere*, belongs to this category.

On a more general level, the task of astrobiology obviously depends on our ability to recognize life even in its strangest forms (i.e., those most removed from terrestrial experience). Contrary to the arbitrary assertions of some critics, the tradition of speculative thinking about alternative forms of life is as old as astrobiological thinking itself.[19] Speculations – now supplemented by computer simulations – concerning whether life can be based on silicon, fluor compounds, solid-state physics or even nuclear forces belong here and are likely to increase in number and quality in the future. The prevailing tendency even in the most conservative astrobiological circles has been to *increase* the robustness of life (e.g., in discoveries of various extremophiles), thus justifying a heightening of our expectations for the possibility of life elsewhere in the multiverse.

---

19. For a classical example, see R. Shapiro and G. Feinberg, 'Possible Forms of Life in Environments Very Different from the Earth' in M. M. Hart and B. Zuckerman (eds) *Extraterrestrials: Where Are They?* (New York: Pergamon, 1982); and for a modern one, F. J Dyson, 'Looking for life in unlikely places: reasons why planets may not be the best places to look for life', *International Journal of Astrobiology* 2, 2003: 103-10. For a very early SF treatment of the theme, see J.-H. Rosny, 'Another World', in COLLAPSE III, 2007: 255-306.

A particular form of surveying is embodied in research on *artificial life* (Alife). From a rather eccentric game of computer scientists (albeit one with august ancestry, with von Neumann), it has become an important mainstream research discipline with wide-ranging influence and an increasing number of applications within fields such as evolutionary computation, cellular automata, genetic algorithms and even evolutionary art.[20] It is often stated that the goal of Alife is to *recreate* biological systems in a digital environment, but there are at least some distinguished researchers, such as ecologist and computer scientist Thomas Ray, who claim that such experiments are actually *creating* a new kind of life.[21] Clearly, if this strong A-life thesis turns out to be correct, this will have important epistemological implications for cosmology as well, since numerical experiments such as Ray's would make the sea shores of the Archipelago amenable to much more precise probing – something alike to the revolution of Gerardus Mercator and Abraham Ortelius in cartography in the 1560s.

Finally and most pertinently to our goal, we can ask, with Tegmark:[22] What are the minimal conditions for a physical environment containing intelligent observers? Tegmark

20. See M. A. Bedau, 'Artificial life: organization, adaptation, and complexity from the bottom up', *Trends in Cognitive Science* 7 (2003): 505-512.

21. T. S. Ray, 'An Evolutionary Approach to Synthetic Biology: Zen in the Art of Creating Life' in A. Ghosh and S. Tsutsui, *Advances in Evolutionary Computing* (NY: Springer, 2003), 479-517. See also C. Vidal, 'The Future of Scientific Simulations: from Artificial Life to Artificial Cosmogenesis', in C. Tandy (ed.), *Death And Anti-Death, Volume 6: Thirty Years After Kurt Gödel (1906-1978)*. In press, preprint at http://arxiv.org/abs/0803.1087.

22. M. Tegmark, 'Is the "Theory of Everything" Merely the Ultimate Ensemble Theory?', op. cit.

lists three basic conditions, namely (1) complexity, (2) predictability, and (3) stability. (He imposes them on mathematical structures describing arbitrary physical laws, in accordance with his 'Platonist' position on the relationship between mathematical and physical worlds; but the usage of these criteria does not really hinge on this philosophical viewpoint.)[23] The first necessary condition is almost self-evident: even the most ardent physicalists are unlikely to deny that an excessively high level of complexity is the reason why, among other things, we have not yet managed to create living or intelligent beings in the laboratory. The other two criteria are meaningful if we consider the operation of measurement by which knowledge is received by observers, an operation which requires both that the results do not fluctuate too much in the past or the future, to preclude the use of inference from past experience, and that habitable conditions exist at least during measurements. Of course, these are necessary, but not sufficient criteria for habitability. The search for sufficient criteria, and thus for the outlines of the Archipelago, continues.

All this (and, arguably, much else) constitutes an 'extended mandate' of astrobiology – and one immediately answering all the conventional criticisms:[24] Almost by definition, it 'looks outward to the general, rather than inward to the particular'. It will, hopefully, provide a much

23. Even more precisely, Tegmark uses the term 'self-aware substructure' in order to pose the problem as mathematical, since on the Platonist viewpoint an observer is nothing else than a part of a wider mathematical structure. But the same general reasoning about the criteria applies if we (i) regard observers as physical systems only approximated by mathematical descriptions, and (ii) have a particular physical mechanism of introducing variations (like the spontaneous symmetry breaking in inflationary cosmologies).

24. E.g. J. Cohen, and I. Stewart, *What Does a Martian Look Like? The Science of Extraterrestrial Life* (Hoboken, NJ: John Wiley & Sons, 2002).

more satisfactory answer to one of the perennial problems of science – Schrödinger's question – in the most general multiverse context.

3. VOYAGES OF DISCOVERY

Geography and cartography would be senseless without an appropriate metric; in the terrestrial case, the units of length (such as kilometers and nautical miles) combined with the angular coordinates (such as longitude and latitude), provide us with a hugely successful description of any explored piece of landmass or ocean. The extension of our analogy to the cartography of the Archipelago of Habitability emphasizes the analogous role of changing various parameters of physics (including the very form of low-energy physical laws). Let us forget, for the purposes of this section, the issue of the altitude of points on an island (i.e. the degree of habitability) and suppose that we are dealing with a single-contour map. Classical anthropic arguments from fine-tuning amassed significant empirical evidence that we cannot change the parameters that describe our universe *very much*, at least as long as we keep other parameters constant.[25] For example, the initial low entropy of our Big Bang seems excessively fine-tuned,[26] as does the amplitude of the primordial density perturbations

25. For compilation of the evidence up to mid-1980s see J.D. Barrow and F. J. Tipler, *The Anthropic Cosmological Principle* (NY: Oxford University Press, 1986). An updated review is C. J. Hogan, 'Why the Universe is Just So', *Reviews of Modern Physics* 72, 2000: 1149-61.

26. R. Penrose, *The Emperor's New Mind* (Oxford: Oxford University Press, 1989); M. M. Ćirković, 'The Thermodynamic Arrow of Time: Reinterpreting the Boltzmann-Schuetz Argument', *Foundations of Physics* 33, 2003: 467-90.

seen as anisotropies in the cosmic microwave background.[27] This would mean that our island is a rather small one, since even small changes in any single coordinate (with other coordinates kept constant) would lead us quickly to the ocean shore. In such a situation, it seems natural that early anthropic thinkers concluded that our island is the only one in existence. They were wrong, but not because of some ulterior and heinous agenda, as it is sometimes implied by opponents of anthropic reasoning; it was perfectly reasonable for them to think so – we might compare their rationality to that of a hypothetical ancient philosopher of Easter Island, pondering the huge ocean surrounding his home.

But contemporary sailors of the Archipelago have been able to refute this prejudice. In his often cited and almost as often poorly understood study, Aguirre[28] finds a 'cold' Big Bang model – a counterfactual one with low entropy-per-baryon in comparison to our actual Big Bang – which is habitable even according to the very high standards posed by the *terrestrial* kind of life. This type of universe is also capable of producing structure, such as galaxies and stars, as well as the chemical building blocks of life; and in such an astrophysical environment, so drastically different from our own in other respects, there is sufficient time for chemical and biological evolution. Some opponents of anthropic reasoning hailed this result as a long-awaited refutation

27. M. Tegmark and M. J. Rees, 'Why is the Cosmic Microwave Background Fluctuation Level 10^{-5}?', *Astrophysical Journal* 499, 1998: 526-32.

28. A. Aguirre, 'The Cold Big-Bang Cosmology as a Counter-example to Several Anthropic Arguments', *Physical Review D* 64, 2001, 083508.

of the alleged 'anthropocentrism' of such reasoning.[29] Whereas what Aguirre does, in fact, is to discover another habitable region in the parameter space – another island of habitability!

While this is a seminal result, it is a far cry from being a 'refutation' or 'disproof' of anthropic reasoning. In fact, supporters of anthropic reasoning have every reason to cheer on Aguirre's bold exploratory voyage: It actually demonstrates that such exploration is meaningful, and that the question of probabilities of observing various parameter values can, at least in principle, be answered quantitatively and operationally. The role of astrobiology sketched in §2 above finds some expression in the endnote of Aguirre's paper, which states:

> I have assumed that the number of independent measurements in a subuniverse is proportional to the number of suitable stars, neglected such effects as, for example, high metallicity leading to more planets upon which multiple civilizations might arise in a single solar system. I have also neglected factors like extinction-causing impacts, radioactivity-induced plate tectonics, etc., which are possibly but not clearly necessary for the evolution of observers.[30]

All these (and many other) factors clearly belong to the domain of astrobiological research. Thus, any elaboration of the classical anthropic arguments, no matter whether supportive or undermining, straightforwardly necessitates

---

29. Cohen and Stewart, *What Does a Martian Look Like?*, op.cit.; see also 'Alien Science: Interview with Jack Cohen and Ian Stewart', this volume; L. Smolin, 'Scientific alternatives to the anthropic principle' (2004), preprint at http://arXiv:hep-th/0407213.

30. Aguirre, 'The Cold Big-Bang Cosmology', op. cit.: n. 18.

the use of astrobiological knowledge. And Aguirre shows that we need such knowledge from our universe (and our experience), even when dealing with other, disconnected parts of the Archipelago.

But Aguirre's is not the only island different from our home island discovered so far. In fact, the island discovered by Harnik, Kribs, and Perez[31] is both larger (in both senses discussed above) and more remote from our home universe: They investigated nothing less than a set of conceivable universes without weak interaction ('weakless' universes). Before engaging in the analysis, they explain the methodology:

> We do not engage in discussion of the likelihood of doing simultaneous tunings of parameters nor the outcome of statistical ensembles of parameters. These questions are left up to the ultraviolet completion, such as the string landscape, which is outside of the scope of effective field theory. Instead, we are interested in 'running the universe forward' from a time after inflation and baryogenesis through billions of years of evolution. We will exploit the knowledge of our Universe as far as possible, adjusting standard model and cosmological parameters so that the relevant micro- and macro-physical outcomes match as closely as possible. We emphasize that this is really a practical matter, not one of principle, since any significant relaxation of the 'follow our Universe' program would be faced with horrendously complicated calculations. Put another way, there is probably a wide range of habitable universes with parameters and structures that look nothing like our Universe. For us, it

31. R. Harnik, G. Kribs, and G. Perez, 'A universe without weak interactions', *Physical Review D* 74, 2006, 035006.

is enough to find one habitable weakless universe about which we can make the most concrete statements, hence matching our Universe as closely as possible.

This truly looks like a bold sailors' manifesto! The difficulties bound to be encountered by any stray explorer in the dangerous waters ('horrendously complicated calculations') are explained, and the independence of the basic approach to the form of the multiverse (i.e. string landscape or any other) explicated. This makes the results of the study still more impressive, since they find at least a single piece of rock above the water in the midst of the ocean – an apparently habitable universe missing so crucial an ingredient of our world as one of the four fundamental low-energy interactions. Whether this is just a rock protruding from the waters or a tip of much larger island is unclear at present; Harnik et al. honestly admit that much.

Why, then, do these authors repeatedly perceive themselves as refuting or undermining anthropic arguments? The reasons are at least twofold. First, most anthropic arguments in the literature (like the one on setting of the electroweak scale, criticized by Harnik et al.) are narrowly or even badly formulated. They are based on narrow-minded calculations of the effects of small (one order of magnitude or so) changes in a small number of parameters, and not on a true insight into the underlying physics, which could indicate the way in which multiple parameters could be varied – at least in principle – whilst retaining habitability. A clear parallel here is with the misguided 'rare Earth' arguments[32] in astrobiology of the form: 'if there were no

---

32. Cf. P. D. Ward and D. Brownlee *Rare Earth: Why Complex Life Is Uncommon in the Universe* (New York: Springer, 2000).

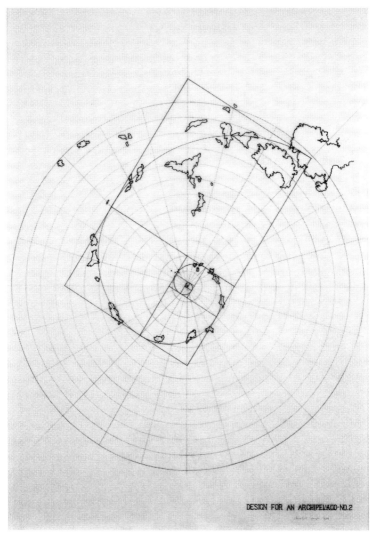

Figure 3. Charles Avery, *Untitled (Design for an Archipelago)* (2008), illustrating both the central metaphor and the possibility of 'deeper' mathematical regularities (here, the logarithmic spiral) underlying the seemingly random position of habitable regions. This is especially appropriate for Platonist multiverses such as Tegmark's, ultimately completely determined by overarching mathematical structures. (Image courtesy of the artist).

Jupiter in the Solar System, the Earth would have been cata-strophically bombarded by large comets and complex life would have been impossible.' Such arguments are clearly dead wrong, since they contain an internal contradiction: If there were no Jupiter, there wouldn't have been a Solar System as we know it at all! It is doubtful whether the Earth would exist at all in such a scenario, and everything else would have been different as well, so the comparison to the realistic case is pointless.[33] Instead, we need a more refined and detailed *physical insight* into the evolution of planetary systems. The same applies to habitability of universes in the anthropic landscape or any form of the multiverse.

The second reason why studies such as Aguirre's or Harnik et al.'s are often misconstrued is that such conclusions are based on a misconstrual of anthropic reasoning itself.[34] The widespread perception of anthropic principle(s) as tele-ological naturally leads to the erroneous conclusion that habitability is, if not identical with the criteria for evolution of *homo sapiens* (such an extremist position is relegated to ID proponents and other religious circles), than at least *centred* on it. According to this way of thinking, it is enough to show that the changing of some parameter by a factor of a few or by an order of magnitude is incompatible with some prerequisite for life as we know it (read: *homo sapiens*) to argue that this parameter must be anthropically selected. In the language of our central metaphor, if you can walk a hundred steps in a particular (single!) direction and get your

---

33. I thank Chris Chyba for pleasant discussion of this point.

34. See, e.g., Cohen and Stewart, *What Does a Martian look Like?*, op. cit.; and Quentin Meillassoux, 'Potentiality and Virtuality', in R. Mackay (ed.) COLLAPSE II: 55-81 (cf. Meillassoux's comment in COLLAPSE IV: 441).

feet wet, that is enough to prove that you live on an island. This logic is anthropocentric and flawed; it has nothing to do with the real meaning of anthropic reasoning. It may well be true that we are indeed living on an island (after all, even Eurasia can be regarded as a rather large island!), but the justification for it is wrong. And yet, it is appealing for the same extrascientific reasons we shall return briefly to in the next section: viz., the rear-guard actions of both positivists and teleologists, leading to a widely accepted anthropocentric 'noble lie'.

In a more general sense, studies such as that of Chavanis on white dwarf stars in an arbitrary number of dimensions,[35] or Adams on stellar evolution with unconventional parameters,[36] are part of the research helping us elucidate the Archipelago. We do not perceive any direct connection between us and white dwarfs at present, but the elegance and simplicity of the problem of such physical objects in D dimensions gives us a feel for the approaches and ways of thinking necessary to sketch out the cartographical task. Obviously, interest in this sort of research has increased significantly in the last couple of years – we might be on the verge of a true Age of Multiverse Exploration!

4. ANTHROPIC SELECTION AND DETRACTION

Steven Weinberg claimed to have predicted the existence of a small positive cosmological constant in the anthropic manner more than a decade before its actual

35. P.-H. Chavanis, 'White dwarf stars in D dimensions', *Physical Review D* 76, 2007, 023004.

36. F. C. Adams, 'Stars in other universes: stellar structure with different fundamental constants', *Journal of Cosmology and Astroparticle Physics* 08, 2008: 010.

observational discovery.[37] This theoretical success opened the way for dramatic expansion of anthropic arguments in cosmology. In the current cottage-industry of multiverse predictions in theoretical physics, a special role is reserved for the equation giving a probability that some observer anywhere in the multiverse measures a feature X:[38]

$$p(X) = \frac{\sum \sigma_n(X) V_n \rho_n^{obs}}{\sum V_n \rho_n^{obs}}, \tag{1}$$

where the index n labels all possible vacuum states (all different low-energy '*physicses*' or different universes); in current versions of string theory there is a finite number of such states, although it is huge (10^{500} or so; see Susskind 2003), but in principle it could be infinite. The latter case could pose some interesting problems in the theory of probability,[39] but in general will not preclude the usage of Equation (1) with appropriate weightings, V_n is the spacetime volume belonging to the universe n, ρ_n^{obs} is the density of observers in the same universe, and

$$\sigma_n = \begin{cases} 1, \text{ if universe } n \text{ has property } X \\ 0, \text{ otherwise} \end{cases}. \tag{2}$$

In principle, V_n is calculable from our understanding of cosmological physics, although in weird enough universes it might be impossible to calculate in practice (or at least

---

37. S. Weinberg, 'Anthropic Bound on the Cosmological Constant', *Physical Review Letters* 59, 1987: 2607-10.

38. See e.g., S.M. Carroll, 'Is Our Universe Natural?', *Nature* 440, 2006: 1132-36.

39. Cf. J.D. Hamkins and B. Montero, 'Utilitarianism in Infinite Worlds', *Utilitas* 12, 2000: 91-96; Tegmark, 'The Mathematical Universe', op. cit.

in finite time available to human cosmologists!). It is also likely to be infinite in some or most of the universes, so some appropriate weighting procedure is certainly necessary. But, of course, the biggest uncertainty comes from the quantity ρ_n^{obs}, the density of intelligent observers. It is usually assumed to be proportional to the density of galaxies, the latter being the main features of the structure of our own universe. But this is at best uncertain, and at worst fantastically wrong for islands outside of our own home island. Obviously, more sophisticated astrobiology is needed here.

How can the concept of the Archipelago of Habitability help us elucidate Equation (1)? Even very cursory thinking points the way toward what I shall dub 'altitude weighting': Obviously, even islands of identical shape on the map can have vastly different habitabilities – the universes in two groups could have a vastly different density of observers. We have thus far discussed only surface coordinates of islands in the Archipelago; but their essential property (which makes them islands) is their altitude profile. Very high points (analogues of the volcano peaks of the Hawaii islands) represent sets of parameters describing extremely bio-friendly universes, in contrast with bare rocks protruding from the waters, where lifeforms are possible but unlikely or very rare. The same pertains to intelligent observers: regions of high altitude will contain the predominant fraction of the entire set of observers in the multiverse. These regions correspond to high values of ρ_n^{obs} in such regions of the parameter space.

Thus, in order to make anthropic arguments cogent against the background of the Archipelago, we need to weight universes by their 'altitude', i.e. the measure of habitability. Clearly, this is a task for astrobiology in the widest sense: As discussed above, the very definition of the Archipelago is contingent upon resolving the issue of criteria for life to arise in a naturalistic manner. But in order to get the altitude profile, we need much more further effort – we need at least some hold on the emergence and dynamics of intelligent observers, traditionally the province of SETI studies (and the recreational discourse of SF books and movies). On the other hand, there is no discontinuity here: by studying already 'traditional' astrobiological themes like the Galactic Habitable Zone,[40] we expect to survey viable SETI targets and assess the density of extraterrestrial civilizations, even if some specific modifications are made when we consider intelligent observers rather than just complex lifeforms.[41] Obviously, much further research needs to be done in that direction. But the encouraging news is that several approaches have been developed recently which encapsulate elements of the future whole picture, notably the counting of observer-moments discussed by Bostrom in philosophical terms,[42] and the counting of the number of possible observations in a particular universe devised by Starkman and Trotta in the physical domain.[43]

40. G. Gonzalez, D. Brownlee, and P. Ward, 'The Galactic Habitable Zone: Galactic Chemical Evolution', *Icarus* 152, 2001: 185-200; C.H. Lineweaver, Y. Fenner & B. K. Gibson, 'The Galactic Habitable Zone and the Age Distribution of Complex Life in the Milky Way', *Science* 303, 2004: 59-62.

41. N. Duric and L. Field, 'On the detectability of intelligent civilizations in the Galaxy', *Serbian Astronomical Journal* 167, 2003: 1-10; M. M. Ćirković and R. J. Bradbury, 'Galactic Gradients, Postbiological Evolution and the Apparent Failure of SETI', *New Astronomy* 11, 2006: 628-39.

42. N. Bostrom, *Anthropic Bias,* op. cit.

43. G. Starkman and R. Trotta, 'Why Anthropic Reasoning Cannot Predict Λ', *Physical Review Letters* 97, 2006: 201301.

There seems to be an epistemological similarity between the proposal of weighting by the astrobiological description ('altitude' in terms of my central metaphor) and Trotta's suggestion[44] that a 'fully Bayesian approach' could resolve the difficulties with anthropic arguments, especially the lack of universal weight criterion for ρ_n^{obs}.

In practice, this task is enormous; perhaps generations of astrobiologists will pass before we get close to quantitative precision. But the enormity of the task should not detract from the fact that it is a well-defined problem from the start. If anything, it should demonstrate how utterly wrongheaded is the classical criticism that the anthropic reasoning is a 'lazy man's approach to science'.[45]

In the remainder of this section, I shall explore some of the more conventional criticisms of anthropic reasoning and discuss how the metaphor of the Archipelago may help us refute or undermine them.[46]

44. R. Trotta, 'Dark Matter: Probing the Arche-Fossil (Interview)', COLLAPSE II, 83-169; R. Trotta and G. D. Starkman, 'What's the trouble with Anthropic Reasoning?' in C. Munoz and G. Yepes (eds), 2nd International Conference on The Dark Side of the Universe, AIP Conference Proceedings 878, 2006: 323-29 (preprint at http://arXiv:astro-ph/0610330).

45. H. R. Pagels, 'A Cozy Cosmology', in J. Leslie (ed.), Modern Cosmology & Philosophy (Amherst: Prometheus Books, 1998), 180-86.

46. I am skipping more bizarre anti-anthropic complaints that occasionally surface in the literature, an example being the charge that 'anthropic principle' is a misnomer (J. Mosterín, 'Anthropic Explanations in Cosmology,' in Hajek, Valdés & Westerstahl [eds], Proceedings of the 12th International Congress of Logic, Methodology and Philosophy of Science [Amsterdam: North-Holland Publishing], after many others). While it might be formally true, as Carter and others readily admitted, it hardly advances discussion of real issues involved. Being, in principle, sympathetic to a programme of excising misnomers from the scientific discourse, may I humbly ask that interested philosophers start with concepts such as 'Hubble's constant', 'planetary nebulae', 'forbidden spectral lines', or even 'quark colours' and 'flavours'?

4.1. BETRAYAL OF THE ENLIGHTENMENT?

There is a rather strange tendency in some scientific and philosophical circles to regard anthropic reasoning as a sort of 'betrayal' of the allegedly sacrosanct traditions of scientific explanation dating from the times of Galileo and Newton. Although this form of criticism has never been clearly and unambiguously formulated, it haunts many recent discussions.[47] Roughly, it alleges that we should rationally explore nature as seen from a completely neutral and immobile 'Archimedean' point – not as real, physical beings evolved through various processes of physical, chemical and biological evolution, but as disembodied abstract observers. Only the former viewpoint, suggest these researchers, yields true causal explanations and satisfies the overall goals of science. Anthropic reasoning does not conform to this model and, consequently, 'has no place in physics or cosmology'.[48] In my view, this is entirely wrong on several counts, including some purely epistemological ones, dealing with the nature of explanation of contingent facts, though I cannot enter this complex topic here.

Instead, I would like to point out that such a rear-guard positivist attitude is in itself bound to end either in contradiction or in mysticism. Are observers natural? It is somewhat surprising to see that the same critics of anthropic reasoning tend to believe in physicalist explanations

47. See, e.g., L. Smolin *The Life of the Cosmos* (Oxford: Oxford University Press, 1997), 'Scientific alternatives to the anthropic principle', (2004), preprint at http://arXiv:hep-th/0407213, and *The Trouble with Physics* (New York: Houghton Mifflin, 2006); Pagels, 'A Cozy Cosmology', op. cit; J. Mosterín, 'The Anthropic Principle in Cosmology: A Critical Review', *Acta Institutionis Philosophiae et Aestheticae* 18, 2000: 111-39, 'Anthropic Explanations in Cosmology', op. cit.; and Quentin Meillassoux, 'Potentiality and Virtuality', op. cit.

48. Pagels, 'A Cozy Cosmology', op. cit.

of mental phenomena, including observership itself. This makes the criticism of anthropic reasoning somewhat close to hypocrisy: If observers are part of the nature to be studied, how can one justify ignoring their properties? Should not they be regarded as parts of the wholeness of reality that is to be rationally and empirically explained? Quite contrary to the detractors' assertions, the anthropic programme of elaboration of observation selection effects – of outlining the properties of the Archipelago of Habitability, in the terms of our metaphor – is the continuation of the Copernican revolutionary spirit in overcoming the apparent specialness not only of the Earth and of life on it, including humans, but of the very physical laws, associated mathematical structures, and our universe in general.

What is really betrayed here – and with good reason – are relics of the Cartesian dualism which underlay the mechanistic philosophy of classical physics for centuries, as well as positivist attitudes in the last century; that is, until modern science progressed sufficiently to tackle the most general questions of the origin of universe, life and intelligence. To approach problems dealing implicitly or explicitly with the properties of observers (e.g., problems in quantum physics or cosmology or astrobiology) in the same manner as, for instance, classical physicists studied the motion of a pendulum or the planet Uranus is not just epistemologically naïve – it is plain wrong.

4.2. How Cozy Is Our Universe?

A charge occasionally brought against anthropic reasoning (especially in older, pre-Weinberg literature) is that its proponents blithely assume that our universe is at the peak of habitability, i.e. 'the best of all worlds' in terms of life and intelligence, although it is clear that one could conceive a universe significantly friendlier for life than our own.[49] While such panglossianism might indeed have been true for the now discarded teleological construals of the anthropic principle(s), there is no reason to retain any such misperceptions any more.

On the contrary, it is clear from the idea of 'altitude weighting' sketched above how easily the Archipelago view can resolve our difficulties. There is no *a priori* reason for us to believe that we are at the top mountain peak of our own island, still less of the entire Archipelago. One may sympathize with Tegmark's view that the requirement that '[o]ur observations are the most generic ones that are consistent with our existence' is a useful prediction in the multiverse,[50] but its meaning depends on the qualification of 'our' type of observer (human? human-like? planetary? carbon-based? evolved?, etc.). We cannot say in advance whether our home-island is mostly flat or very rugged. Our real altitude and the height profile of our vicinity is a matter for rational and empirical investigation; we should conduct many numerical experiments and calculate how far in various directions we are from both the peak(s) and the shores of our home island. Suppose, for the sake of simplicity, that there is just a single peak, corresponding to the most habitable universe in our region. Determining our distance from the peak is then equivalent to answering the

49. Echoes of this position can be found in, e.g., J. Maynard-Smith and E. Szathmáry, 'On the likelihood of habitable worlds', *Nature* 384, 1996: 107.

50. M. Tegmark, 'Is "The Theory of Everything" Merely the Ultimate Ensemble Theory?', op.cit.

question of how much various parameters would need to be simultaneously changed in order for the number of predicted observers to be increased. Determining our distance from sea level is equivalent to answering the question of how much various parameters would need to be simultaneously changed in order for the universe to cease to be habitable. We may have different intuitions as to the answers to these questions, but the bottom line is that this is a problem to be answered by quantitative astrobiological modelling.

4.3. Imprecisely Defined Shores?

Klee laments the fact that anthropic arguments are numerically imprecise, often by an order of magnitude or more, and stretch the meanings of terms 'of the same order of magnitude' or 'of similar order of magnitude'.[51] He calls this 'mathematical sharp practice' and concludes that it is usually motivated by extrascientific, namely theistic, reasons. Apart from the old moral about taking up the sword and perishing by it,[52] this criticism sounds like a whiggish charge that Pedro Álvares Cabral or Fernando de Magallanes did not use precise maps; their errors in navigation were often an order of magnitude or more larger than what we in the GPS age know about the *correct* geography. Are their discoveries any the less appreciable for that undeniable fact? Do we mock them – or do we rather

---

51. R. Klee, 'The Revenge of Pythagoras: How a Mathematical Sharp Practice Undermines the Contemporary design Argument in Astrophysical Cosmology', *British Journal for the Philosophy of Science* 53, 2002: 331-54.

52. See M. A. Walker and M. M. Ćirković, 'Anthropic Reasoning, Naturalism and the Contemporary Design Argument', *International Studies in the Philosophy of Science* 20, 2006: 285-307, for Klee's own numerical mistakes, as well as his conflating of mathematical and physical fine-tunings.

celebrate their achievements, while emphasizing the simple means they had at their disposal? Understanding that we are at the very beginning – an overstatement, if anything – of the exploration of the Archipelago of Habitability should lead us naturally to expect large errors in our positioning of its shores – how could it be otherwise?

4.4. THE PROBLEM OF SWARMING ADVANCED OBSERVERS

In a thought-provoking paper, Olum argues that 'a straightforward application of anthropic reasoning and reasonable assumptions about the capabilities of other civilizations predicts that we should be part of a large civilization spanning our galaxy.'[53] This has been quoted by Carroll[54] and others as an instance of anthropic reasoning giving unacceptable results even within a single universe. Starting from the assumption of an infinite universe (following from the inflationary paradigm), Olum conjectures that there are civilizations much larger than ours (consisting of about 10^{10} observers). Spatial extent and the amount of resources at the disposal of such large civilizations would lead, in principle, to much larger number of observers (for example, 10^{19} observers). Now, even if 90 percent of all existing civilizations are small ones similar to our own, anthropic reasoning suggests that the overwhelming probabilistic prediction is that we live in a large civilization. Since this prediction is spectacularly unsuccessful on empirical grounds, with the probability of such failure being about 10^{-8}, something seems clearly wrong here.

---

53. K. Olum, 'Conflict between anthropic reasoning and observation', *Analysis* 64, 2004: 1-8.

54. Carroll, 'Is our Universe Natural', op. cit.

There are several ways out of Olum's problem, as he himself points out. For instance, we may conceive of a future redefinition of the concept of 'observer' (e.g., in the 'hive-mind' scenarios popular in SF), which would skew the Bayesian factor and resolve the paradox. But even if we restrict ourselves to our universe, there are less strong medicines at our disposal. It can be shown that the knowledge of the particular present epoch, together with some rather uncontroversial astrophysical assumptions, is sufficient to undermine – or, more precisely, to *postpone* – the applicability of Olum's argument.[55] However, this way out may not be open when we generalize to the entire spacetime (understood in a sufficiently wide sense) of the Archipelago – in that case we should ask the question: 'Why we don't find ourselves in a universe where almost all observers belong to large civilizations?' Although this question has not been pursued thus far, one possible approach could be that such universes are strongly suppressed for some at present unclear reason (say, that the observer-moment count peaks strongly before a typical large civilization anywhere can develop). Obviously, this remains a problem for anthropic reasoning generalised to the multiverse in the spirit of Equation (1) above.

4.5. THE PROBLEM OF FREAK OBSERVERS

One of the recently discovered difficulties facing the application of anthropic reasoning to the multiverse is that of so-called freak observers, also called Boltzmann's brains.

---

55. M. M. Ćirković, 'Too Early? On the Apparent Conflict of Astrobiology and Cosmology', *Biology and Philosophy* 21, 2006: 369-79.

Although prefigured by Price, Rees, Bostrom[56] and some other thinkers, it was explicitly posed in the 'disturbing' study of Dyson, Kleban, and Susskind[57] as a consequence of the new standard cosmology dominated by constant vacuum energy (positive cosmological constant). Such a cosmology leads asymptotically to a future-eternal de Sitter spacetime. This is equivalent (in the eschatological limit of future eternity) to a thermal state with a characteristic temperature $\sim 10^{-29}$ K. At first glance, such a low temperature coupled with the extreme dilution of matter at such late epochs is unlikely to yield anything interesting, but in fact like any thermal system, such a late vacuum will fluctuate at a nonzero rate per unit spacetime volume. And out of such fluctuations, across large eschatological time spans, complicated systems, e.g. intelligent observers, can arise, again at a nonzero rate. Since de Sitter spacetime is eternal, such 'freak observers' will be infinite in number (in fact, their production rate will exponentially increase with time) and will thus completely overwhelm 'normal' observers, like us, who emerged through physical, chemical, and biological evolution. Why, then, are *we* not freak observers?

Several recent publications show that the threat has been taken seriously. In particular, Page[58] argues that the simplest answer to the puzzle is that the future is finite and

56. H. Price, *Time's Arrow and Archimedes' Point* (Oxford: Oxford University Press, 1996); M. J. Rees, *Before the Beginning: Our Universe and Others* (Cambridge, MA: Helix Books, 1997); Bostrom, *Anthropic Bias*, op. cit.

57. L. Dyson, M. Kleban and L. Susskind, 'Disturbing implications of a cosmological constant', *Journal of High Energy Physics* 10, 2002: 011.

58. D. N. Page, 'The Lifetime of the Universe', *Journal of the Korean Physical Society* 49, 2006: 711-14 (preprint at http://arXiv:hep-th/0510003).

that our universe will vanish before Boltzmann's brains start to dominate the total observers' census. On a more optimistic note (at least from the point of view of non-freak observers), Carlip shows that the time variation of fundamental constants can lead to a small measure of freak observers,[59] and Vilenkin demonstrates that the same effect is achieved by the bubble nucleation in de Sitter vacuum under some fairly reasonable assumptions.[60]

From the present point of view, the problem of freak observers is easily generalized to a multiverse, since de Sitter spacetime is usually regarded as the source of an inflationary self-reproducing fractal. A rather uncontroversial aspect of anthropic reasoning is that we need to suppress the measure of freak observers in the entire Archipelago (and, clearly, Page's recipe will not work for a multitude of universes) in order to explain our evolution and our ordered observations. Although this problem will require further work, the good news is that there are ways out, such as those indicated in Carlip's and Vilenkin's studies.

5. PROSPECTS FOR AN AGE OF EXPLORATION?

In this essay, I have argued that the bridge between cosmology and particle physics on one side and astrobiology (and certain other 'mundane' disciplines, like artificial life, evolutionary theory, and so on) on the other, can be achieved through an exploration of cosmological parameter space. The Archipelago of Habitability – the set of habitable

59. A. Carlip, 'Transient observers and variable constants, or repelling the invasion of the Boltzmann's brains', *Journal of Cosmology and Astroparticle Physics* 6, 2007: 001.

60. A. Vilenkin, 'Freak observers and the measure of the multiverse', *Journal of High Energy Physics* 01, 2007: 092.

domains in the multiverse – seems to be a useful metaphor which directs our efforts towards an elucidation of the relationship between astrobiology and cosmology in a wider perspective. It offers directions for tight interdisciplinary collaboration between scientists interested in the properties of life, and those interested in the grand-scale structure of physical reality. It also offers great opportunities for philosophers – notably, the opportunity to generalize classical anthropic reasoning to the entire Archipelago, where all teleological and other unnecessary baggage is explicitly discarded. The relationship between the Archipelago and other multiverses containing intelligent observers considered in both philosophical[61] and scientific literature remains to be elaborated.

I have also attempted to argue that we may expect a true Age of Exploration of this Archipelago. Is this taking a metaphor too far? Not necessarily, even beyond Borges' idealistic statement – following Chesterton – that a really good metaphor cannot be taken too far; considering how dramatically the informatic revolution has changed our thinking about 'simulated' vs. 'real' worlds, it would be premature to claim that theoretical research on other habitable universes is any more intrinsically speculative than the very concepts of 'computer virus' or 'genetic algorithm' or even 'quantum computer' were a quarter of century ago. At the dawn of the new millennium, not only studies on the observable consequences of the existence of other universes,[62] but also intriguing arguments on simulating

61. E.g. D. Lewis, *On the Plurality of Worlds* (Oxford: Blackwell, 1986).

62. E.g., A. Aguirre, M.C. Johnson and A. Shomer, 'Towards observable signatures of other bubble universes', *Physical Review D* 74, 2007, 063509.

Figure 4. René Magritte's *The Beyond* (1938). The juxtaposition of an artifact and an apparently inhospitable planetary surface (remarkably prescient of our contemporary photographic images of the Martian surface) poses the age-old problem of the distinction between 'natural' and 'artificial' in a general context.

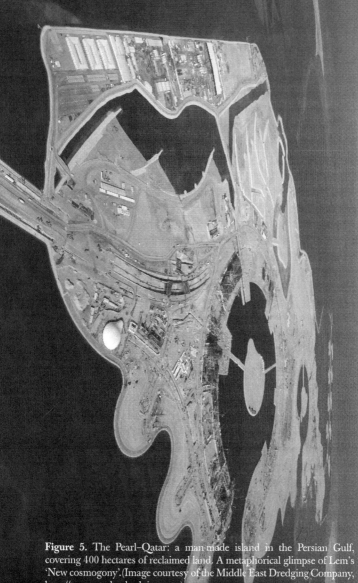

Figure 5. The Pearl–Qatar: a man-made island in the Persian Gulf, covering 400 hectares of reclaimed land. A metaphorical glimpse of Lem's 'New cosmogony'.(Image courtesy of the Middle East Dredging Company, http://www.medcodredging.com).

entire universes,[63] are threads of the same dynamic research activity – threads tightly entangled and intertwined, like the 'natural' and the 'artificial' in Magritte's painting. Further elucidation of this latter, perennial dichotomy could be an unexpected and welcome philosophical benefit.

Ultimately, I have used the concept of the observer here in a purely passive sense, in accordance with the only valid interpretation of anthropic reasoning as observational selection. But what about the vast future times for intentional action accorded to us (and other intelligent observers in the multiverse) by physical eschatology? Could the rules be changed, at least in principle and in the fullness of time, and parts of the landscape modified by intentional influence, like the build-up of artificial islands in today's world (figure 5)? Fortunately, at least two visionary pioneers strode, with giant steps, in that direction; we should keep silent in the huge shadows of Olaf Stapledon[64] and Stanislaw Lem.[65]

63. N. Bostrom, 'Are You Living in a Computer Simulation?', *Philosophical Quarterly* 53, 2003: 243-55.

64. O. Stapledon, *Star Maker* (London: Methuen, 1937).

65. S. Lem, 'The New Cosmogony', in S. Lem, M. Kandel (ed.) *A Perfect Vacuum* (Evanston: Northwestern University Press, 1993), 197-227.

Where Are They?
Why I Hope the Search for Extraterrestrial Life Finds Nothing[1]

Nick Bostrom

When water was discovered on Mars, people got very excited. Where there is water, there may be life. Scientists are planning new missions to study the planet up close. NASA's next Mars rover is scheduled to arrive in 2010. In the decade following, a Mars Sample Return mission might be launched, which would use robotic systems to collect samples of Martian rocks, soils, and atmosphere, and return them to Earth. We could then analyze the sample to see if it contains any traces of life, whether extinct or still active. Such a discovery would be of tremendous scientific significance. What could be more fascinating than discovering life that had evolved entirely independently of life here on Earth? Many people would also find it heartening to learn that we are not entirely alone in this vast cold cosmos.

1. First published in *MIT Technology Review*, May/June 2008: 72-7. Reprinted with permission.

But I hope that our Mars probes will discover nothing. It would be good news if we find Mars to be completely sterile. Dead rocks and lifeless sands would lift my spirit.

Conversely, if we discovered traces of some simple extinct life form – some bacteria, some algae – it would be bad news. If we found fossils of something more advanced, perhaps something looking like the remnants of a trilobite or even the skeleton of a small mammal, it would be *very* bad news. The more complex the life we found, the more depressing the news of its existence would be. Scientifically interesting, certainly, but a bad omen for the future of the human race.

How do I arrive at this conclusion? I begin by reflecting on a well-known fact. UFO-spotters, Raelian cultists, and self-certified alien abductees notwithstanding, humans have, to date, seen no sign of any extraterrestrial intelligent civilization. We have not received any visitors from space, nor have our radio telescopes detected any signals transmitted by any extraterrestrial civilization. The Search for Extra-Terrestrial Intelligent Life (SETI) has been going for nearly fifty years, employing increasingly powerful telescopes and data mining techniques, and has so far consistently corroborated the null hypothesis. As best we have been able to determine, the night sky is empty and silent – the question 'Where are they?' thus being at least as pertinent today as it was when Enrico Fermi first posed it during a lunch discussion with some of his physicist colleagues back in 1950.

Here is another fact: There are on the order of 100 billion stars in our galaxy alone, and the observable universe contains on the order of 100 billion galaxies.

In the last couple of decades, we have learnt that many of these stars have planets circling around them. By now, several hundred exoplanets we have discovered. Most of these are gigantic, but this is due to a selection effect: It is very difficult to detect smaller exoplanets with current observation methods. (In most cases, the planets cannot be directly observed. Their existence is inferred from their gravitational influence on their parent sun, which wobbles slightly when pulled towards a large orbiting planet; or alternatively by a slight fluctuation in their sun's perceived luminosity which occurs when it is partially eclipsed by the exoplanet.) We have every reason to believe that the observable universe contains vast numbers of solar systems, including many that have planets that are Earth-like at least in the sense of having a mass and temperature similar to those of our own orb. We also know that many of these solar systems are much older than ours.

From these two facts it follows that there exists a 'Great Filter'.[2] The Great Filter can be thought of as a probability barrier. It consists of one or more highly improbable evolutionary transitions or steps whose occurrence is required in order for an Earth-like planet to produce an intelligent civilization of a type that would be visible to us with our current observation technology. You start with billions and billions of potential germination points for life, and you end up with a sum total of zero extraterrestrial civilizations that we can observe. The Great Filter must therefore be powerful enough – which is to say, the

---

2. I borrow this term from Robin Hanson's 'The Great Filter – Are We Almost Past It?' (http://hanson.gmu.edu/greatfilter.html), a paper which presents an argument similar to the one expounded here.

critical steps must be improbable enough – that even with many billions of rolls of the dice, one ends up with nothing: no aliens, no spacecraft, no signals, at least none that we can detect in our neck of the woods.

Now, an important question for us is, just where might this Great Filter be located? There are two basic possibilities: It might be behind us, somewhere in our distant past. Or it might be ahead of us, somewhere in the millennia or decades to come. Let us ponder these possibilities in turn.

Consider first the possibility that the filter is in our past. This would mean that there is some extremely improbable step in the sequence of events whereby an Earth-like planet gives rise to an intelligent life form comparable in its technological sophistication to our contemporary human civilization. Some people seem to take it for granted that evolution of intelligent life on this planet was straightforward – lengthy, yes, complex, sure, yet ultimately inevitable or nearly so. Carl Sagan appears to have held this view; he once wrote that 'the origin of life must be a highly probable circumstance; as soon as conditions permit, up it pops!'[3] But this view might well be completely mistaken. There is at any rate hardly any evidence to support it. Evolutionary biology, at the moment, does not enable us to calculate from first principles how probable or improbable the evolution of intelligent life on Earth was. Moreover, if we look back at the history of life on this planet, we can identify a number of evolutionary transitions each one of which is a plausible candidate Great Filter.

---

3. C. Sagan, 'The abundance of life-bearing planets', *Bioastronomy News* 7(4): 1–4.

For example, perhaps it is very, very improbable that even simple self-replicators should emerge on any given Earth-like planet. Attempts to create life in the laboratory by mixing water and gases believed to have existed in the early atmosphere on Earth have failed to get much beyond the synthesis of a few simple amino acids. No instance of abiogenesis has ever been observed.

The oldest confirmed microfossils date from approximately 3,500 million years ago, and there is tentative evidence that life might have existed a few hundred million years prior to that date, but no evidence of life before 3,800 million years ago. Life might well have arisen considerably earlier than that without leaving any traces. There are very few preserved rock formations this old and such as have survived have undergone major remoulding over the eons. Nevertheless, there is a period lasting several hundreds of millions of years between the formation of Earth and the first known life. The evidence is thus consistent with the hypothesis that the emergence of life required an extremely improbable set of coincidences, and that it took hundreds of millions of years of trial-and-error, of molecules and surface structures randomly interacting, before something capable of self-replication happened to appear by a stroke of astronomical luck. For aught we know, this first critical step could be a Great Filter.

Since we cannot rerun the history of life multiple times to obtain rigorous statistics, it is difficult to determine conclusively the 'difficulty' of any given evolutionary development. There are, however, some criteria that we can use to identify evolutionary transitions that are at least good candidates for being a Great Filter, i.e. that are both extremely improbable and practically necessary for the eventual emergence of intelligent technological civilization. One criterion is that the transition should have occurred only once. Flight, sight, photosynthesis, and limbs have all evolved several times here on Earth, and are thus ruled out. Another indication that an evolutionary step was very improbable is that it took a very long time for it to occur even after its prerequisites were in place. A long delay suggests that vastly many random recombinations had to be tried before one was found that worked. Perhaps several improbable mutations had to occur all at once in order to leap from one local fitness peak to another: the mutations might individually be deleterious and only fitness-enhancing when they occur together. (The evolution of *Homo sapiens* from one of our recent hominid ancestors, such as *Homo erectus*, happened rather quickly on geological timescales, so this step would be a relatively weak candidate for a Great Filter.)

The original emergence of life appears to meet these two criteria. As far as we know, it might have occurred only once and it might have taken hundreds of millions of years for it to happen even after the planet had cooled down sufficiently to enable a wide range of organic molecules to be stable. Later evolutionary history offers additional candidates for the Great Filter. For example, it took some 1.8 billion years for prokaryotes (the most basic type of single-cell organism) to evolve into eukaryotes (a more complex kind of cell with a membrane-enclosed nucleus). 1.8 billion years is a long time, and as far as we know eukaryotes evolved only once, making this transition an excellent possible Great Filter. Other strong candidates include the rise of multi-cellular organisms and sexual reproduction.

So one possibility is that the Great Filter is behind us. This would explain the absence of observable aliens. Why? Because if the rise of intelligent life on any one planet is sufficiently improbable, then it follows that we are most likely the only such civilization in our galaxy or even in the entire observable universe. (The observable universe contains approximately 10^{22} stars. The universe might well extend infinitely far beyond the part that is observable by us, and may contain infinitely many stars. If so, then it is virtually certain that there exists an infinite number of intelligent extraterrestrial species, no matter how improbable their evolution on any given planet. However, cosmological theory implies that, due to the expansion of the universe, any life outside the observable universe is and will forever remain causally disconnected from us: it can never visit us, communicate with us, or be seen by us or our descendants.)

The other possibility is that the Great Filter is after us, in our future. This would mean that there is some great improbability that prevents almost all technological civilizations at our current human stage of development from progressing to the point where they engage in large-scale space-colonization and make their presence known to other technological civilizations. For example, it might be that any sufficiently technologically advanced civilization discovers some technology – perhaps some very powerful weapons technology – that causes its extinction.

I will return to this scenario shortly, but first I shall say a few words about another theoretical possibility: that the extraterrestrials are out there, in abundance but hidden from our view. I think this is unlikely, because if extraterrestrials do exist in any numbers, it's reasonable to think at least one species would have already expanded throughout the galaxy, or beyond. Yet we have met no one.

Various schemes have been proposed for how an intelligent species might colonize space. They might send out 'manned' space ships, which would establish colonies and 'terraform' new planets, beginning with worlds in their own solar system before moving on to more distant destinations. But much more likely, in my view, would be colonization by means of so-called 'von Neumann probes', named after the Hungarian-born prodigy John von Neumann, who included among his many mathematical and scientific achievements the development of the concept of a universal constructor. A von Neumann probe would be an unmanned self-replicating spacecraft, controlled by artificial intelligence, capable of interstellar travel. A probe would land on a planet (or a moon or asteroid), where it would mine raw materials to create multiple replicas of itself, perhaps using advanced forms of nanotechnology. These replicas would then be launched in various directions, thus setting in motion a multiplying colonization wave.[4] Our galaxy is about 100,000 light years across. If a probe were capable of travelling at one-tenth of the speed of light, every planet in the galaxy could thus be colonized within a couple of million years (allowing some time for the bootstrapping process that needs to take place between a probe's landing on a resource site, setting up the necessary infrastructure, and producing daughter probes). If travel speed were limited to 1 percent of light speed, colonization might take twenty

4. This scenario was developed by Frank Tipler in 1981.

million years instead. The exact numbers do not matter much because they are at any rate very short compared to the astronomical time scales involved in the evolution of intelligent life from scratch (billions of years).

If building a von Neumann probe seems like a very difficult thing to do – well, surely it is, but we are not talking about a proposal for something that NASA or the European Space Agency should get to work on today. Rather, we are considering what would be accomplished with some future very advanced technology. We ourselves might build von Neumann probes in decades, centuries, or millennia – intervals that are mere blips compared to the lifespan of a planet. Considering that space travel was science fiction a mere half century ago, we should, I think, be extremely reluctant to proclaim something forever technologically infeasible unless it conflicts with some hard physical constraint. Our early space probes are already out there: Voyager 1, for example, is now beyond our solar system.

Even if an advanced technological civilization could spread throughout the galaxy in a relatively short period of time (and thereafter spread to neighboring galaxies), one might still wonder whether it would opt to do so. Perhaps it would rather choose to stay at home and live in harmony with nature. However, there are a number of considerations that make this a less plausible explanation of the great silence. First, we observe that life here on Earth manifests a very strong tendency to spread wherever it can. On our planet, life has spread to every nook and cranny that can sustain it: East, West, North, and South; land, water, and air; desert, tropic, and arctic ice; underground rocks, hydrothermal vents, and radioactive waste dumps; there are even living beings inside the bodies of other living beings. This empirical finding is of course entirely consonant with what one would expect on the basis of elementary evolutionary theory. Second, if we consider our own species in particular, we also find that it has spread to every part of the planet, and we have even established a presence in space, at vast expense, with the international space station. Third, there is an obvious reason for an advanced civilization that has the technology to go into space relatively cheaply to do so: namely, that's where most of the resources are. Land, minerals, energy, negentropy, matter: all abundant out there yet limited on any one home planet. These resources could be used to support a growing population and to construct giant temples or supercomputers or whatever structures a civilization values. Fourth, even if some advanced civilization were non-expansionary to begin with, it might change its mind after a hundred years or fifty thousand years – a delay too short to matter. Fifth, even if some advanced civilization chose to remain non-expansionist forever, it would still not make any difference if there were at least one other civilization out there that at some point opted to launch a colonization process: that expansionary civilization would then be the one whose probes, colonies, or descendants would fill the galaxy. It takes but one match to start a fire; only one expansionist civilization to launch the colonization of the universe.

For all these reasons it seems unlikely that the galaxy is teeming with intelligent life and that the reason we haven't seen any of them is that they all confine themselves to their home planets. Now, it is possible to concoct scenarios in which the universe is swarming with advanced civilizations every one of which chooses to keep itself well hidden from our view. Maybe there is a secret society of advanced civilizations that know about us but have decided not to contact us until we're mature enough to be admitted into their club. Perhaps they're observing us, like animals in a zoo. I don't see how we can conclusively rule out this possibility. But I will set it aside for the remainder of this essay in order to concentrate on what to me appears to be more plausible answers to Fermi's question.

A disconcerting hypothesis is that the Great Filter consists in some destructive tendency common to virtually all sufficiently advanced technological civilizations. Throughout history, great civilizations on Earth have imploded – the Roman Empire, the Mayan civilization that once flourished in Central America, and many others. However, the kind of societal collapse that merely delays the eventual emergence of a space-colonizing civilization by a few hundred or a few thousand years would not help explain why no such civilization has visited us from another planet. A thousand years may seem a long time to an individual, but in this context it's a sneeze. There are planets that are billions of years older than Earth. Any intelligent species on those planets would have had ample time to recover from repeated social or ecological collapses. Even if they failed a thousand times before they succeeded, they could still have arrived here hundreds of millions of years ago.

To constitute an effective Great Filter, we hypothesize a terminal global cataclysm: an existential catastrophe. An existential risk is one where an adverse outcome would annihilate Earth-originating intelligent life or permanently and drastically curtail its potential for future development. We can identify a number of potential existential risks: nuclear war fought with stockpiles much greater than those that exist today (maybe resulting from future arms races); a genetically engineered superbug; environmental disaster; asteroid impact; wars or terrorist acts committed with powerful future weapons, perhaps based on advanced forms of nanotechnology; superintelligent general artificial intelligence with destructive goals; high-energy physics experiments; a permanent global Brave-New-World-like totalitarian regime protected from revolution by new surveillance and mind control technologies. These are just some of the existential risks that have been discussed in the literature, and considering that many of these have been conceptualized only in recent decades. It is plausible to assume that there are further existential risks that we have not yet thought of.

The study of existential risks is an extremely important albeit rather neglected field of inquiry. But here we must limit ourselves to making just one point. In order for some existential risk to constitute a plausible Great Filter, it is not sufficient that we judge it to have a significant subjective probability of destroying humanity. Rather, it must be of a kind that could with some plausibility be postulated to destroy virtually all sufficiently advanced civilizations. For instance, stochastic natural disasters such as asteroid hits and super-volcanic eruptions are unlikely Great Filter candidates, because even if they destroyed a significant number of civilizations we would expect some civilizations to get lucky and escape disaster; and some of these civilizations could then go on to colonize the universe. Perhaps the most likely type of existential risks that could constitute a Great Filter are those that arise from technological discovery. It is not far-fetched to suppose that there might be some possible technology which is such that (a) virtually all sufficiently advanced civilizations eventually discover it and (b) its discovery leads almost universally to existential disaster.

So where is the Great Filter? Behind us, or not behind us?

If the Great Filter is ahead of us, we have still to confront it. If it is true that almost all intelligent species go extinct before they master the technology for space colonization, then we must expect that our own species, too, will go extinct before reaching technological maturity, since we have no reason to think that we will be any luckier than most other species at our stage of development. If the Great Filter is ahead of us, we must relinquish all hope of ever colonizing the galaxy; and we must fear that our adventure will end soon, or at any rate, prematurely. Therefore, we had better hope that the Great Filter is behind us.

What has all this got to do with finding life on Mars? Consider the implications of discovering that life had evolved independently on Mars (or some other planet in our solar system). That discovery would suggest that the emergence of life is not a very improbable event. If it happened independently twice here in our own back yard, it must surely have happened millions times across the galaxy. This would mean that the Great Filter is less likely to occur in the early life of planets and is therefore more likely still to come.

If we discovered some very simple life forms on Mars, in its soil or under the ice at the polar caps, it would show that the Great Filter must exist somewhere after that period in evolution. This would be disturbing, but we might still hope that the Great Filter was located in our past. If we discovered a more advanced life form, such as some kind of multi-cellular organism, that would eliminate a much larger stretch of potential locations where the Great Filter could be. The effect would be to shift the probability more strongly to the hypothesis that the Great Filter is ahead of us, not behind us. And if we discovered the fossils of some very complex life form, such as of some vertebrate-like creature, we would have to conclude that the probability is very great that the bulk of the Great Filter is ahead of us. Such a discovery would be a crushing blow. It would be by far the worst news ever printed on a newspaper cover.

Yet most people reading about the discovery would be thrilled. They would not understand the implications. If the Great Filter is not behind us, it is ahead of us.

So this is why I'm hoping that our space probes will discover dead rocks and lifeless sands on Mars, on Jupiter's moon Europa, and everywhere else our astronomers look. It would keep alive the hope for a great future for humanity.

Now, it might be thought an amazing coincidence if Earth were the only planet in the galaxy on which intelligent life evolved. If it happened here – the one planet we have studied closely – surely one would expect it to have happened on a lot of other planets in the galaxy also, which we have not yet had the chance to examine? This objection, however, rests on a fallacy: It overlooks what is known as an 'observation selection effect'. Whether intelligent life is common or rare, every observer is guaranteed to find themselves originating from a place where intelligent life did, indeed, arise. Since only the successes give rise to observers who can wonder about their existence, it would be a mistake to regard our planet as a randomly-selected sample from all planets. (It would be closer to the mark to regard our planet as though it were a random sample from the subset of planets that did engender intelligent life: this being a crude formulation of one of the sane elements extractable from the motley ore of ideas referred to as the 'anthropic principle'.)

Since this point confuses many, it is worth expounding it slightly. Consider two different hypotheses. One says that the evolution of intelligent life is fairly easy and happens on a significant fraction of all suitable planets. The other hypothesis says that the evolution of intelligent life is extremely difficult and happens perhaps only on one out of a million billion planets. To evaluate their plausibility in light of your evidence, you must ask yourself, 'What do these hypotheses predict that I should observe?' If you think about it, it is clear that both hypotheses predict that you should observe that your civilization originated in places where intelligent life evolved. All observers will observe precisely that, whether the evolution of intelligent life happened on a large or a small fraction of all planets. An observation selection effect guarantees that whatever planet we call 'ours' was a success story. And as long as the total number of planets in the universe is large enough to compensate for the low probability of any given one of them giving rise to intelligent life, it is not a surprise that a few success stories exist.

If – as I hope is the case – we are the only intelligent species that has ever evolved in our galaxy, and perhaps in the entire observable universe, it does not follow that our survival is not in danger. Nothing in the above reasoning precludes the Great Filter from being located both behind us *and* ahead of us. It might both be extremely improbable that intelligent life should arise on any given planet, and very improbable that intelligent life, once evolved, should succeed in becoming advanced enough to colonize space.

But we would have some grounds for hope that all or most of the Great Filter is in our past if Mars is indeed found to be barren. In that case, we may have a significant chance of one day growing into something almost unimaginably greater than we are today.

In this scenario, the entire history of humankind to date is a mere instant compared to the eons of history that lie still before us. All the triumphs and tribulations of the millions of peoples that have walked the Earth since the ancient civilization of Mesopotamia would be like mere birth pangs in the delivery of a kind of life that hasn't really begun yet. For surely it would be the height of naiveté to think that with the transformative technologies already in sight – genetics, nanotechnology and so on – and with thousands of millennia still ahead of us to perfect and apply these technologies and others that we haven't yet conceived of, human nature and the human condition will remain unchanged for all future times. Instead, if we survive and prosper, we will presumably develop into some kind of posthuman existence.

So this is why I conclude that the silence of the night sky is golden, and why, in the search for extraterrestrial life, no news is good news. It promises a potentially great future for humanity.

None of this means that we ought to cancel our plans to have a closer look at Mars. If the red planet ever harboured life, we might as well find out about it. It might be bad news, but it would tell us something about our place in the universe, our future technological prospects, the existential risks confronting us, and the possibilities for human transformation: issues of considerable importance.

It is impossible to know in advance what insights might be gleaned by applying the kind of careful and systematic study to such big questions that we apply every day to smaller and less consequential technological and scientific problems. There may be surprising arguments and ideas out there merely waiting to be discovered. Some of these might even turn out to have practical ramifications of such importance as to change our whole scheme of priorities. Perhaps the greatest benefit from the SETI program will result if it prompts thinking about these larger matters.

Theoretically, smart ambitious scholars could start thinking without waiting for such prompts. Expensive instruments, however, have a way of lending scientific status and respectability to a field of inquiry. Academics are keen to put as much distance as possible between themselves and the kooks and cranks that flock to these big questions. If large telescopes, NASA satellites, and complicated mathematical data analysis are involved, it becomes harder for outside observers to mistake the work for the ramblings of UFO-nuts and other crackpots. There may be no signals from space, yet those with their antennas tuned to more anthropomorphic wavelengths are sure to pick up a buzz of social signaling in people's attitudes towards the search for extraterrestrial beings. Such social background noise might in fact be one of the main obstacles to intellectual progress on many big-picture topics.

Random Sampler from a Blocktime Animation

Keith Tyson

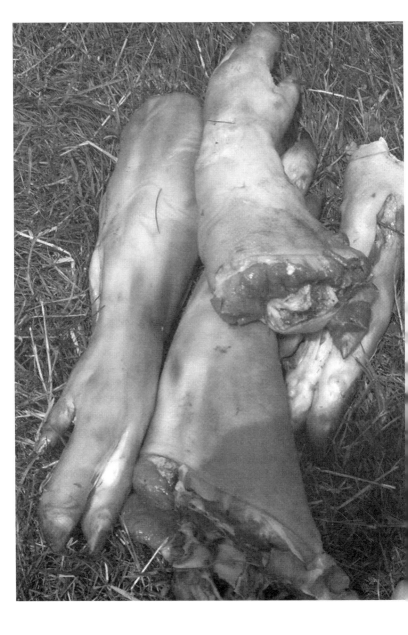

The Phoenix of Nature:
Kant and the Big Bounce

Martin Schönfeld

For Fred Beiser, Mike Friedman, and Paul Eisenberg.[1]

There is a profound concept, the Phoenix of Nature, which deserves another look. Recent theoretical progressions are structuring information in startling ways. In light of this emerging information gestalt, a clarification of the Phoenix seems timely. The point is to advance towards a future integration of Kant.

The Phoenix of Nature appears in Kant's second book, Universal History of Nature and Theory of the Sky. It emerges only once, in part two, chapter seven (Academy Edition 1:321), but it can be understood as the idea that holds the book together. Universal History of Nature was published anonymously in 1755. Most printed copies were committed to the flames, supposedly accidentally, but probably intentionally. Its key idea was provocative. Kant's authorship contributed to his academic marginalisation until 1770.

1. Frederick C. Beiser (Syracuse) first pointed me towards the 'phoenix of nature' as a lacuna in Kant interpretation. Michael Friedman (Stanford) helped me to understand the scientific and heuristic relevance of Kant's thought. Paul Eisenberg (Indiana) patiently discussed with me my misgivings about Schopenhauer's criticism of Kantian philosophy. When I thought the Copernican turn precluded identification of Nature's deep structure, in Schopenhauer's or any other way, Paul Eisenberg encouraged me to look for a new reading of the Copernican turn, to integrate Kant's critical legacy with Kant's metaphysical and cosmological heirs. I thank them for inspiration.

The Phoenix is not part of conventional interpretations of Kant. It would be sensible for this situation to change, not least because this would allow mainstream scholarship to step out of its self-imposed isolation. Other research approaches, by workers in other disciplines, recognize the Phoenix and its implications. But a bridging of the disciplines, however timely, comes at a price. Philosophy will need to abandon its self-complacent, self-serving scepticism, deal at last with the patterns of outward reality, and become once more what it had been in Kant's enlightened day: *Weltweisheit* or world wisdom.

1. CONVENTIONAL NEGLECT: OMITTING THE PHOENIX

Historians of philosophy know that Kant wrote for nearly sixty years, from 1745 to 1802, but most of the scholarly attention is focused on what Lewis White Beck called the 'astonishing decade', the 1780s, which saw the publication of major works – the *Critiques*, the *Groundwork*, and *What is Enlightenment*, to name just a few.[2] The texts prior to the first *Critique*, the pre-critical writings, from 1746 to 1768, are by and large ignored. The critical works are available and taught in college. The early texts are not even read by most Kant experts. This is not because the early texts are juvenilia; they aren't: Kant wrote his first book, *Living Forces*, when he was in his twenties, the second, *Universal History*, in his thirties, and the third, *One Possible Proof-Ground for a Demonstration of Divine Dasein*, when pushing forty.

---

2. 'I know of no way to describe the 1780s except to say that they were the astonishing decade.' L W Beck, *Early German Philosophy: Kant and his Predecessors* (Cambridge, Mass.: Harvard, 1969), 433.

The critical work has generated a mountain of commentary and analysis, while studies on the early texts are few and far between. Conventionally, we think of the critical Kant as belonging to a small handful of great thinkers, but we think of the early Kant as a flawed figure with an inconsequential body of work. The difference in reception between the two halves of the Kantian oeuvre could hardly be any starker.

The book on the Phoenix, *Universal History of Nature*, is neither well-known nor in print.[3] A literature search of the Phoenix will come up empty, at least as long as one scans bibliographies of Kant scholars. *Kant-Studien* has existed for a century, but its first article on that book appeared only a few years ago (2003). The article's title is just the book title ('Kants "Allgemeine Naturgeschichte und Theorie des Himmels" (1755)'), revealing how basic the scholarship has remained.[4] The paper falls in clear sections: on views before Kant, on the book, part I, part II, and on views after Kant.[5]

3. There is an online translation, *Universal Natural History and Theory of the Heavens*, by Ian Johnston at Vancouver Island University, at http://records.viu.ca/~johnstoi/kant/kant2e.htm. The website, dated September 2008, and accessed October 2008, refers to a print edition by Richer Resources Publications (Arlington, VA), which, however, is not listed in the catalogue of the press. An earlier translation, also called *Universal Natural History and Theory of the Heavens*, by Stanley Jaki, was published by Scottish Academic Press (Edinburgh, 1981), and is out of print. The first translation, by William Hastie, titled *Kant's cosmogony, as in his essay on the retardation of the rotation of the earth and his natural history and theory of the heavens*, appeared in 1900; it was reprinted by Greenwood (New York, 1968), and University of Michigan Press (Ann Arbor, MI, 1969); both editions are no longer available. The Cambridge Edition of the Works of Immanuel Kant, ed. Paul Guyer and Allan Wood, has slated *Universal History of Nature* to appear in the volume *Natural Science*, ed. Eric Watkins, but this volume is nearly ten years overdue, and no fixed publication date has been set. In English, Kant's second book is not available in print.

4. To my knowledge, there is no publication in *Kant-Studien* on Kant's first book, *Living Forces*, 1747, to date either.

5. S. Lalla, 'Kants "Allgemeine Naturgeschichte und Theorie des Himmels" (1755),' *Kant-Studien* 94, 2003: 426-53.

The Phoenix isn't mentioned; neither is part III. After twenty-seven pages, the author concludes in the even-handed way that has become typical of conventional philosophy: Kant's approach was promising but also weird; his ideas were interesting but problematic; today it'd be tough to make scientific sense of them; their content is unverifiable, and this is probably a good thing.[6] Conclusions of this sort show two things: the scholarly consensus in first-rate philosophy journals – and the isolation of philosophy from scientific disciplines.

The differences between the early texts and the critical work come down to a contrast in perspectives. This contrast hinges on the so-called Copernican Turn. According to *Critique of Pure Reason* (B xvi) we tend to assume that concepts conform to objects, but doing so hasn't led to progress in metaphysics; so we might as well turn it upside down and assume the opposite, that *objects conform to concepts*, and see whether this would lead to progress. A corollary of the Copernican Turn is that any thing we take as an object is already an object conforming to concepts, which means an object seen is an object changed. When looking at things as they are in themselves we organize impressions into concept-conforming representations; it is these representations that we look at. Things in themselves are inaccessible. We are cognitive versions of King Midas: whatever we touch

6. Lalla, op. cit., 453: 'Rein retrospektiv hatte Kant einen vielversprechenden Ansatz geliefert, die Anfänge der eigenen Naturgeschichte explanativ einzuholen, um sich so ein solides Fundament für die Bestimmung aller sich aus dieser Urphase ergebenden Prozesse zu geben. Laplaces Glaube an die Vollständigkeit und die vollständige Verfügbarkeit aller dafür notwendigen Faktoren ist angesichts einer Quantenphysik nur noch schwer nachvollziehbar. Ob die Hypothese einer zeitlosen Determination des Gegebenen astronomisch sinnvoll ist (unabhängig davon, ob es anthropologisch wünschenswert ist), steht also heute, wie damals, buchstäblich in den Sternen.'

doesn't turn into gold but into appearance. Perception alters the perceived. And here's the rub: The early texts are precisely inquiries into things as they are in themselves. The Copernican Turn seems to rule such inquiry out and thus invalidate the early texts.

2. Challenging the Copernican Turn: The Conceptual Route to the Phoenix

But first appearances can be deceptive. That the Copernican Turn is an obstacle for grasping things as they are in themselves doesn't mean the obstacle is insurmountable. Yet that there may be a way around an invalidation of the early inquiries doesn't mean that the Copernican Turn was a failure either. It wasn't. It was a stunning success. The *Critique* changed discourse to such an extent that its year of publication divides what led up to it, Early Modern Thought, and what played out afterwards, the Age of Modernity. Kant's proposal settled the debate between rationalists and empiricists. Over the question of the roots of knowledge, rationalists stress the internal activity of the mind and appeal to mathematics as a case in point. Empiricists stress the external passivity of the mind and appeal to pretty much everything else. Kant integrated both views in a bigger picture: the mind is passively absorbing data and actively shaping appearances. The mind is passive and active. Cognition is an interactive process. Interactivity is the Midas Touch of perception, and since we perceive only what is absorbed-plus-shaped, the unshaped things in themselves elude our grasp. The conclusion of their indeterminacy is an effective weapon for social freedom. The critical work delivered the *coup de grace* to religious dogma. The elusiveness of the thing in itself means that transcendent truth is obscure and cannot be enforced. The critical insight was a milestone along the way toward more enlightened, secular, and open societies.

But freedom, in excess, is indulgence; there can be too much of a good thing. Ultimate religious truths are not ultimate natural patterns. Conceptually they are distinct. While the critical release from religious dogma is a lasting legacy, the critical suspension of metaphysical inquiry is not. Contrary to what one might expect, the Copernican Turn doesn't entail total inaccessibility of things as they are in themselves. There is a way to get to them, indirectly, through the environmental backdoor, so to speak.

Consider what things in themselves are: mind-independent material taken up in the cognitive process. While following the Copernican Turn we know *something* is mind-independent. Something is out there.

'Out there' are environmental structures that are mind-independent parts of reality. For a subject to *prevail* in such structures requires that the subject's representations match the real thing. If they fail to match up, the subject would be cognitively dysfunctional. It would bump into things, not procreate, be eaten, and soon die.[7] But a subject happily

---

7. D Hoffman, in 'The Interface Theory of Perception,' forthcoming in *Object Categorization: Computer and Human Vision Perspectives*, ed. S. Dickinson et alia (Cambridge University Press), argues that, on evolutionary grounds, it is *not* the case that our senses have been shaped to the end of estimating true properties of the world, but instead that 'perceptions constitute a *species-specific user interface* that guides behaviour in a niche' (3). This approach seems to run counter to my isomorphism thesis, but I think it is compatible with my suggestion. Isomorphism does not mean identity. Our visual perception of a cave is distinct from its auditory perception by a bat. It seems hard to imagine what it is like to be like a bat, and what sonic picture of the cave a bat might represent to its mind. Clearly the sonic cave-representation is as much a species-specific user interface as a visual image of the cave by humans. However,

surviving in the mind-independent environment is different: it shapes absorbed sense data into appearances; it makes objects conform to concepts – but does so in such a way that the structure of its representation is an isomorphic echo of the structure of its environment. Conceptual form mirrors environmental form. For elementary evolutionary reasons, rational cognition makes objects conform to concepts that have worked out. Thus objects conform to concepts that fit. Things as they are in themselves are inaccessible and yet isomorphic mirrors of cognized appearances, at least in the case of surviving subjects. Accordingly the critical path leads to ultimate natural patterns after all. In this light, the Copernican Turn doesn't invalidate the results of Kant's early pursuits; it suspends them awaiting confirmation. For the concept at issue, the Phoenix, confirmation seems to have arrived.

---

isomorphism means mapping by a rule. And while a sonic map differs from the visual map, both are related such that component information in either not only translates to the appropriate node in the respective other map, but also translates to the cave as it exists independent of any perceiver. As both maps work, humans walking in a cave are capable of avoiding stalagmites looming in the flashlight, just as it is possible for a bat flying there to swerve around the same stalagmites echoing its cries. In this way, the Copernican Turn fits to a cognitive realism. Things as they are in themselves emerge as isomorphic mirrors of cognized appearances, as mentioned. It should further be noted that this use of 'thing in itself' differs from the usage in Schopenhauer, for instance, who takes 'thing in itself' as referring to a universal quintessence, and not the individuated structure of nature. L. W. Beck, in the glossary to the third edition of *Critique of Practical Reason* (New York: Kessinger, 2004), xxv, adds a clarification that '*Ding an sich* is an expression Kant employs only once in the second *Critique*, his usual locution being *Ding an sich selbst*. According to Gerold Prauss (*Kant und das Problem der Dinge an sich* [Bonn, 1974]), the latter locution is adverbial rather than adjectival, and elliptical for "thing regarded as it is in itself". The distinction […] suggests that there are two *kinds* of things, viz., appearances and things in themselves, whereas the second suggests that there is one kind of thing in two contexts (as it appears, and as it is regarded in itself)'. The isomorphism thesis I wish to submit concerns the 'latter' kind; thus suggesting a 'two-aspect' interpretation. The price my thesis pays is that its acceptance does interpretive violence to Kant such that a problem left unresolved according to the textual evidence would find an arguable resolution upon further thought.

3. A UNIVERSAL SINGLE RULE: THE PHOENIX

The Phoenix of Nature is the idea that all environmental structures are subject to the rule of rise and fall. Everything oscillates, from simplicity to complexity to simplicity, along a line of quasi-reincarnations. No matter how long winter lasts, there'll be another spring. Such is life. Such is nature. In fact, such are all natures. In the beginning of the chapter on the Phoenix, Kant notes:

> The Universe, with its immeasurable greatness, endless diversity, and beauty, which shines up at all angles, puts us in a state of silent wonder. And whenever the idea of all this perfection fires up the power of imagination, the understanding falls into a state of delight, as soon as one considers how so much splendour and grandeur flows from a single universal rule, in eternal and right tact.(1:306.16-23)[8]

Nietzsche praised the Pre-Socratic depth of *Universal History of Nature*.[9] Like Anaxagoras or Heraclitus, Kant suspects *ek-pyrosis*, the eternal recurrence of *world burn*. Thus rise follows fall follows rise. For Nietzsche, the shape of quintessence, Kant's Phoenix, is a 'kind of swinging', a 'sort of vibration,' which, slowed down, would look like a

---

8. Kant, *Werke* (Academy Edition), 1:306.16-23: 'Das Weltgebäude setzt durch seine unermeßliche Größe und durch die unendliche Mannigfaltigkeit und Schönheit, welche aus ihm von allen Seiten hervorleuchtet, in ein stilles Erstaunen. Wenn die Vorstellung aller dieser Vollkommenheit nun die Einbildungskraft rührt, so nimmt der Verstand andererseits eine andere Art der Entzückung ein, wenn er betrachtet, wie so viel Pracht, so viel Größe aus einer einzigen allgemeinen Regel mit einer ewigen und richtigen Ordnung abfließt.'

9. Nietzsche, *Philosophie im tragischen Zeitalter der Griechen* (*Philosophy in the Tragic Age of the Greeks*), § 17, in *Sämtliche Werke: Kritische Studienausgabe*, ed. G Colli, M Montinari (Munich/Berlin: DTV/De Gruyter 1980), 1:865.

dancing mathematical figure or a moving formal frame.[10]
The largest formal frame – the largest environment – is
the Universe. In German, 'universe' is the *All*. This isn't a
static background against which nature's dance plays out.
The *All*, the background, itself is dance. It is a chain steadily
swinging from trough to peak to trough, or from a prone
state to an evolved state to a prone state. Some cosmologists call the Phoenix 'the Big Bounce'. Here's Kant's take
on the Phoenix:

> The Phoenix of Nature burns himself up only to return from
> his ashes, come back to life, and be young again. If we now
> follow the Phoenix through all infinity of time and space, and
> if we see how Nature, even in the aspect of decay and obso-
> lescence, is not depleted of raw emergence; if we see how, at
> the other edge of creation and in the realm of unformed, raw
> matter, Nature proceeds with steady steps toward expansion of
> the plan of Divine unfolding and fills all time and all space with
> its miracles – if one sees all this, then the mind, pondering such
> vistas, will sink into deep wonder. (1:321.13-22)[11]

Between remarks on universal rule and the Phoenix, Kant
details the relation of emergence and entropy:

---

10. Nietzsche, *Werke*, 1:866.2-4: 'eine bewegte mathematische Figur [...] eine Art der
Schwingung'.

11. Kant, *Werke* (Academy Edition), 1:321.13-26: 'Wenn wir diesen Phönix der Natur,
der sich nur darum verbrennt, um aus seiner Asche wiederum verjüngt aufzuleben,
durch alle Unendlichkeit der Zeiten und Räume hindurch folgen; wenn man sieht, wie
sie sogar in der Gegend, da sie verfällt und veraltet, an neuen Auftritten unerschöpft
und auf der anderen Grenze der Schöpfung in dem Raum der ungebildeten rohen
Materie mit stetigen Schritten zur Ausdehnung des Plans der göttlichen Offenbarung
fortschreitet, um die Ewigkeit sowohl, als alle Räume mit ihren Wundern zu füllen:
so versenkt sich der Geist, der alles dieses überdenkt, in ein tiefes Erstaunen'. For the
translation above, note that I read *sie* ('she,' 1:321.16) as denoting nature.

It appears that the end, fated to the worlds as to all matters natural, is subject to some law. Recognizing this law will lend the theory a new touch, a touch of rightness. By this law, the end touches those worlds closest to the cosmic centre first, just as conception and organization had first started next to this centre. From there, doom and destruction radiate outward step by step in ever farther reaches from the centre. Through general dissipation of motion, the whole universe, having completed its period, will eventually be buried in uniform chaos. Yet Nature on the other side, at the opposite edge of the evolved cosmos, is busy steadily spawning worlds from the raw stuff of scattered elements. Nature on one side decays at centre. Nature on another side is young and fertile in new creations. So the evolved cosmos is placed in between, bounded by limits on either side – the ruins of destroyed nature, and a chaos of a still unformed nature. And if we imagine that (as would be likely) the time-span of a world matured to perfection outlasts that of a world forming up, then regardless of all the damage wreaked constantly by transience, the Universe's circumference will nonetheless and on the whole expand. (1:319.19-1:320.2)[12]

---

12. Kant, *Werke* (Academy Edition), 1:319.19-1:320.2: 'Es scheint, daß dieses den Welten, so wie allen Naturdingen verhängte Ende einem gewissen Gesetze unterworfen sei, dessen Erwägung der Theorie einen neuen Zug der Anständigkeit giebt. Nach demselben hebt es bei den Weltkörpern an, die sich dem Mittelpunkte des Weltalls am nächsten befinden, so wie die Erzeugung und Bildung neben diesem Centro zuerst angefangen: von da breitet sich das Verderben und die Zerstörung nach und nach in die weiteren Entfernungen aus, um alle Welt, welche ihre Periode zurück gelegt hat, durch einen allmählichen Verfall der Bewegungen zuletzt in einem einzigen Chaos zu begraben. Andererseits ist die Natur auf der entgegengesetzten Grenze der ausgebildeten Welt unablässig beschäftigt, aus dem rohen Zeuge der zerstreueten Elemente Welten zu bilden, und indem sie an der einen Seite neben dem Mittelpunkte veraltet, so ist sie auf der andern jung und an neuen Zeugungen fruchtbar. Die ausgebildete Welt befindet sich diesemnach zwischen den Ruinen der zerstörten und zwischen dem Chaos der ungebildeten Natur mitten inne beschränkt, und wenn man, wie es wahrscheinlich ist, sich vorstellt, daß eine schon zur Vollkommenheit gediehene Welt eine längere Zeit dauern könne, als sie

4. Ultimate Natural Pattern: The Big Bounce

Kant stares into the abyss, and the abyss stares back. Such a reflected stare can easily turn monstrous. And still he marvels, with a smile.[13] What he is doing in *Universal History of Nature* is to map out the history of histories. Nature's history is universal in space; it concerns everything that coexists. It is also universal in time, concerning everything that ever was and ever will be. Kant looks for structure and finds it. He claims to see the ultimate natural pattern. Is this madness? Conventional philosophers, whose trade is to shrink Big Questions down to harmless nuggets, would of course nod, emphatically. But they would be wrong. Kant's gaze is clear-sighted. His speculation in *Universal History of Nature* is coherent and systematic. His contentions agree with the facts as we know them and have emerged as anticipations of what we are meeting now at the boundaries of knowledge. The Phoenix of Nature, swinging to entropy and back, has returned to academic discourse as the Big Bounce.

Since the Big Bounce is not yet as familiar as the Big Bang, one might as well start with the latter, 13.7 billion years ago, when nature flared outward from a prone singularity. The Big Bang is at the heart of the research consensus known as the Standard Model. The Big Bang is the rational inference from the red-shift of galaxies far

---

bedurft hat, gebildet zu werden: so wird ungeachtet aller der Verheerungen, die die Vergänglichkeit unaufhörlich anrichtet, der Umfang des *Universi* dennoch überhaupt zunehmen.'

13. F. Nietzsche, *Jenseits von Gut und Böse*, § 146, *Werke*, 5:98: 'Wer mit Ungeheuern kämpft, mag zusehn, dass er nicht dabei zum Ungeheuer wird. Und wenn du lange in einen Abgrund blickst, blickt der Abgrund auch in dich hinein.' ('He who fights with monsters should look to it that he himself does not become a monster. And when you gaze long into an abyss the abyss also gazes at you.' F. Nietzsche, *Beyond Good and Evil*, trans. R.J. Hollingdale (London: Penguin, 1990).

outside the Milky Way, a red-shift first measured nearly a century ago. Distant light reaches us in elongated wavelengths without exception. Chased through a prism, such light unfurls into lopsided rainbows: skinny in the blue, fat in the red. The one explanation that has held up (and hardened through other confirmed predictions) is that light red-shifts as its sources recede from us and each other. Like dough rising, nature expands outward. Like raisins in the dough, nebulae pull away from one another. Like a coil being stretched, wavelengths of their reddening light lengthen to an observer. So much is clear: a chorus of data tells us that nature expands like a wavefront of a primordial, bygone bang.

A recent addition to the Standard Model is the Big Rip. It is the rational inference from the acceleration of cosmic expansion measured a decade ago.[14] Galaxies are pulling away from one another, and from us, faster than they used to. The travelling wavefront is gaining velocity. Nature's expansion is speeding up. Yet any given acceleration, of any frame within another, eventually hits the tolerance limit of the framework of acceleration. When the limit is hit, the dynamic geometry will reorder itself, which is a polite way of saying that things will fly apart.[15]

---

14. P Garnavich et al., 'Constraints on cosmological models from Hubble Space Telescope observations of high-z supernovae', *Astrophysical Journal* 493, 1998: L 53; S Perlmutter et al., 'Discovery of a supernova explosion at half the age of the universe,' *Nature* 391, 1998: 51-54; A G Riess et al, 'Observational evidence from supernovae for an accelerating universe and a cosmological constant,' *Astronomical Journal* 116, 1998: 1009-1038. For a summary, cf. 'Special Report: revolution in cosmology,' *Scientific American* 280.1, 1999: 45-6.

15. M Edesio et al., 'Does the Big Rip survive quantization?' *General Relativity and Gravitation* 38, 2006: 1609-1622, B Gumjudpai, 'Slow-roll, acceleration, the Big Rip, and WKB approximation in a non-linear S-type formulation of scalar field cosmology,' *Journal of Cosmology and Astroparticle Physics* 6, 2008: JCAP 09, 2008: 028.

Big Rip points to Big Crunch.[16] When things rip, the fabric that holds them will tatter and unravel. While one tends to think of a dimensional fabric as what holds things together, it may be more exact to think of it as what holds them apart. Untethered from their place, nothing will hold the displaced at bay. Ripped, the fabric and its places will buckle, crumple, and fold. It'll crunch.

The Big Crunch would stop at a singularity. This is the Universe squeezed together as tight as it gets; parameters shoot off to infinity or nearly so. It is the null point. It is a prone state harbouring the Big Bang and contains all the conditions for yet another cosmic inflation. So the cycle starts all over again. Ergo the Big Bounce.[17] As Big Bounce, the Phoenix returns and suggests the ultimate natural pattern.

5. Perspectival Convergence on Absolutes

Conventional philosophers are so in love with questions that they are at a loss what to make of answers. Thus scholarly lacunae perpetuate themselves, and inconvenient truths such as the Kantian cosmogony are best ignored. But one can play the scepticist game only for so long. In the end, information prevails. Remember how the *Critique*

---

16. S Elitzur et al., 'From Big Bang to Big Crunch and beyond,' *Journal of High Energy Physics* 6, 2002: JHEP 0206, 2002: 017.

17. N Turok et al., 'From Big Crunch to Big Bang with AdS/CFT,' *arXiv* version 3, 12/27/07, 0711.1824; G Niz, N Turok, 'Classical propagation of strings across a Big Crunch/Big Bang Singularity,' *Physical Review D* 75, 2007: 026001; M Brown et al, 'The Phantom Bounce: A New Oscillating Cosmology', *Journal of Cosmology and Astroparticle Physics* 6, 2008: JCAP 03, 2008: 002; P Dzierzak et al., 'Quantum Big Bounce,' *arXiv* version 1 10/17/08 0810.3172.

ends: anybody, so Kant says, can do research any way they like. But research that leads somewhere is not only systematic but also on a track that is equidistant from two extremes: the Hume extreme, denying everything, and the Wolff extreme, affirming everything. By themselves, doubt and dogma are sterile. It's only what's in between that is fertile. Between them unfolds the critical path. If we follow it, odds are that we'll answer the Big Questions that have troubled reason for so long.[18] Thus the critical path leads to ultimate patterns. While absolutes are nowadays outside the philosopher's comfort zone, they are the bread and butter of cosmology. Absolutes are the limits of reality, edges so extreme that they are invariably the same. The Phoenix wave of the cosmos, the Big Bounce, is such an absolute, and so are its geometro-dynamic parts: the trough that is the Big Bang; the peak that triggers the Big Rip; the fall-to-trough that is the Big Crunch; and the rise-to-peak that follows the Big Bang.

The Big Bounce makes news because it is the convergent outcome of two distinct research programs. Theoretical physics involves two major rival approaches to the ultimate limit. One is string theory, and another is loop

18. *Critique of Pure Reason*, conclusion, A 856/B 886; in *Werke*, 3:552. Compare Kemp Smith's translation: 'As regards those who adopt a *scientific* method, they have the choice of proceeding either *dogmatically* or *skeptically*; but in any case they are under obligation to proceed *systematically*. I may cite the celebrated Wolff as a representative of the former mode of procedure, and David Hume as a representative of the latter, and may then, conformably with my present purpose, leave all others unnamed. The *critical* path alone is still open. If the reader has had the courtesy and patience to accompany me along this path, he may now judge for himself whether, if he cares to lend his aid in making this path into a high-road, it may not be possible to achieve before the end of the present century what many centuries have not been able to accomplish; namely to secure for human reason complete satisfaction in regard to that with which it has all along so eagerly occupied itself, though hitherto in vain.' See Kant, *Critique of Pure Reason* (New York: St Martin's press, 1965), 668-9.

quantum gravity theory. String theoreticians have insisted on the possibility of a Big Bounce for years already.[19] This insistence didn't raise many eyebrows since string theory is full of strange claims. But in 2008, researchers who work for the competition, loop quantum cosmology, and who proceed from quite different assumptions, have arrived at just the same conclusion once more.[20]

Inquiries that are on to something exhibit certain traits. One sign is that investigators find themselves suddenly very busy. Activity teems, publications abound, and bibliographies grow longer and longer. Another sign is that inquiries that come from different theoretical locations, use different tools, and approach a question from different angles suddenly find themselves converging on the same answer. When inquiries draw close to an absolute, a relative convergence fuses the perspectives into one view.

So it appears the cosmos is indeed how Kant describes it: *a place in between* and bounded by limits on either side (1:319.32-33). Looking backwards, we see the Big Bang as a bottleneck from a past universe. Looking forwards, we see cosmic acceleration as the first harbinger of future ruin and another Big Bang.

Thus philosophers who wish to break with the conventionality of their field can no longer afford to ignore

19. M Gasperini, G Veneziano, 'The pre-Big Bang scenario in string cosmology,' *Physics Reports* 373.1-2, Jan 2003: 1-212, hep-th/0207130; non-technical version: G Veneziano, 'The myth of the beginning of time,' *Scientific American* 290.5, May 2004: 54-65.

20. The cover title of the October 2008 issue of *Scientific American* has the headline: 'Forget the Big Bang: Now it's the Big Bounce – quantum gravity theory predicts the universe will never die.' See also M Bojowald, 'Follow the bouncing universe,' *Scientific American* 299.4, 2008: 44-51; cf. online version 'Big Bang or Big Bounce?' and M Bojowald, 'Loop quantum cosmology,' *Living Reviews in Relativity* 11.4, July 2008, lrr-2008-4.

Kant's second, burned book, and its core idea, the Phoenix of Nature. For a decade now, string theorists have pointed out the genius of the early Kant, and a handbook on cosmology issued in 1998 from these quarters character-ises the cosmogony of *Universal History* as 'the essence of modern models'.[21] After the corroboration from loop quantum gravity, sceptical loopholes would seem to have closed. Now we may wonder what this conceptual triumph means. Determining this, I suspect, defines philosophy's task in this century. Let the scientists figure out the answers to the Great Questions, and let the philosophers add the answers up, rationally, synthetically, and thereby fill the void of monotheistic bankruptcy by crafting a new world wisdom.

21. P. Coles, ed., *The Routledge Companion to the New Cosmology* (London/New York: Routledge, 1998), 240.

On Creation in the Total Extent of its Infinity in Both Space and Time[1]

Immanuel Kant
Translated by Martin Schönfeld

The Universe, with its immeasurable greatness, endless (1.306) diversity, and beauty, which shines up at all angles, puts us in a state of silent wonder. And whenever the idea of all this perfection fires up the power of imagination, the understanding falls into a state of delight, as soon as one considers how so much splendour and grandeur flows from a single universal rule, in eternal and right tact. If the picture of all this perfection now stirs the power of imagination, the understanding derives another type of delight, when it observes how so much splendour and grandeur flows from a single universal rule, in an eternal and justified order. The Sun, with its powerful attraction at the centre of all orbital rings, forces the inhabited planets of its system to cruise eternal rounds. The planetary world system, as we have seen, is completely made up of the basic stuff of all world-matter. Originally, this matter was spread out. The fixed stars, which the eye finds in the hollow deep of the sky – an abundance that seems to suggest a kind of waste-fulness – are all suns and system-centres similar to our own.

---

1. Chapter Seven of Kant's *Allgemeine Naturgeschichte und Theorie Des Himmels oder Versuch von der Verfassung und dem mechanischen Ursprunge des ganzen Weltgebäudes, nach Newtonischen Grundsätzen abgehandelt* [*Universal History of Nature and Theory of the Heavens or An Essay on the Constitution and the Mechanical Origin of the Entire Structure of the Universe Based on Newtonian Principles*] (1755). Page numbers in the margin refer to the Akademie edition of Kant's Work.

The method of analogy suggests that these far-flung systems were formed in the same way as the one in which we live. The method of analogy further suggests that these systems, too, evolved from the smallest particles of basic matter. These particles used to fill the infinite sweep of Divine Presence, which we call empty space.[2]

(1.307)   If it appears now that all worlds and world-structures share a pattern of emergence; that among the elements the force of attraction is unlimited and universal, and the force of repulsion is just as efficacious and general; and that at infinity the large and the small are both small – if this is all true, should then not all world-structures organize as one network and systematically interact as well? A systematic interplay, to wit, that would be equal to that of the celestial bodies in our solar neighborhood? And if this is so, would the world-structures then not have to link up just like Saturn, Jupiter, and Earth do, all of which are systems of their own, and yet connect into even larger system?[3]

2. The 'infinite sweep of Divine Presence' (*diesen unendlichen Umfang der göttlichen Gegenwart*) raises a question as to how to read the text. Kant often uses words such as 'God,' 'Divine,' and 'revelation' (*Gott, göttlich, Offenbarung*), making the text sound like an exercise in rational theology. Yet the actual claims made by Kant suggest that such a conventional reading is misleading. Here, God and Nature merge; Nature is creative; and 'God' appears to denote a kind of 'universal world spirit' or 'Proteus of Nature'; see also the 1754 essay *Aging Earth* (2:211.29 and 2:212.15). While Kant hesitates to come out as a pagan ('free-thinker') or pantheist ('Spinozist'), we should note that such views were not tolerated in Germany until the Jacobi-Mendelssohn controversy in 1783. *Universal History of Nature* was written in the context of censorship. In 1725, Christian Gabriel Fischer (1686-1751), professor of natural philosophy, espoused pagan-pantheist perspectives; he was fired from the Albertina, banned from Königsberg, and exiled from Prussia.

3. Earlier in the book (Part I), Kant considers the Milky Way and other galaxies. He reasons that an analogy obtains between the evolution and structure of the Milky Way and other galaxies. He infers that the Milky Way is a star cluster rotating around a central axis; centrifugal forces flatten the poles, make the equator bulge, and compress the cluster into a disk (1:249-252). William Herschel confirmed Kant's conception in 1811. In 1750, five years before Kant published *Universal*

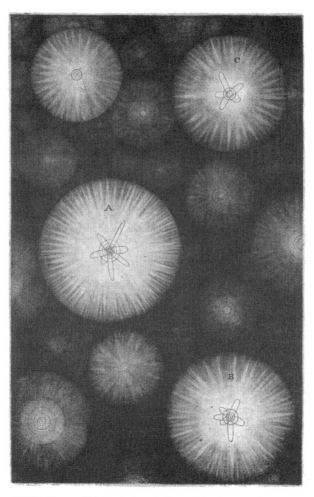

Plate XVII in Thomas Wright's *An Original Theory or New Hypothesis of the Universe* (1750): 'A kind of perspective View of the visible creation, wherein A represents the Sun, B, that supposed round Syrius, and C, the region about Rigel. The rest is a promiscuous Disposition of all the Variety of other Systems within our finite Vision, as they are supposed to be posited behind one another, in the infinite Space, and round every visible Star. That round every Star then we may justly conjecture a similar system of Bodies, governed by the same Laws and Principles with this our solar one, though to us at the Earth for very good Reasons invisible.'

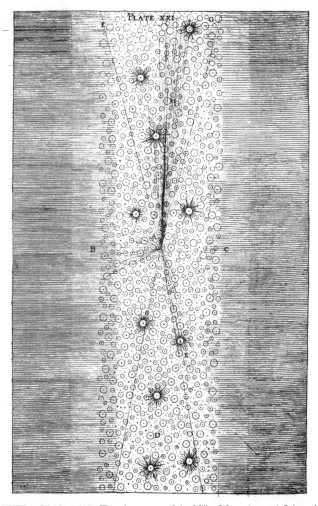

Plate XXIII in Wright (1750): The phenomena of the Milky Way – 'a vast infinite gulph, or Medium, every Way extended like a plane, and inclosed between two Surfaces [...] all the Stars scatttered promiscuously [...] as to fill up the whole Medium with a kind of regular Irregularity of Objects.'

Suppose you take a given point within the boundless space in which all the suns of the Milky Way formed. Suppose further that at that very point Nature's evolution from chaos arose by an unknown cause. Then the greatest concentration of mass will have accreted there. So a body of huge attractive force will have condensed. This will have given the galactic centre-point the power to draw all other emergent star systems into a vast enveloping sphere, and to make them sink toward itself as their gravity-well. Thereby the point will have forged a system around itself, analogous to the system created by the Sun in its own small sphere, and made from the same elementary basic matter that had moulded the planets. Observation makes this conjecture virtually certain. The star cluster emerges as a system because it serves as a frame of reference for a collectively shared plan, just as the planets, clustering around the Sun, are the frame of our solar system. The Milky Way is the zodiac, as it were, of these higher world-structures. These structures hardly deviate from the zodiac-zone; their light always illuminates the ribbon of the Milky Way. Similarly, the planetary zodiac glints in discrete spots through the sunshine illuminating these spheres, even though these spheres are just a few sparse points. In the higher world-structure, each sun creates with orbiting planets a system of its own. That suns everywhere form systems, is a circumstance that does not prevent such suns from being elements of an even larger system – just like the fact that Jupiter or Saturn serve as centres to their lunar companions does not prevent such planets from being integrated into the tight

History, Thomas Wright suggested the idea of a disk-like Milky Way, but, as various commentators have pointed out, the credit should go to Kant: Wright only states the notion while Kant explains it.

organization of a larger system. Is it not possible to see in this precise agreement of organization – Milky Way here, solar system there – the same cause, and the same type of causation?

So: if the stars are organized as a system whose circumference is informed by the gravitational sphere of its central mass, then will it not be likely that even more star systems (1.308) – more Milky Ways, as it were – evolved in the boundless field of space? Earlier we were amazed to see celestial figures arise as such star systems – such Milky Ways, if I may express myself thus – that cohere by a communally shared design.[4] Such star systems show themselves in elliptic guises, because they are angled at various degrees against the eye. Infinite distances from the eye weaken their light to a gleam. Their diameter is, so to speak, infinities and infinities larger than that of our solar system. And yet, these star systems have surely evolved in the same way and unfolded from the same causes; furthermore, the

---

4. The idea that the fuzzy blobs faintly visible on a dark and clear night could be star clusters originated with Thomas Wright, who called them 'knots of stars'. Kant read a review of Wright's *Original Theory and Hypothesis of the Universe* (1750) in *Freie Urteile und Nachrichten zum Aufnehmen der Wissenschaften und Historie überhaupt* (1751). Just as Kant extrapolates from our solar system to the Milky Way, so he extrapolates from the latter to other galaxies. Calling them 'foggy stars' (*neblichte Sterne*, 1:254-1:255), he argues they are not just knots, but rather *systems* of stars. In 1761, Johann Lambert suggested a similar view in *Cosmologische Briefe*. In the 1780s, Charles Messier prepared a catalogue listing 103 nebulae. In 1802, William Herschel published a catalogue of 2,500 nebulae; in the 1830s, his son, John Herschel, added 1,300 more. In 1864, William Huggins discovered through spectrographic analysis that nebulae differ from stars and speculated they are of some luminous fluid. At the end of the nineteenth century, most astronomers assumed nebulae were proto-stars *inside* the Milky Way. Kant's idea, that nebulae are Milky Ways in their own right, was marginalised. In the 1920s, Heber Curtis revived Kant's idea, calling such nebulae 'island universes'. In 1924, Edwin Hubble examined M 31 (the Andromeda nebula), determined its location to be outside the Milky Way, and verified Kant's idea. See M. Schönfeld, *Philosophy of the Young Kant* (Oxford: Oxford University Press, 2000), 116 and 272.

Nebula NGC346 (Credit: NASA,ESA,Hubble Heritage Team [STScI/AURA]).

same dynamic engine that had structured them continually maintains them.

Now, if we see these star systems, in turn, as links in the great chain of Nature as a whole, then we will have just as much reason as before to think of these links as being concatenated in reciprocal networks.[5] By the law of primordial evolution that governs all Nature, we should think of these connections as already weaving another system. That even greater system would be ruled by the gravitational pull of a central body inside its regular frame, with an even larger attractive force than all the others considered thus far.[6] The force of attraction is the cause of the systematic organization among the stars of the Milky Way. This force is active even in the distances of these world structures. In fact, its power is such that it would actually knock them out of their systematic places and bury the world in inexorably looming chaos, if it were not for the steady radiation of centrifugal forces serving as counterweights. In their interplay, attractive and centrifugal forces yield the relation that grounds systematic organization. Attraction connects substances through mutual dependencies. Now, surely, this force must be a property of matter, and it must reach as far as co-presence, which is a property of space. Speaking more precisely, attraction must be the very relation that unites the parts of Nature in one space. Hence attraction stretches through the whole sweep of space towards the depth of infinity. Light reaches us from these distant systems, but

---

5. 'Star systems' (*Sternensystemata*), here, are galactic systems; see Kant's previous paragraph.

6. This is the first conjecture in history about the possibility of a Local Group in the Virgo Cluster.

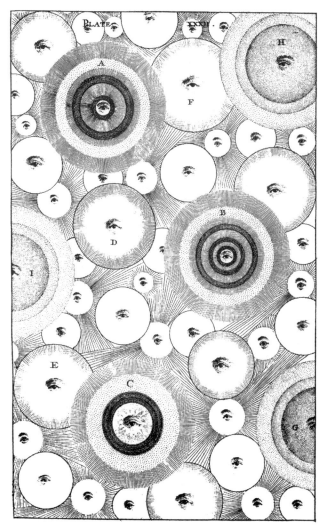

Plate XXXII in Wright (1750): A sectional view of 'the endless Immensity [...] an unlimited Plenum of creations not unlike the known Universe'.

light is merely an impressed motion. Should then not attraction reach that far, too? Attraction is the primordial source of motion; it is more ancient than motion, and it (1.309) does not need external causes. Also, attraction cannot be stopped by any obstacle, since it acts without resistance in the inner reaches of matter, even when Nature is fully at rest. Considering this, I ask: Will attraction not have set star systems in motion as well? And will attraction then not be the cause of all the systematic connection and the permanence of Nature's links, which protects them from dissolution here, just as in the smaller frames?

But then, what is going to be the ultimate end of these systematic arrangements? Where will creation ever stop? Note that creation, since it is proportional to the might of Infinite Being, cannot have boundaries at all. Enclosing the realm of revelation within a sphere of the radius of the Milky Way does not bring us one step closer to the infinity of God's creative power than putting this realm into a ball the size of an inch. All that is finite, involves limits, and can be measured, is equally far away from infinity. Is it not incoherent to conceive of a divinity as acting with an infinite small part of its creative potential? Or to take the infinite power of divinity as a force inert and sealed up, forever wanting for some way of showing itself adequately? This power, after all, is the cornucopia of the true boundlessness of natures and worlds. So, is it not far more decent – or, to say it again, with more precision: is it not *necessary* – to take creation as it would have to be such as to testify to that very

7. Kant's first question appears to refer to the Christian concept of a coming eternal afterlife (*künftige Folge der Ewigkeit* 1:309.34). The infinity of 'varieties and change' (*von Mannigfaltigkeiten und Veränderungen* 1:309.35) comes into play in that an eternal afterlife counts as real eternity only if it is an actually infinite time span. The essence

power that cannot be measured by any yardstick? Thus the cosmic field of the revelation of the Divine traits must possess the infinity of these traits themselves.

Eternity would not be big enough to contain the traits (1.310) of a Supreme Being unless infinity is also expressed as a spatial field. Complexity, form, beauty, and perfection are certainly relations of elementary fields and substances that constitute the stuff of the cosmic system. This is evident in the eternal designs crafted by Divine Wisdom. It is also appropriate to this wisdom that such designs unfold by implanted universal laws along unconstrained courses. So, with sound reason, we can say that organisation and design of the world will occur along a time flow, step by step, as the

* [*Kant's footnote*] The concept of the world's infinite extension has opponents among the experts of metaphysics; a recent example is *Magister* Weitenkampf. Now since these gentlemen cannot grant this idea because of the alleged incoherence of the notion of a set without numerical limits, I just want to ask this: When eternal afterlife comes, will not its future flow contain a genuine infinity of varieties and change?[7] And is not this infinite set fully present once and for all in the Divine Understanding? (1:310) Now, if it were possible that God realised in a successive series the notion of infinity that presents itself to His understanding, why should not the same concept be able to denote another infinity, in a *connected network* that is spatial? And if this were so, would it not thereby make the circumference of the world without borders? While one seeks for an answer to this question, let me use this opportunity to solve a problem related to an explanation of the nature of numbers; a question deserving of clarification. A power guided by supreme wisdom reveals itself in creation: does the set of actually created revelations constitute a fraction compared to the set of what this power *could* have created?

of time is flow, visible in varieties and change. Without change there is no time; and without time, there is no eternity – if eternity were *outside* time, it would be a stasis and thus nothing. Christians distinguish between creator and creation, conceiving the former as active and infinite, the latter as passive and finite. Echoing the views of Martin Knutzen (1713-51), Johann Weitenkampf (1726-58) argued against a possibly infinite extension of nature. Knutzen, a Christian, held the chair of metaphysics and logic in Königsberg when Kant attended college. As a teacher, Knutzen promoted Weitenkampf and Friedrich Buck (1722-86), but made Kant drop out in 1748 over his *True Estimation of Living Forces* (w. 1744-47, p. 1749). Weitenkampf and Buck were candidates for Knutzen's succession in 1751; Buck gained the chair of metaphysics and logic in 1756.

unfolding of a stock of created Nature-stuff. The sole direct effect crafted by Divine Presence is pure matter, whose properties and powers ground all change. Hence Divine Presence must at one point be so rich and complete that the development of its compositions in the flow of eternity can radiate along a plan that has everything that can be; that does not accept any measure; and that, in short, is infinite.

So: since, now, creation must be spatially infinite, too – or, at least, has been actually infinite over matter already from the start, and is bound to be infinite as regards form via an evolutionary process – then it follows that cosmic space will teem with an infinite number of worlds. Now, earlier we said that systematic connection informs all specific parts. Does this mean that systematic connection will also inform the Whole? Will the Universe, the All of Nature, be structured as a unified system, by the bond of attraction and repulsion? Yes indeed, I say. For imagine (1.311) there were only isolated world systems, without a shared link to a whole, and that these systems made up an actually infinite set. Imagine, further, a precise equilibrium among all the attractive forces of all these disparate parts from all sides; an equilibrium that would protect such a system from the ruin threatened by such mutual inward attraction. Clearly, this scenario requires such a perfectly exact determination of dynamically balanced distances that the tiniest shift would pull the Universe into doom, surrendering it to collapse. While such a pull may take eons, it will inexorably lead to this end. A cosmic organization that does not sustain itself without a miracle lacks the property of permanence that is a trait of Divine choice. To such choice it would be far more appropriate if the whole creation were made into a single system.

Plate XXXI in Wright (1750): '[A]s the visible creation is supposed to be full of siderial Systems and planetary Worlds, so on, in like similar Manner, the endless Immensity is an unlimited Plenum of creations not unlike the known Universe; a partial view of Immensity, or without much Impropriety perhaps, a finite view of Infinity.'

Galaxy NGC1672 (Credit: NASA,ESA,Hubble Heritage Team [STScI/AURA]-ESA/Hubble)

In this system, all the worlds and world structures that fill up the whole spatial infinity form a network around a common centre. A scattered swarm of world systems would collapse with undiminished momentum into doom and destruction no matter how far apart they were from one another, unless systematic motions create a relational order towards one universal centre. Such a cosmic mid-point would be the attractive centre of the Universe and the column that holds up Nature.

Nature's universal centre and gravity-well is the same in Nature's evolved and raw states. At this centre mass would surely concentrate towards the greatest attraction. Its gravitational field would hold all worlds and structures which have been produced over time and will be produced unto eternity. One can probably assume that Nature started to form around this universal centre and gravity-well. There the systems would also cluster with maximum density. The farther they were placed from the centre, the thinner their dispersion would be, until they lost themselves in the infinity of space. We can identify this rule by analogy with our solar system. Indeed, its makeup serves to illustrate a further dynamic feature: over vast distances the pull of the primary body at the centre fuses with the attractive forces of orbiting sub-systems so that the systematic attraction radiates essentially from one mass against even farther systems. This will help us to comprehend the whole of (1.312) Nature, in the whole infinity of its sweep, as one single system.

Now let us see how Nature's universal system evolves in lawful mechanical ways from a material striving towards complexity. In the infinite spatial dispersion of the elementary, primordial matter, there must be a place with the highest density of basic material. There evolution happens first. This process yields the mass that is the column sustaining the Universe. Granted, infinite space does not really have a centre point. But if one considers a given relationship based on real degrees of primordial mass density, one can arguably speak of a centre-point within infinity – it would simply be the place of peak material density. Outside this centre, density rarefies according to distance. The formation of a mass with maximum attraction defines the centre as the gravity-well into which all other elementary matter will sink, even when such matter is simultaneously weaving its own specific networks. So it will not matter how far the evolution of Nature reaches – this centre of the infinite sphere of creation unifies the entire cosmos into a system.

Now here is something vital that demands applause and deserves full attention. It is this: As a consequence of Nature's organization according to the described system, creation, or rather, Nature's evolution, begins at this centre-point, spreads out step by step in steady progression, towards all farther reaches, and fills infinite space with worlds and subordinate systems along the flow of eternity. Let us savour this vision for a moment with quiet pleasure. I find nothing that elevates the human spirit to nobler reverence than the part of the theory that concerns creation's successive completion. This part opens to the spirit a vista into the boundless field of omnipotence. As soon as one grants that matter, or the stuff of world formation, is not homogenously scattered in the whole spatial infinity of Divine (1.313) Presence, but is instead spread out according to a law, which

392

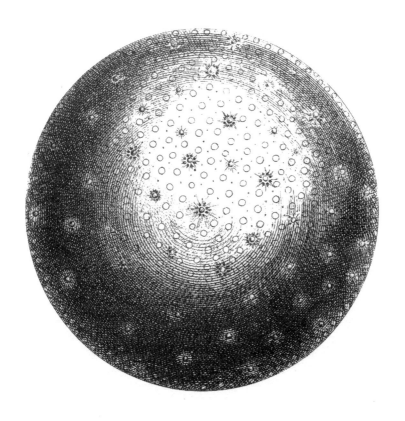

Plate XXIV in Wright (1750): 'A representation of the convexity, if I may call it so, of the intire creation, as a universal Coalition of all the Stars consphered round one general Center, and as all governed by the same Law.'

is perhaps a law concerning particle density, then Nature's first stirring will have tied the start of evolution to this centre-point. After this start, and as the next evolutionary step, the space beyond the centre shapes worlds and world-orders into a systematic structure around this centre. This happens gradually and over time. The span of a given time is proportional to the size of the work to be completed. In any finite time-period it is possible to structure only a finite sphere around this centre-point. The infinite remainder, meanwhile, will quarrel with confusion and chaos. The farther areas in such infinity are from the sphere of evolved Nature, the further they will be from a state of full evolution. Seen from our perspective in the Universe, it would seem as if we looked at wholly completed creation and, so to speak, at an infinite array of systematically connected world-orders. And yet, from what has been said, it follows that we must be quite close to the centre-point of Nature; at any rate so close that Nature has already evolved from chaos here and attained its appropriate perfection. But if we could step outside this evolved sphere, we would see chaos. The random scattering of elements is inversely proportional to the proximity to the centre-point. The closer the scattering is, the more it will have already partially emerged from the raw state and be on its way toward full evolution. But the farther the scattering is, the more it will lose itself with each outward step into utter dispersion. If we could travel outside this sphere, we would see how the spatial infinity of Divine Presence and its store-house of possible natural forms are buried in a night of silence, a night filled with matter that serves as building material for future generations of worlds. Impulses set this matter into motion.

A faint stirring will be the onset of the very motions that are going to make these boundless desert-spaces come alive. Many millions of years and centuries will perhaps go by before our home-sphere of evolved Nature will expand to thrive in these spaces with that kind of completion that is its feature now. And perhaps a time span of similar length will have to pass before Nature takes such a great step (1.314) into chaos. But how long it will take does not matter, for the sphere of evolved Nature is incessantly busy with its expansion. Creation is not the work of an instant. Creation starts with the production of an infinity of substances and matters. It then continues with producing ever higher levels of fertility throughout eternity. Millions of years, no; whole mountain ranges of millions of centuries will pass, during which always new worlds and world-orders come into existence and reach maturity, one by one, in remote reaches far from Nature's centre. Whatever systematic organization the parts have with respect to one another, all of them attain a universal relation to the cosmic mid-point that had become the primordial and creative centre through the gravitation of its extraordinary mass. The infinity of future time-flows will make all spaces of God's presence wholly come alive. Step by step, this infinity will turn these spaces into the regularity that is appropriate to the fittingness of Divine design. If we could, with bold imagination, sum up the whole eternity, as it were, in a single notion, then we would also be able to see the whole spatial infinity filled with world-orders and thus see creation complete. But in the flow of eternity futures are always infinite and pasts always limited. So the sphere of evolved Nature can only be an infinitely small part of the essence that carries the

Young stars in the extended arms of the Southern Pinwheel Galaxy M83 (Credit: NASA/ JPL-Caltech/VLA/MPIA)

seed of future worlds, and that seeks to evolve from chaos over shorter or longer periods. Creation is never done. Creation has a beginning but not an end. creation is constantly in the process of generating new dawns of Nature, new things, and new worlds. The work that it completes is proportional to the time the work takes. Creation needs an eternity to animate the whole boundless reach of infinite spaces with worlds without number and end. One can say of it what the greatest of the German poets writes about it: (1.315)

> Infinity! Who can fathom you?
> For you worlds are days, and humans are instants;
> Perhaps the thousandth sun is now turning,
> And a thousand more are still in store.
> Like a clock, animated by a weight,
> A sun hurries on, moved by divine force:
> Its spring winds down, and another strikes,
> You, though, stay the same and count them not.
>
> von Haller[8]

It is no small delight to sweep one's power of imagination beyond the boundary of completed creation and outward into the arena of chaos, and to see how Nature is first half-raw, outside the sphere of the unfolded world, and then loses itself into the distance, along all degrees and gradations of imperfection into utter unformed space. Some might say such audacity deserves rebuke. Is it blameworthy to feign a hypothesis and to praise it as a model of rational delight? Is it perhaps all too arbitrary to contend that Nature is created

---

8. Albrecht von Haller (1708-1777), *Unvollkommene Ode über die Ewigkeit* (1743; alternative title *Unvollkommnes Gedicht über die Ewigkeit*), stanza 4; cf. 1:315. Compare also the nice translation by Ian Johnston at http://records.viu.ca/~johnstoi/kant/kant2e.htm.

only in its infinitely small part; that infinite spaces are still fighting with chaos; and that in the far future these spaces will contain entire armies of worlds and world-orders, in all their order and beauty? I am not so committed to the consequences of my theory, that I would not see how this speculation – a successive expansion of creation through infinite spaces filled with creative material – is vulnerable to the reproach of indemonstrability. Granted, this map of infinity contains a model that seems destined to be hidden forever from human understanding. And yet, I expect from those readers who know how to estimate degrees of probability, that they do not reject out of hand and as sheer lunacy such a map. I expect this, especially if one considers the method of analogy. For analogies must always and everywhere guide us as soon as the understanding lacks the thread of incontrovertible proof.

Now, one can support the analogy through acceptable reasons as well, and the reader, whose approval I hope to gain, may perhaps add even more important ideas. We need to keep in mind that creation has the trait of (1.316) permanence only through a balance between the universal striving of attraction permeating all parts of nature, and an equally universal counter-striving. With centrifugal forces, this counter-striving sufficiently repels the inclination of attraction towards collapse and chaos. Together these strivings constitute Nature's universal systematic order. This compels us to assume a cosmic centre that holds all parts of the Universe in a relation of connectivity, and it is this that turns Nature into a system. Add to this the notion of the evolution of astrophysical bodies from dispersed elementary matter, as was explicated in the previous chapters. Since we do not tie this notion to any specific system here but instead apply it to Nature at large, we assume a primordial chaos of elementary matter dispersed in space. Such chaos, in natural fashion, must generate a centre of the entire creation. The whole of Nature is a sphere of active mass that coheres in this centre. In this way, a universal relation obtains that integrates all worlds into a single framework. But in infinite space it is hardly possible to conceive of a type of scattering of primordial matter that leads to a true centre point and gravity-well of Nature as a whole, unless Nature enacts lawfully, increasing entropy from this point outward toward its farthest reaches. Such a law will also posit a difference in time needed by a system in the various regions of infinite space to bring its unfolding to fruition and maturity. This interval would be the shorter the closer the area of an evolving world-order is to the creative centre. At the centre it takes less time to create the systematic unfolding than in the distance, for material elements are more densely concentrated in the former. Since they are more thinly dispersed in the distance, they will accrete later into organization.[9]

9. Kant's idea is that things closest to the stellar or galactic centre would form first and those farthest away, last. This is an aspect of his famous Nebular Hypothesis, verified by G. Kuiper and K. v. Weizsäcker in 1949. According to this hypothesis, put forward elsewhere in *Universal History*, a condensing cloud ripples with tides and forms a gravity-well to concentrate matter until it lights up. The flow of matter to this well – the future Sun – deflects laterally through internal collisions. The laterally-deflected matter revolves around the proto-Sun. The revolving matter coheres into orbital bands. Thus the solar system grows from a cloud. Orbital bands become lumpy; bigger lumps absorb smaller ones; the matter clusters condense into planets. Planets form sooner the closer they are to the centre. The farther one travels from the Sun, the deeper one looks into its past: beyond Neptune wait the old lumpy orbital bands – the Kuiper Belt. Even farther out, beyond the orbital bands, one arrives at the oldest shrouds of the rippling cloud – the Ort Cloud.

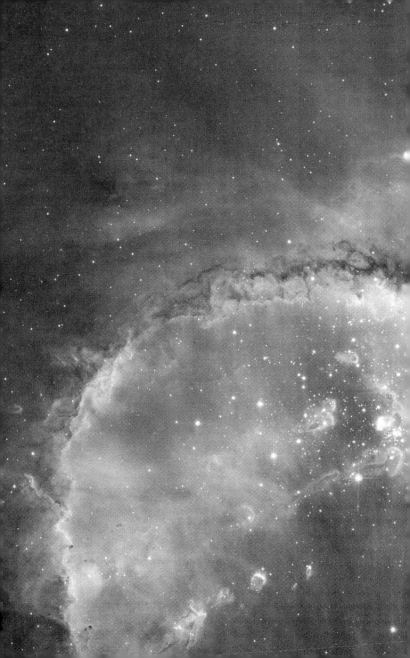

If one considers now the whole hypothesis developed here, and considers it in its full scope, over both what I have said, and what I shall still lay out, one will not think that the boldness of its implications is inexcusable. (1.317) Every world-order that matures to perfection has a growing and inexorable tendency toward its own doom. This may be counted among the reasons that warrant that the Universe is more fertile in the production of worlds in other areas, to compensate for its deterioration elsewhere. The full range of known Nature may be as small as an atom compared to what is hidden from view above or below our sights, but it still confirms this fertility of Nature. This fertility is boundless, for it is the exertion of Divine Power itself. Countless animals and plants are daily destroyed and fall prey to transience. And yet, no less are created by unexhausted fertile powers of Nature elsewhere to repopulate the emptiness. Large stretches of inhabited land emerge from the seas in an auspicious epoch and are again buried by them, but elsewhere Nature fills the gaps, makes other lands from the watery depths, and blankets the new lands with more fertile riches. In the same way, worlds and world-orders fall apart and are swallowed up by abyssal eternities, and yet creation is constantly busy crafting new evolutions in other celestial regions, compensating loss with gain.

One should not be surprised to see that God's works are transient even on their largest scale. Everything finite, everything with a beginning and an end, contains the mark of limited nature – it has to perish; it has to end. The span of a world-order is so long-lasting in virtue of the magnificence of its designs that it approaches eternity when seen from our perspective. Perhaps thousands, perhaps millions of centuries go by without the destruction of world-orders. And yet a vanity within all finite natures is constantly busy at work to destroy them. Eternity may have all sorts of eons, but in the end all eons lead through steady decline at last to the moment of downfall. *Newton*, that great admirer of God's traits in the perfection of His works, connected deep insight into Nature's grandeur with great reverence for the revelation of Divine Omnipotence. In virtue of the natural trend of the mechanics of motions towards decline, he (1.318) found it necessary to announce in advance Nature's decay. If, as a central consequence of frailty, a systematic organization gets over eons of time even the tiniest conceivable step closer to the state of dissolution, then there must come a moment in the infinite run of eternity when gradual loss will have exhausted all motion.

We must not regret the downfall of a world system as a true loss for Nature. Nature demonstrates its wealth in a kind of wastefulness. While some of its parts pay tribute to transience, Nature maintains its entire scope of perfection through countless new creations. How many flowers and insects are destroyed by a single cold day! But even though they are magnificent works of art and proofs of Divine Omnipotence, how little are they missed! Abundance replaces this loss elsewhere. Humans, the apparent masterpiece of creation, are not exempt from this law either. Nature shows itself just as rich, just as unexhausted in creating the greatest of creatures as in creating the least of them. Nature shows that even their doom is a necessary shadow in the abundance of her suns, since their creation costs her nothing. Destructive consequences of contagion, earthquakes, and floods wipe whole nations off the map, but it never seems that this is to Nature's detriment. In the same way, whole worlds and systems leave the stage after having played their role. The infinity of creation is so large that a world or a Milky Way of worlds appears by comparison just as small a flower or an insect compared to the Earth. And while Nature decorates eternity with its mutable creations, God keeps busy forming the the basic stuff that develops into even grander worlds.

> Who sees with equal eye, as God of all,
> A hero perish, or a sparrow fall,
> Atoms or systems into ruin hurl'd,
> And now a bubble burst, and now a world
> Alexander Pope[10]

(1.319) So let our sight get used to these terrifying upheavals. They are the common paths of providence. Let us see them with a kind eye. And indeed, nothing fits better than this sight to the wealth of Nature. For if a system of worlds, in the long course of its duration, exhausts all the diversity that its organization can contain, and becomes a redundant link in the chain of beings, then nothing will be more appropriate than for it to play the final role in the drama of the unfolding transformations of the Universe. Paying its dues to mortality is the final role of any finite thing. As we have suggested, Nature shows already in the small parts of its whole notion the very rule of its way that eternal Fate prescribes to everything. And I say it again: Size is no obstacle to doom. For everything that is large becomes

---

10. Alexander Pope (1688-1744). *Essay on Man* (1733-34), Epistle 1, lines 87-90. Kant cites a very literal translation by B. H. Brocke (1740); cf. 1:318

404

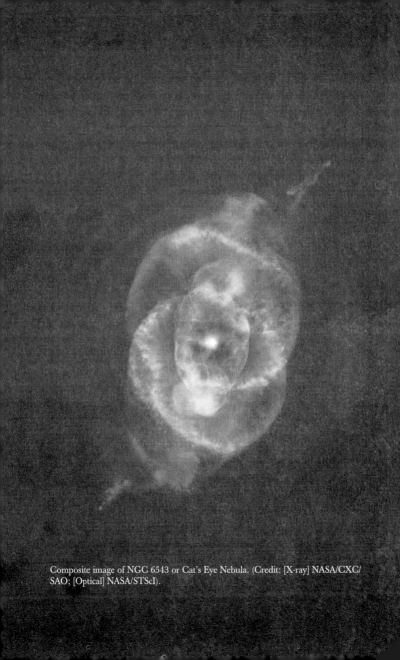

Composite image of NGC 6543 or Cat's Eye Nebula. (Credit: [X-ray] NASA/CXC/ SAO; [Optical] NASA/STScI).

small, and becomes, as it were, a point if compared to the infinity that creation represents in unlimited space and in the flow of eternity.

It appears that the end, fated to worlds as to all matters natural, is subject to some law. Recognizing this law will lend the theory a new touch, a touch of rightness. By this law, the end touches those worlds closest to the cosmic centre first, just as conception and organization had first started right next to this centre. From there, doom and destruction gradually radiate outward into ever farther reaches from

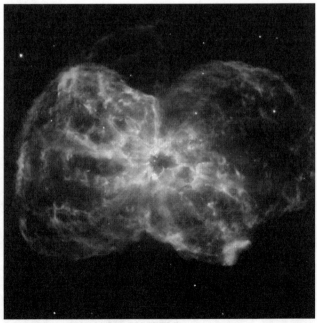

Solar Nebula (credit NASA,ESA, K.Noll[STScI]).

the centre. By general dissipation of motion, the whole Universe, having completed its period, will eventually be buried in uniform chaos. And yet, at the opposite limit of the evolved sphere, Nature is steadily busy spawning worlds from the raw stuff of scattered elements. That is to say, at the one limit Nature rots at the centre, and at the other limit Nature is young and fertile in new creations. Thus the unfolded world is placed in between, constrained by either boundary: The ruins of nature already destroyed; and the chaos of nature yet unformed. And if we imagine, as would be likely, that the length of time of a thriving mature world outlasts that of a young world forming, then regardless of all the damage done by transience, the Universe's circum- (1.320) ference will nonetheless and on the whole expand.

Now if we want to leave room, finally, for an idea that is just as plausible as it is appropriate to Divine works, then the satisfaction given by such an account of Nature's mutations will soar to the highest degree of delight. Nature is capable of hoisting itself out of chaos into regular order and elegant systematicity. Yet a diminution of motions sinks Nature into new chaos. Is it impossible to believe that Nature might be equally capable of reconstituting itself just as easily from this new chaos as from the old, and of renewing its former structure? The standstill of the machine brought the springs to rest that impelled the stuff of dissipated matter towards motion and order. But could these springs not be wound up once more by the rarefied field of forces? And could they not once again be curbed by the very same general rules toward harmony, whereby original evolution had come about? One won't have to tarry long with misgivings, as soon as one considers the following: A terminal weakening of orbital motions within the world system will make planets and comets without exception crash into the Sun. The Sun, in turn, will absorb an immeasurable energy increase through the admixture of so many big lumps. This energy increase will be especially great since distant spheres of the solar system consist of the lightest and most combustible materials of nature, by the theory previously laid out. Through new nourishment and the most volatile matter, the fire will flare up into greatest violence. It will doubtless not only dissolve everything into its smallest elements but also radiate and dissipate them into the very same distant spaces that such matters had occupied before the first evolution of Nature. This radiation and dissipation will happen through a force of expansion proportional to the heat, and with a velocity not weakened by any resistance in the dimensional medium. The near-total dissolution of its matter then dampens the violence of the central conflagration. By next linking attractive and repulsive forces, the old productions and systematically related motions will be repeated with no lessening of regularity. In this way Nature will organize a new world system.[11] When a particular

(1.321) planetary system decays in this way; when it reorganizes itself by essential forces out of such disorder; when it even repeats this process more than once – eventually an era is bound to come, when even the great system of stars will decay in its motions and sink into chaos. There is little doubt that the concentration of such a boundless lot of fiery charges (which these burning suns are) will dissolve in nameless glow, dissipate in the old realm of its evolutionary

11. This may well be the first conjecture in history about generations of stars. According to current knowledge, the first and long extinct generation consisted of blue hydrogen stars; in their nuclear furnace, the heavier elements of the periodic table formed that make up the more recent populations of stars. The younger a star is (such as the Sun), the higher will be its metal content.

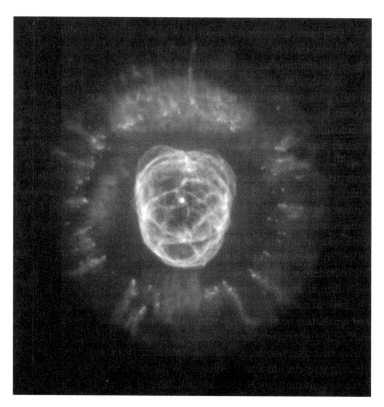

Eskimo Nebula (Credit: NASA, Andrew Fruchter and the ERO Team [Sylvia Baggett (STScI), Richard Hook (ST-ECF), Zoltan Levay (STScI)]). A photograph of a dying star. 'Ten thousand years ago this halo of gas and dust was part of the central star. The aging star then expelled its outer layers into space in successive bursts, forming what astronomers call a planetary nebula. All ordinary stars like the Sun will eventually meet a similar fate.' (Carl Sagan, *The Varieties of Scientific Experience*, London and New York: Penguin, 2006, 267.)

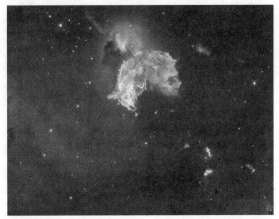

Supernova Remnant 63A. (Credit: NASA, ESA, HEIC, and The Hubble Heritage Team [STScI/AURA]).

sphere, and accordingly supply the materials to new evolutions by the same mechanical laws. In this way the emptiness can come alive again with worlds and systems. The **Phoenix of Nature** burns itself up only to return from its ashes, come back to life, and be young again.[12] If we now follow the Phoenix through all infinity of time and space, and if we see how Nature, even in the aspect of decay and obsolescence, still has the power for new creations; if we see how, at the other edge of creation and in the realm of unformed, raw matter, Nature proceeds with steady steps toward the expansion of the plan of Divine unfolding, and fills all time and all space with its miracles – if we see all this, then the mind, pondering such vistas, will sink into

---

12. My emphasis: On the 'Phoenix of Nature' see my own contribution to this volume.

deep wonder. Yet the mind is discontent with this grandiose object whose transience can never appease the soul, and wishes to get to know that very being up close whose understanding and grandeur are the light source shining through the whole nature as from a centre. With what kind of reverence shouldn't the soul regard its own being, considering that it is supposed to survive all these transformations? It can tell itself what the philosopher-poet says about eternity:

> When next a second Nothingness will bury this world,
> When from the All nothing will stay but the place,
> When still other skies, bright with other stars,
> Will have completed their course:
> Then you will be as young as now, just as far from death,
> And be as eternally future-bound as you are today.
>
> von Haller[13]

O how happy will reason be, when, among the tumults (1.322) of the elements and the ruins of nature, it is set on a steady height that lets it see the wreckage caused by the frailty of things in the world as if it were a current rushing by its feet. A happy blessedness, which reason may not even dare to wish for, is taught by the Revelation as what we can hope for with conviction. When the shackles that bind us to the vanity of creatures fall off in the very instant that is tuned to the transformation of our essence, the immortal ghost, freed from the dependence of finite things, will find the pleasure of true luck-spiritedness in the community with infinite being. Nature as a whole has a universal

13. Albrecht v. Haller (1708-1777), 'Unvollkommene Ode über die Ewigkeit' (first printing 1743).

and harmonious relation to the well-falling of divinity. Nature is capable of filling a rational creature, which finds itself joined to the arch-source of all perfection, with nothing but steadfast contentment. Seen from this central perspective, Nature will display pure safety, pure integrity, on all sides. Its mutable scenes fail to unsettle the happy poise of a ghost once raised to such height. In foretasting this state with sweet hope, a mind which is still embodied, can already train its mouth in singing these songs of praise that once will sound in all eternities.

> When, once in time, the frame of the world flees back into its own nothingness
> And the work of your hands does not differentiate by day and night anymore:
> Then my moved character, firmed by you, should try,
> To draw to your throne in honour and respect of all your power
> My mouth, filled with thanks, should through all eternities
> Prepare unending praise to you and your majesty;
> And yet no praise would be perfect – for o Sir! So tall are you,
> That eternity won't suffice to give praise fit to your dignities.
>
> Joseph Addison[14]

---

14. Joseph Addison (1672-1719), 'Some Pieces of Divine Poetry', stanzas 12 and 13, *Spectator* 453 (9 Aug 1712); Kant cites a rather free translation by Louise v. Gottsched, b. Kulmus ('die Gottschedin', 1713-62). The poem above is a literal re-translation from Gottsched's paraphrase. Compare Addison's original: 'When Nature fails, and day and night / Divide thy works no more, / My ever grateful heart, O Lord, / Thy mercy shall adore. / Through all Eternity to Thee / A joyful song I'll raise; / For, oh! Eternity's too short / To utter all Thy praise.'

Prospects for Post-Copernican Dogmatism: The Antinomies of Transcendental Naturalism

Iain Hamilton Grant

For it is not because there is thinking that there is being, but rather because there is being that there is thinking.
Schelling[1]

[T]he fundamental error of dogmatism [...][is to] search outside the I in order to discover the ultimate ground of all that is in and for the I.
Fichte[2]

What is the dogmatism against which transcendental philosophy launched its Copernican revolution? Since Kant's invention of the thing-in-itself, we are apt to think dogmatism in terms of an access problem,[3] and therefore to conclude that any philosophy is dogmatic that, through insufficient attention to its own conditioning, denies that there is an access problem. Yet characterising dogmatism as

---

1. F. W. J. Schelling, *Sämmtliche Werke*, ed. K F. A. Schelling, 14 vols (Stuttgart und Augsburg: Cotta, 1856-61), vol. XIII, 161 n., trans. B. Matthews, *The Grounding of Positive Philosophy* (New York: SUNY, 2007), 203 n.

2. J. G. Fichte (1971) *J. G. Fichtes sämmtliche Werke*, ed. I. H. Fichte, 8 vols (Berlin: Walter de Gruyter, 1971), vol. IV, 174, trs. D. Breazeale and G. Zöller, *The System of Ethics* (Cambridge: Cambridge University Press, 2005), 165.

3. For an excellent recent account of the access problem, see Chapter One of Quentin Meillassoux's *After Finitude* (London: Continuum, 2008).

access-positivism does little to define it positively, providing only a formal regression to inhibit speculative or rational egress beyond reflection, as the Fichte citation above makes sun-clear. Nevertheless, the Fichtean egress-prohibition has latterly been posited as a positive criterion of 'philosophically effective' transcendental arguments:

> The transcendental argument must not invalidly infer objective and/or unrestricted conclusions from purely subjective and/or merely parochial premises.[4]

Again, following Fichte, this criterion is expressly designed to counter any claim to a 'transcendental naturalism', which comes close, as Bell claims, to an oxymoron.[5] It follows from the above criterion that the only valid transcendental argument is one that demonstrates and asserts the parochial subjectivism of its premises. What is striking is that the double assertion of subjectivity and parochialism is asserted against the rest of being or nature. We must ask, however, whether the Bell-Fichte subjective parochialism thesis does in fact exhaustively define transcendentalism, so that to reject the one is to dismiss the viability of the other, and thus to assert that there can be no other basis for transcendental philosophy. If this is so, in so far as transcendentalism's parochialism constitutes its putative value, it also constitutes grounds for its rejection. If not, we cannot conclude a transcendental naturalism to be oxymoronic.[6]

---

4. D. Bell, 'Transcendental Arguments and Non-Naturalistic Anti-Realism', in R. Stern (ed.) *Transcendental Arguments. Problems and Prospects* (Oxford: Oxford University Press, 1999),189-210, at 192.

5. Ibid., 194.

6. The prospect of a naturalistically grounded transcendental philosophy is precisely

Consider, for example, Schelling's claim above: It is a transcendental argument in that it stipulates what conditions the possibility of thinking without reducing these conditions to any given or particular domain of objects. Hence Kant's having noted, with regard to Schelling's *System of Transcendental Idealism*, that 'transcendental idealism is realism in an absolute sense'.[7] In accordance with this absolute realism, Schelling's thesis stems from his ontological naturalism:[8] Being is the necessary condition of thinking and not vice versa.

The point to note is that neither claim is inherently inconsistent, that both are transcendental, and accordingly, that transcendental positions are themselves open to counterpositions. Given this, in what follows, we shall argue that transcendental philosophy is itself a dogmatism,[9] and

what Kant sought by way of the 'ether proofs' in the *Opus postumum*, trans. by E. Förster, (Cambridge: Cambridge University Press, 1993), 62-99. Transcendental philosophy is then defined as the 'system of *ideas*, which are problematic (not assertoric) in themselves [...] but must nevertheless be thought as possible forces affecting the rational subject' (ibid., 250), necessitating a *dynamica generalis* (ibid., 224) to ground *both* the system of objects *and* the system of ideas.

7. *Opus postumum*, op. cit., 255.

8. 'Anything whose conditions simply cannot be given in nature, must be absolutely impossible' (Schelling, *Werke* III, 571). Although it could be argued that the 'positive philosophy' of the *Grounding* is incompatible with the 'negative philosophical' theses of the *System of Transcendental Idealism*, this would be to disguise the extent to which Schelling's naturalism is precisely the kind of 'absolute realism' with which Kant identifies 'transcendental idealism'.

9. As indeed Fichte claims in the 'Review of *Aenesidemus*': 'the [Dogmatic] system holds open the possibility that we might someday be able to go beyond the boundary of the human mind, whereas the Critical system proves that such progress is absolutely impossible, and it shows that the thought of a thing possessing existence and specific properties in itself and apart from any faculty of representation is a piece of whimsy, a pipe dream, a nonthought. And to this extent the Humean system is sceptical and the Critical system is dogmatic – and indeed negatively so' (*W* I, 16; Eng trans. by D. Breazeale in *Fichte: Early Philosophical Writings*, Ithaca: Cornell University Press, 1988, 70-1).

shall do so on the basis of the applicability of three criteria specified by transcendental philosophers for the identification of dogmatism. These criteria are:

C.1 *Logical*: the susceptibility of dogmatic systems to internally consistent but antinomic counter-systems.[10]

C.2 *Metaphysical*: the attempt to provide a ground or cause of beings external to the I, or to satisfy the Principle of Sufficient Reason;[11] and

C.3 *Ontological*: the thesis that beings are things or objects.[12]

---

10. '[Reason, in] its dogmatic employment [...] lands us in dogmatic assertions to which other assertions, equally specious, can always be opposed' (Kant, *Critique of Pure Reason*, trans. N. Kemp Smith, London: Macmillan, 1958, B22-3; hereafter CPR). '[I]n the dogmatic procedure of reason [...] unavoidable contradictions of reason with itself have long since undermined the authority of every metaphysical system yet propounded' (CPR: A10/B23-4). In 'the dispute between the idealist and the dogmatist [...] reason gives us no principle of choice [... and n]either of these two systems can directly refute its opposite' (Fichte, *Werke* I, 429-432; trans. by P. Heath and J. Lachs, *The Science of Knowledge*, Cambridge: Cambridge University Press, 1982, 12-14).

11. While metaphysics, 'as science [...] has to deal [...] only with itself and the problems which arise entirely from within itself, and which are imposed upon it by its own nature, not by the nature of things which are distinct from it' (CPR: B23), 'dogmati[sm] claim[s] acquaintance with the constitution of the object fuller than that of the counter-assertion' (CPR: A388). See also Fichte, *Werke* IV, 174; *System of Ethics*, trans. and ed. by Daniel Breazeale and Günter Zöller (Cambridge: Cambridge University Press, 2005), 165: '[T]he fundamental error of dogmatism [...][is to] search outside the I in order to discover the ultimate ground of all that is in and for the I'. Wayne Martin confirms this diagnosis in his *Idealism and Objectivity: Understanding Fichte's Jena Project* (Stanford: Stanford University Press, 1997), 37: 'dogmatists are not identified simply as those who assert that things-in-themselves exist; rather they are those who assert that things in themselves constitute the ground of experience'.

12. '[D]ogmatic enquiry concern[s] things (objects), [whereas] a *critical* enquiry concern[s] the limits of my possible knowledge' (CPR: A758/B786). Dogmatism thus 'requires an insight into the nature of the object such that we can maintain the opposite of what the proposition has alleged in regard to this object [...] claiming acquaintance with the constitution of the object fuller than that of the counter-assertion' (CPR: A388). 'Any philosophy is [...] dogmatic, when it equates or opposes any thing to the self as such;

Since (3) can itself be construed as satisfying (2), it may be subsumed under it. Our purpose in stating it separately is threefold. Firstly, to highlight the crucial role played by 'things' not only in the determination of the nature of dogmatism, as above, but also in the development of transcendental philosophy's *ontology*, for which the concept 'thing-in-itself' asserts only the most elementary determination of existents; but transcendental philosophy is itself dogmatic when it concludes that *therefore they exist at all*, and that this is how being is, as when, for instance, it asserts that 'concepts of relation presuppose things which are absolutely [*schlechthin*] given, and without these are impossible'.[13] That is, the condition of possibility of objects of intuition – even of their distinction – is simply 'things absolutely given'. At this point, transcendental philosophy, whose 'supreme concept [...] is the division into the possible and the impossible', can avoid dogmatic ontological commitment only at the cost of antithesis:

Thus the object of a concept to which no assignable intuition whatsoever corresponds is = nothing. That is, it is a concept without an object (*ens rationis*), like noumena, which cannot be reckoned among the possibilities, although they must not for that reason be declared to be also impossible.[14]

Although the 'things absolutely given' on which the objects of intuition depend are neither possible nor

and this it does in appealing to the supposedly higher concept of a thing (*ens*), which is thus quite arbitrarily set up as the absolutely highest conception. In the critical system, a thing is what is posited in the self; in the dogmatic, it is that wherein the self is itself posited' (Fichte, *Werke* I, 119-120; *Science of Knowledge*, 117).

13. CPR: A284/B340.

14. CPR: A290/B346-7.

impossible, and therefore not susceptible of a transcendental investigation, their existence cannot be denied: The very essence of the dialectic, or the unavoidable errors entailed by reason's own nature, we might say. Yet as Kant's naturalistic inquiries continue (the analysis of fundamental forces in the *Metaphysical Foundations*, for example; that work's assuaging of Kant's doubts concerning chemistry as a science, and its possible applicability to emergent neuroscience; or more explicitly, the 'ether proofs' of the *Transition from Metaphysics to Physics*),[15] this possible-impossible determination *that there are things* becomes increasingly open to dispute: Perhaps things are not 'absolutely given', but instead forces assume ontological and explanatory priority over things. At issue here is the susceptibility of parochial (in Bell's sense) transcendentalisms to naturalistically driven ontological change. By criterion (1), then, the revealed contestability of a thing-based ontology demonstrates the transcendental philosophy's propensity for dogmatism.

The second reason for the initial separation of condition (3) from (2) is to accommodate a recent argument made by Wayne Martin concerning Fichte's identification of dogmatists not 'simply as those who assert that things-in-themselves *exist*' but rather as 'those who assert that things-in-themselves *constitute the ground of experience*'; or, in other

---

15. See Kant, *Aus Soemmering, Über das Organ der Seele, Ak.* XII, 33-7, trans. by Anulf Zweig as 'From Soemmmering's *On the organ of the soul*' in Immanuel Kant, *Anthropology, History and Education*, ed. by Gunter Zöller and Robert Louden (Cambridge: Cambridge University Press, 2007), 219-226; and Alexander Ruerger, 'Brain water, the ether, and the art of constructing systems', *Kant-Studien* 86, 1995: 26-40. The *Transition between Metaphysics and Physics* was the working title by which what became Kant's *Opus postumum* was contemporarily known (cf. Schelling, *Werke* VI, 8).

words, that 'the I is a thing'.[16] Such arguments – properly parochial, in Bell's sense – highlight the implicit assertion that an argument is transcendental if and only if it avoids dogmatic assertion and *therefore* susceptibility to counter-assertion ('things-in-themselves do/do not exist'). Such transcendentalisms therefore tend to propose a metaphysics without ontology. The third and final reason for the initial distinction is therefore to raise the question as to whether this is possible. For dogmatisms, by contrast, argue that *any consistent metaphysics is an ontology, and any consistent ontology is a metaphysics*.

Consider a metaphysical problem such as causality. When Kant examines self-organisation in the third *Critique*, he makes precisely the claim that its ubiquity in experience cannot warrant any assertion or denial of its existence in nature. Yet this 'problematic' address to natural causality nevertheless finds that it is 'necessary for reason to think' that 'matter can receive more and other forms than it can get through mechanism'.[17] Rational necessity avoids ontological commitment if and only if it does not entail that the theses concerning matter and causation so necessitated are *not* theses concerning matter and causation at all, but only reason; or, in other words, if the thesis, although rationally necessary, is contradictory. If the rational necessity so identified is not to be contradictory, then they are indissociably ontological theses. In other words, a resolutely

---

16. Martin, *Idealism and Objectivity*, op. cit., 36-7.

17. I. Kant, *Kants gesammelte Schriften* (Henceforth *Ak.*), ed. Königlich Preussischen Akademie der Wissenschaften (Berlin: Georg Riemer, later Walter de Gruyter, 1900-), vol. V, 411; trans. W.S. Pluhar, *Critique of Judgment* (Indianapolis: Hackett, 1987).

problematic metaphysics must either satisfy the principle of sufficient reason, or break the law of non-contradiction. Neither, for the same reason, can ontology be separated from metaphysics unless the latter does not concern being at all. If it does not, it can only concern not-being, and is then not metaphysics, but meontology. If it does, then the distinction is untenable. Or ontology is not concerned with being, but with the reason-of-being, its *logos*. Such an account must either again face the problems encountered by Kant's 'rational necessity', or the reason-of-being must become the sole focus of ontological enquiry. This is why many of the immediate post-Kantians understood the transcendental undertaking as a 'critique of natural cognition'[18] or of the 'natural antithetic';[19] that is, an inquiry into the nature of reason itself.

It is precisely this that Schelling's thesis about being denies. For it asserts not only that being is the necessary *condition* of thinking, but also that being is *first* necessary *in order that there be* thinking; being is the cause and ground of thinking, so that the Sufficient Reason for thinking is indistinguishable from ontology. Schelling's is, on this reading, a transcendental dogmatism, specifying conditions of possibility by satisfying criteria (1) and (2) above. As to the non-separable criterion (3), Schelling will indeed deny, following from the force-ontologies developed by early experiments in electromagnetism, that 'things' can provide an adequate ontological basis for either the natural sciences or for speculative naturalism. If this is taken to mean that

18. Schelling, *Werke* XI, 526.

19. CPR: A407/B434.

any ontological thesis resting on forces rather than things is for that reason non-dogmatic, then the difference between transcendental and dogmatic naturalisms rests on contingent differences in the ontologies of the natural sciences.

The dilemma initially facing a transcendental naturalism is accordingly that it must either assert determination by contingent entities of whatever nature (things, forces) or assert parochialism and admit that even in those of its theses that putatively address nature, no such address takes place insofar as the 'nature' in question is *phenomenal only*. The problem with this perhaps over-familiar claim, for those of us steeped in Kantian lore, is that there is an implicit assertion that nature as it is in itself is separable from nature *kat' anthropon*, as Kant says – nature as it appears *for us*. For this asserts in turn that phenomenal nature *is not nature*, which therefore transcendental philosophy *does not and cannot address*. This is exactly the problem that Kant encounters when he attempts the transition, firstly, from the dogmatic naturalism of his pre-critical to the properly critical works; and secondly, from metaphysics to physics in his final accounts of transcendental philosophy. If the Copernican revolution does not resolve this problem, then the problems Kant encountered remain ours: How, if at all, is a nondogmatic account of the relation of reason to nature possible?

1. Every Consistent Dogmatism is a Naturalism

How then is the Critical system different from what was previously described as the Humean one? The difference consists entirely in this: the Humean system holds open the possibility that we might someday be able to go beyond the boundary of the human mind, whereas the Critical system proves that such progress is absolutely impossible, and it shows that the thought of a thing possessing existence and specific properties *in itself* and apart from any faculty of representation is a piece of whimsy, a pipe dream, a nonthought. And to this extent the Humean system is sceptical and the Critical system is dogmatic.[20]

If thetic be the name for any body of dogmatic doctrines, antithetic may be taken as meaning not dogmatic assertions of the opposite, but the conflict of the doctrines of seemingly dogmatic knowledge in which no one assertion can establish superiority over the other.[21]

It would be a matter of considerable irony that a *Copernican* revolution in philosophy should have put paid to the project of a *Universal Natural History* – were it true. It does not, however; yet this is precisely what it is considered to have achieved: Having put an end to worries about how to adequate intellect to thing, since things must now instead comply with intellect. Yet how is any 'unthinged' naturalism to survive the revolutionary injunction? Are such 'things' reducibly those that are intellect-compliant, or are all things so? Must they be made so? Of necessity or by

20. Fichte, *Werke* I, 16; *Early Philosophical Writings*, ed. and tr. Daniel Breazeale (Ithaca: Cornell University Press, 1988), 70-71.

21. CPR: A420/B448.

reconstruction? If the occasion for the revolution is that it has proven impossible to integrate reason with nature as it is in itself, what becomes of the problem of the integration of reason and nature after it?

It is immediately evident that not only does the problem of nature not disappear from the transcendental philosophy, but also that, as the critical project progresses, it resumes the central role it enjoyed under Kant's precritical or dogmatic-naturalist period. The engagement with chemistry in the first *Critique*, which persisted long afterward;[22] the problem of the teleological judgment of nature with regard to the *actuality* of self-organising beings in the third. But nowhere is this cohabitation of dogmatic naturalism with transcendental philosophy more immediate than in Kant's final, unfinished project, known under the title *Transition from Metaphysics to Physics*,[23] with its ether deductions and its attempt to square transcendental deduction with *ontogenesis*.[24]

22. For a survey of Kant's chemism, see M. Lequan, *La chemie selon Kant* (Paris: PUF, 2000). On Kant and the sciences more generally, see M. Friedman, *Kant and the Exact Sciences* (Cambridge: Harvard University Press, 1992), E. Watkins (ed.) *Kant and the Sciences* (Oxford: Oxford University Press, 2001), and M. Friedman and A. Nordmann (eds), *The Kantian Legacy in Nineteenth-Century Science* (Cambridge: MIT, 2006). For a substantial philosophical account of the persistence of naturalism in the critical philosophy, see J. Edwards, *Substance, Force and the Possibility of Knowledge* (Berkeley: University of California Press, 2000), and for the naturalism in the *Opus postumum*, E. Förster, *Kant's Final Synthesis* (Cambridge: Harvard University Press, 2000). For my own account of the conflict between somatism and field physics in Kant's philosophy of nature, see *Philosophies of Nature After Schelling*, 2nd edition (London: Continuum, 2008).

23. Schelling, *Werke* VI, 8: 'In the year 1801 he [Kant] was still labouring, in those few hours in which his power of thinking remained free, on a work: *Transition from Metaphysics to Physics* which, had age allowed him to complete it, would doubtless have been of the greatest interest.'

24. What I have in mind here is the *Transition*'s discussions of 'how matter becomes a physical body' (Kant, *Ak*. XXI, 476-7). I discuss this in *Philosophies of Nature after Schelling*, op. cit., 59-81.

Allowing that the Copernican revolution was expressly undertaken to eradicate (at least Kant's) dogmatic naturalism; and acknowledging also that the problem Kant held dogmatism incapable of resolving is the integration of reason and nature into a single and consistent philosophical system; then the purpose of the critical philosophy is to prepare a transcendental resolution of reason and nature. The beginnings of this can be seen in the first *Critique*'s account of nature as 'the dynamical whole of all appearances', as opposed to 'world', which designates 'the mathematical sum-total' thereof.[25] Dynamics is invariably the means whereby the transcendental philosophy undertakes to avoid the fate of dogmatic naturalism without eliminating nature. Force-fields provide, by disputing criterion (3), above, egress from dogmatism without sacrificing nature, while the dynamical categories enable a reconstruction of reason as itself a dynamical and productive system. In the overt transcendental naturalism of the ether deductions, ether will finally integrate freedom with natural causality in a single, necessary and a priori, physical medium, long after the failure of the third *Critique*'s analogical attempt to achieve the same end. Of the ether, Kant writes that

> the question is whether it is to be regarded, not just as a *hypothetical material*, in order to explain certain appearances, but a real world-material – given *a priori* by reason and counting as a principle of the possibility of the experience of the system of moving forces [...] The existence of this material, and the necessity of its *a priori* presupposition, I now prove *a priori* in the following manner.[26]

---

25. CPR: A418-9/B446.

26. Kant, *Ak.* XXI, 216; *Opus postumum*, ed. and tr. Eckhart Förster (Cambridge:

With this, Kant seems to condemn his physics to the same fate as his geometry: Changes in the sciences apparently undermine the a priori necessities Kant ascribes to their theses. At the same time, therefore, the transcendental project in general is opened to charges of dogmatism on the grounds of susceptibility to antinomic dispute. Yet the reason why Kant argues for the a priori necessity of the ether as world-material is this: that *dynamics composes being from actions, not things.* As Kant writes, 'the moving forces of matter are what the moving subject itself does to [other] bodies'.[27] The twofold gambit of this claim, as of any transcendental naturalism, is that the transition from things to actions is sufficient both to avoid dogmatic traps concerning antithetical ontologies of things-in-themselves (are such disputes only possible between rival claims as to the nature of *things?*); and to integrate reason and nature into a single system susceptible to determination by free and self-constitutive acts (ontogenesis, categorial synthesis, etc.), now cast as causes. The problem is *whether the transcendental determination of nature is in fact a determination of nature at all,* i.e., a determination 'at once *a priori* and physically conditioned',[28] or merely a determination of the nature of Reason. If nature is *not* so determined, then things are not intellect-compliant, and dogmatism's inconclusiveness or revisability becomes the price to pay for the failure of the Copernican experiment. If it *is*, then the question is *either*: What kind of nature is it that is directly determinable in accordance, as Kant twice stipulates, with the 'power of

Cambridge University Press, 1993), 67.

27. Kant, *Ak.* XXII, 326; *Opus postumum*, op. cit., 110.

28. E. Förster in Kant, *Opus postumum*, op.cit., xi, citing *Ak.*XXII, 138-9; 46.

desire' as cause?;[29] *or*: What is the nature of reason such that it can so determine nature?

It is freedom and/or reason – or their *necessary combination*, as Fichte was first to point out – that denaturalises as a precondition of nature taken as an objective of transcendental philosophy. Accordingly, transcendental anti-naturalism has its avatars: Heidegger, for instance, in *On the Essence of Ground* (1929), comparing the dogmatic with the transcendental concept of 'world' in Kant's *Inaugural Dissertation* and first *Critique*, respectively, concludes in strict accordance with the replacement of the dogmatist's things with actions, that 'world never *is*, but *worlds*'.[30] Thus 'there are reasons' why, Heidegger insists, 'nature is apparently missing [from this account], not only nature as an object of natural science, but also nature in an originary sense':[31] Nature is not original, but only appears as a determination of world *for* a form of attention paid to it.

While Heidegger's remains a Copernican transcendentalism, Husserl's 1934 work 'Foundational Investigations of the Phenomenological Origin of the Spatiality of Nature: The Originary Ark, the Earth, Does not Move' reverts to a more Cartesian, or *Archimedean* strategy. In a reprise of the first of the antinomies of pure reason,[32] the essay begins the search for a 'a transcendental theory of natural

---

29. Kant, *Ak.* V, 9n: *Critique of Practical Reason*, trans. L.W. Beck (New York: Macmillan, 1993) and *Ak.*V 177 n., *Critique of Judgment*, op. cit., 16.

30. Heidegger, 'Kant's Thesis about Being' in M. Heidegger, *Pathmarks*, ed. W. McNeill (Cambridge, Cambridge University Press, 1998), 126.

31. Ibid., 370 n. 59.

32. CPR: A426/B454ff.

scientific knowledge'[33] by arguing *against* the 'absurdity – indeed, the absurdity' of naturalistic accounts of the origins of world, and *for* a world that is instead constituted by and for experience. Nature and its causes are not things, but 'elaborated intuitions', and *for experience*, indeed, as its condition, the Earth, even as a body, *does not move*. The paradox is alarming: What began with the Copernican revolution has returned, on transcendental grounds, to Ptolemaic geocentrism, to a 'restitution of a sense of the earth as ground beyond Copernicus', as Merleau-Ponty describes Husserl's undertaking.[34]

Such transcendentalisms amplify their Kantian inheritance, and in particular the problem of whether a transcendental naturalism *can supply* a naturalism at all. In light of these latter examples, the answer would clearly be in the negative. For precisely this reason, the post-Kantian fate of the transcendental project reveals something about that project in turn – its susceptibility to antinomy:

THESIS	ANTITHESIS
Nature precedes the thinking it spawns	Thinking precedes the Nature it thinks

What is important to note is that the antinomy revolves around the problem of ontological as opposed to conscious priority, just as Schelling's thesis stipulates. A naturalistic

33. E. Husserl, 'Foundational Investigations of the Phenomenological Origin of the Spatiality of Nature: The Originary Ark, the Earth, Does not Move' (1934) in Maurice Merleau-Ponty, *Husserl at the Limits of Phenomenology*, trans. and ed. Leonard Lawlor and Bettina Bergo (Evanston: Northwestern University Press, 2002), 117-131: 117)

34. Ibid., 67.

ontological solution will therefore think this priority in terms of physical conditionality, while a transcendental anti-naturalist solution will, by contrast, think it in terms of the co-natality of *Ich* and *nicht-Ich* (Fichte), of experience and its ground (Husserl), or of the priority of projection over world (Heidegger). We will return to these solutions below.

The antinomy or 'natural antithetic' echoes either side of the transition in Kant's own work from dogmatic to transcendental naturalism. For example, the *Universal Natural History* provides reasons for the critical project that are themselves naturalistic:

> If one looks for the cause of impediments, which keep human nature in such a deep debasement, it will be found in the crudeness of the matter into which his intellectual [*geistige*] part is sunk, in the unbending of the fibres and in the sluggishness and immobility of fluids which should obey its stirrings. The nerves and fluids of his brain deliver only gross and unclear concepts [...].[35]

In this light, Kant's post-Copernican attention is directed not away from nature, but towards the nature of 'self-constituting' reason,[36] a 'natural dialectic'. In the above passage, nature clearly conditions thinking; while in the post-Copernican period, the causes of such impediments

---

35. Kant, *Ak.* I, 356.

36. 'Transcendental philosophy is the autonomy of ideas, insofar as they form, independently of everything empirical, an unconditioned whole, and reason constitutes itself to the latter as a separate system' (Kant, *Ak.* XXI, 79; *Opus postumum,* op. cit., 246). This is also clear from CPR, where Kant defines critical philosophy as that 'science [which] has to deal [...] only with itself and the problems which arise entirely from within itself, and which are imposed upon it by its own nature, not by the nature of things which are distinct from it' (B23).

are found to 'aris[e] from the very nature of our reason'.[37] Thus we have a first element, corresponding to criterion (1) above, in a definition of the dogmatism it is the Copernican project to supplant:

D.1 *Any philosophy is dogmatic whose theses can be antinomically disputed.*[38]

It follows from this that, if transcendental theses are susceptible to antinomy, their assertion is dogmatic. Since they are so susceptible, then it cannot be concluded that the Copernican revolution entails the elimination of dogmatism, which is why naturalism remains a problem for transcendental philosophy.

A second element towards a definition of dogmatism may also be drawn from Kant's neuro-anatomical critique of human reason. It is clear from the above passage, as well as from other works of the 1750s and 60s, that the dogmatism at issue during the critical revolution is indeed any metaphysics that might support a *dogmatic naturalism*. On one view, the critique of such naturalism attests to Kant's conversion to the 'experimental method' in the consideration of nature, leaving all a priori reasonings regarding nature blinded by their want of experimentally derived intuitive content. On another, however, it is not empty concepts but the determination of causes that presents the problem. The *Universal Natural History* makes it clear that the causes of conceptual confusion are the materials from which the brain is composed. 'Dogmatism in its pure

---

37. CPR: A669/B697.

38. '[The] dogmatic employment [of reason …] lands us in dogmatic assertions to which other assertions, equally specious, can always be opposed' (CPR: B23).

form is materialism', wrote Hegel.[39] It is not that this must necessarily be wrong, but rather that the determination of the specific causes of contingent things is held to determine reason in turn. That is, if a contingent neural architecture (others are conceivable) is responsible for unclear concepts, then reasoning concerning concepts is duly inflected by such neurology. This is why the first *Critique* stipulates that while the proper means for 'determining the limits of [all] possible knowledge' are a priori, 'when my ignorance is contingent [*zufällig*] it must incite me [...] to a dogmatic enquiry concerning things (objects)'[40] – precisely because it is the principle of the Copernican revolution that it is not objects that determine thought, but rather thought that determines objectality. Fichte makes the point explicitly:

> It is by the *principle of causality* that dogmatism wishes to explain this nature of intelligence in general, as well as its particular determinations.[41]

This is extremely telling: Not only does it clarify the reasons for Kant's apparent abandonment of the geological, cosmological and mechanical investigations that preoccupied him during his precritical period, but specifies a dimension of dogmatism that, though often overlooked, remains crucial in the struggles of the post-Kantian philosophers against the mechanistic materialism then migrating from the natural sciences into philosophy (hence Fichte's constant complaints against Spinoza).

39. G.W.F Hegel, *The Difference Between Fichte's and Schelling's System of Philosophy*, ed. and trans. by H.S. Harris and Walter Cerf (New York: SUNY, 1977), 126.

40. CPR: A758/B786.

41. Fichte, *Werke* I, 436; *The Science of Knowledge*, ed. and tr. Peter Heath and John Lachs (Cambridge: Cambridge University Press, 1982), 17.

D.2 *Any philosophy is dogmatic for which (physical) contingencies determine the possibilities of reason*

It should be noted that D.2 adds to C.2 and 3, insofar as the latter stipulate that dogmatism locates the ground of being in things, which D.2 recasts in terms of determinability. Thus, rather than rejecting the world of physically contingent states of affairs, transcendental naturalism will, on the above grounds, argue for the primacy of actions determining by free causes over objects determined in accordance with necessity.

2. THE NECESSARY INDETERMINACY OF BEING

The claim that dogmatism is in fact dogmatic naturalism is supported not only by Kant's overt assertion that dogmatism always entails the assumption of the principle of (efficient) causality in its explanations,[42] that is, of the things (*cosa*) which ground experience, but also by subsequent anti-dogmatist philosophers, chief amongst whom is Fichte. Yet the rejection of causal explanations in metaphysics is only one element of a transcendental naturalism designed to replace it; an additional, *ontological* part of this programme

---

42. See, for example, Kant's attempts to determine the causes involved in a putative alteration of the Earth's axial rotation (*Ak.* I, 183-191) and of 'The Age of the Earth, physically considered' (*Ak.* I, 193-214). Critically reflecting on this procedure in the Antinomy of pure reason, Kant writes: 'the assertions of the thesis, on the other hand, presuppose, in addition to the empirical mode of explanation employed within the series of appearances, intelligible [*intellektuelle*] beginnings; and to this extent its maxim is complex. But as its essential and distinguishing characteristic is the presupposition of intelligible beginnings, I shall entitle it the dogmatism of pure reason' (CPR A466/B494). Finally, in the *Critique of Judgment*, Kant notes: 'Now as we talk about the systems that try to explain nature as concerns final causes, we must note carefully that the dispute among all of them is dogmatic – i.e., the dispute is about objective principles concerning the possibility of things, whether through causes that act intentially or only those that act unintentionally' (*Ak.* V, 391).

derives from Kant's critique of the primacy of the law of non-contradiction, initially presented in the *New Elucidation* (1755). Proposition I of that work states that 'there is no unique, absolutely first, universal principle of all truths'.[43] The ground of this argument stems from the problems into which basic ontological propositions fall if the law of non-contradiction is held to fulfil the office of such a principle. Drawing on Parmenidean propositions (what is, is; what is not, is not), Kant argues that any truly simple proposition must be either affirmative or negative. If the one, then not the other, and so neither can be universal, since an affirmative proposition cannot be the principle of a negative one, and vice versa. Even the proposition that might be held indirectly to prove the above assertion false, namely, that 'everything of which the opposite is false, is true',[44] is itself an affirmative rather than a negative proposition; just as its antithesis, that is, 'everything of which the opposite is true, is false', is a negative one. Since neither can be derived from its antithesis, neither could have a foundation save in itself, from which it follows that there are two propositions, rather than one unique one. Moreover, from the combination of these two propositions the principle of identity is derived. Kant states this concisely in the following terms: 'whatever is, is, and whatever is not, is not'.[45] The principle of identity is *synthetic* and *necessarily true*, but not a priori, insofar as the principle maintains the difference between being true of reason and being true of things.

---

43. Kant, *Ak.* I, 388; *Theoretical Philosophy 1755-1770*, trans. and ed. by David Walford and Ralf Meerbote (Cambridge: Cambridge University Press, 1992), 6.

44. *Ibid.*

45. Kant, *Ak.* I, 389; *Theoretical Philosophy*, op. cit., 7.

The pertinence of Kant's adoption of this Parmenidean couple[46] consists in its abandonment of a *single* first principle, and its replacement with *two* such principles on the one hand, and their *derived synthesis* in the Principle of Identity on the other. This synthetic aspect is further borne out when we consider the place of existence [*Dasein*] and not-being [*Nichtsein*] in the first *Critique*'s Categories of Modality.[47]

TABLE OF CATEGORIES

I *Of Quantity*:	Unity	Plurality	Totality
II *Of Quality*:	Reality	Negation	Limitation
III *Of Relation*:	Of Inherence and Subsistence	Of Causality and Dependence	Of Community (Reciprocity)
IV *Of Modality*:	Possibility-Impossibility	Existence-Nonexistence	Necessity-Contingency

In the considerations concerning the Table of Categories added in the B-Edition, Kant asserts that Modality and Relation belong to the *dynamical* categories, Quality and Quantity to the *mathematical*. The distinction is significant since the latter are concerned with objects of intuition and the former with their *existence*. In all cases, Kant notes, 'the third category in each class always arises from the combination of the second category with the first'. According to the Categories of Modality, then, 'necessity is just the

46. Parmenides DK 28 B2: 'the only ways of inquiry to be acknowledged are: one, that <that which is> is, and it is impossible for it not to be […] another, that It is not, and must needs not be – this, I tell you, is a path that is utterly indiscernible, for you could not know that which is not, for that is impossible, nor utter it'. I follow Cornford's translation and insertion, *Plato and Parmenides* (London: Routledge and Kegan Paul, 1939), 30-31. Importantly, Parmenides' argumentation proceeds by antitheticals, a procedure that Plato's *Parmenides* repeats and of which Kant's dialectic is a direct heir.

47. CPR: A80/B106.

existence which is given through possibility itself'.[48] This reiterates what the *New Elucidation* had already affirmed: that existence is necessary and non-existence impossible.

Descending from the synthetic, while 'all a priori division of concepts must be made by dichotomy',[49] the dynamical categories operate by *dichotomous antitheses* of concepts. On the scale of systems rather than concepts, the principle of identity explicitly sanctions extra-systemic contradictions between those that are affirmatively and those that are negatively grounded, setting up the problem the Transcendental Dialectic examines between antinomic systems. To these formal concerns, the *New Elucidation*'s protocritical yet still dogmatic argumentation adds a material element: In keeping with its Parmenidean source, Kant draws expressly *ontological* consequences from the principle of identity. It is not the identity of any particular content that is established by the principle, but rather the primary differentiation of being from not-being, and therefore the identity of what is as what is. Both principles are self-identical, insofar as their contraries facilitate no derivation: 'Being is not', that is, does not yield any derivables, not even nothing.[50]

---

48. Ibid., B110-111.

49. Ibid., B110.

50. Kant expressly disputes that the product of a contradiction is nothing: '"+ A – A = 0", [or i]n other words, affirming and negating the same thing is impossible or [*sive*] nothing' is true iff 'you invest the sign of the negative concept with the power of cancelling [*vim tollat*] the affirmative concept' (*Ak.* I, 390; 1992: 9). This power of cancellation, however, is precisely what the principle of contradiction presupposes, but that the principle of identity denies as active between assertions and negations. With no such power, nothing cannot derive from the combination of something with something that is not. The power of cancellation operates only between identicals, so that Kant rephrases the principle of identity thus: '*whatever is not not, is*', where the two 'nots' cancel each other out (*Ak.* I, 389; 1992: 8). In effect, Kant is arguing that the impossible is not nothing, but is impossible.

Accordingly, 'whatever is *not not*, *is*'[51] avoids the trap of asserting the being of what is not, or of asserting the being of 'not-being' (Parmenides' 'way of opinion').

Ontologically, the important consequence of both this Parmenidean and modal argumentation is that *all predication is of what is* and *no predication can be of what is not*. Being is not therefore a predicate, as the critical Kant will assert,[52] but rather that of which all predicates are predicates, the referent or *Bedeutung* of all predication, regardless of its *Sinn*.[53] In other words, no information is or can be given as to what is: all that is specified concerning being is that it is *impossible* that it is not. This modal account is an important first element of the ontology transcendental philosophy presupposes but cannot own without reverting to dogmatism. The elucidation of this ontology will therefore demonstrate that transcendentalism offers a new species of dogmatism in philosophy.

We are not alone in affirming an ontology underlying the transcendental project. For example, Heidegger notes in his address to 'Kant's Thesis About Being', that the thesis at issue does not affirm that beings or *things* are, and thus does not even inform us as to whether being is comprised

---

51. Kant, *Ak.* I, 389; *Theoretical Philosophy*, op. cit., 8.

52. CPR: A598/B626.

53. This elicits a dimension often overlooked in the Fregean account of the *Bedeutungen* of propositions. In 'On *Sinn* and *Bedeutung*' (1892), Frege writes 'all true sentences have the same *Bedeutung*' (in Beaney [ed.] *The Frege Reader* [Oxford: Blackwell, 2000], 159), namely, as the 'Comments' on that essay (1892) make clear, 'the True'. Just as Kant claims all predication is of being, so Frege argues that since all propositions aim at the True, 'thought and Being are the same' (ibid., 174). Finally, in 'Thought' (1919), Frege generalizes this account to the classical Platonic triumvirate: 'Just as "beautiful" points the way for aesthetics and "good" for ethics, so do words like "true" for logic' (ibid., 325).

solely of beings. All Kant's thesis tells us is that 'being is obviously not a real predicate'. Heidegger identifies this as the 'negative thesis about being'.[54] The 'positive thesis', by contrast, characterises being as

> the positing of a thing, of certain determinations as existing in themselves. [55]

From this we gain a sense of the dogmatism inherent in ontological determination, while at the same time the properly critical element is foregrounded. In this late analysis of Kant's ontology,[56] Heidegger takes the entirety of the above proposition as constituting the 'positive assertion', despite its containing two distinct – and perhaps antithetical – sub-theses: First, being is identified with *positing*; second, positing is identified not only with determination, but with determinations 'as *existing in themselves*'. That the first sub-thesis fulfils the critical requirements of this ontology is evident from the *positing*: It is not that things are in this or that way that makes the proposition a transcendental one, but the *positing* of things as this or that mode of existence (*agit, facit, operatur, dirigit*).[57] That this is so will become especially evident not only in the *Selbstsetzungslehre* and the 'Ether deductions' of the *Opus postumum*, but also in

---

54. M. Heidegger 'Kant's thesis about being', op. cit.

55. CPR: A598/B626.

56. Heidegger's first published examination of Kant's ontology is *Kant and the Problem of Metaphysics* (1929, trans. by R. Taft, Bloomington: Indiana University Press, 1997), an analysis to which he returns in 'Kant's Thesis about Being' (1961) and *What is a Thing?* (1962, trans. by W. B. Barton and V. Deutsch, Chicago: Regnery, 1968).

57. 'Nature *causes* (*agit*). Man *does* (*facit*). The rational subject acting with consciousness of purpose *operates* (*operatur*). An intelligent cause, not accessible to the senses, *directs* (*dirigit*).' (Kant, *Ak*. XXI,18; *Opus postumum*, 224-5)

Kant's heirs' (especially Fichte's) accounts of the constitutive or determining role of the *act* of positing with regard to the *facts* so posited. Against these Copernican credentials, the second sub-thesis automatically triggers accusations of dogmatism, at least insofar as the term applies to all metaphysics that takes as its object the determination of things 'existing in themselves'.

The question then concerns the relation between the two sub-theses; whether, that is, the first sub-thesis's identification of being with positing is identical with or different from the second sub-thesis's identification of positing and determination. If it is, then being is determinable *in itself* by positing; if not, then the being of the positing is not equivalent to the determination so posited. Note that from the thesis that being is what all predication is of, it follows that all predication must be the determination of being. Meanwhile, positing posits *determinations* as 'existing in themselves'. It does not, that is, determine anything *that* exists in itself, but *makes* determinations exist in themselves. In effect, this is what a second constituent of Kant's modal ontology stipulates: 'I have been reproached', Kant writes,

> for defining the power of desire as the power of being the cause, through one's presentations, of the actuality of the objects of these presentations [*die Definition des Begehrungsvermögens als Vermögens, durch seine Vorstellungen Ursache von der Wirklichkeit der Gegenstände dieser Vorstellungen zu sein*].[58]

Just as the thesis that all predication is of what is critically buttresses the *New Elucidation*'s modal proposition concerning being, viz., that it is impossible that it is not, so

---

58. Kant, *Ak.* V, 177 n., citing *Ak.*V, 9 n.

the thesis that being is a positing of determinations existing in themselves turns into an account of the determining causes of *actuality*. From this, we derive an initial statement of Kant's ontology:

Being is necessarily indeterminate if actuality is determinable.

Or, in practical terms:

The necessity of contingency is necessary for the determinability of the actual.

It is precisely at this juncture that a comment Hegel makes in the *Difference Between Fichte's and Schelling's System of Philosophy* with regard to Kant's table of categories acquires significance as regards the investigation of a transcendental dogmatism. The framing of Hegel's comment is, in this regard, especially instructive. In Kant's deduction,

> The identity of subject and object is limited to twelve acts of pure thought [*reine Denkthätigkeiten*] – or rather to nine only, for modality really determines nothing objectively; the nonidentity of subject and object essentially pertains to it.[59]

Firstly, that the categories are to fulfil the 'identity of subject and object', that is, satisfy the speculative proposition, may seem like Hegel's own imposition. Yet it is Kant who stipulates that, although the categories in general constitute 'all original pure concepts of synthesis that the understanding contains within itself *a priori*',[60] the dynamical categories are in addition 'concerned with existence'.[61]

59. Hegel, *The Difference Between Fichte's and Schelling's System of Philosophy*, op. cit., 80.

60. CPR: A80/B104.

61. Ibid., B110.

With what existence? Categories or acts of thought that had no such effects could satisfy no subject-object or concept-intuition identity. In other words, although the categories cannot determine a priori the existence and specific differentia of particular matters, the categories of modality are nonetheless held to posit 'determinations existing in themselves'. Yet we have seen how the transcendental philosophy demonstrates the necessity attaching to existence as the ground for its determination, which extends, in the form of practical reason, to the determination of actuality (*Wirklichkeit*) as such. Why then does Hegel expressly deny this determination, asserting instead that Kant's categories of modality 'determine nothing objectively' and that 'the nonidentity of subject and object essentially pertain to it'?

The criticism hinges on the claim that the categories of modality, *qua* categories of the understanding, are determining only of forms of thought, and thus provide a merely subjective determination of actuality. Hence it can be denied that anything is thereby determined *objectively*. Further, this is necessarily the case insofar as these categories are premised on the non-identity of subject and object, which the ontology supporting the Copernican revolution presupposes: The determination of reason is simply not the determination of things. In other words, if it is through the *positing* that 'determinations exist in themselves', then these determinations have existence only consequent upon their positing. Since, at the same time, no determinations can be made of things-in-themselves, then the categories of modality, especially those of existence and non-existence, 'determine nothing objectively'.

While possessing no capacity for objective determination, the categories do nevertheless determine the *only possible actions* that speculative reason can perform, *regardless of whether such performances obtain* or are *actualised*. As we have seen, the transition to *actuality* is not an element of speculative reason, but a power only practical reason can effect. To effect is ultimately to determine actuality in accordance with freedom as the only *unconditioned* and *necessary* cause.[62] Accordingly, since it is a necessary presupposition of the Copernican revolution that being is determinable but not determining, being so determined is actuality: Subjectivity remains impotent in being, but powerful in actuality.[63] The reason for this is the Copernican thesis that objects are determinable for reason while reason is not determinable by objects, which entails that objective determination – that is, determination of existents anterior to determination – is impossible. Neither existence nor any of the other categories can therefore be extended to objects as such, but only to actuality, by positing. If being has no 'objective' side, in what then does nature consist? Grasping the implications, it is Fichte who is Kant's true heir, exactly as he claimed, when, in the *Science of Knowledge*, he characterises the object for the subject as the *nicht-Ich*, finally subjectivising all nature. 'Is it true' then, as Georges Cuvier asked his erstwhile professor of comparative anatomy, Carl Friedrich Kielmeyer, 'as the Kantians seem to maintain', that

---

62. Ibid., A418-9/B446-7.

63. Kant was never as clear as Fichte about this: 'if the Science of Knowledge should be asked, how then, indeed, are things-in-themselves constituted, it could offer no other answer save, as we are to make them. [… H]ence we can never speak of the existence of an object without a subject' (Fichte, *Werke* I: 286; *Science of Knowledge*: 252).

external nature [...] may be deduced from *a priori* principles, i.e., those that are present prior to all experience […] – in short, from the nature of our minds [?][64]

The problem is excellently posed: if there are principles prior to all experience, then external nature emerges only *after* its subjective determination. Thus Hegel's intervention clarifies the ontology presupposed by transcendentalism, and articulates its dichotomous structure: Nature cannot be objectively but only subjectively determined; therefore objective nature is of necessity objectively indeterminate in itself. By contrast, Cuvier's problem suggests that it is only if the deduction of external nature is *not* the deduction of external nature that a subject-object dichotomy is conceivable. Rather than the subject-object pair, the Cuvier question (so like Jacobi's challenge to Kant)[65] works out the implications of the priority of thinking over being asserted by transcendental naturalism. Both sets of concerns, however, present an antinomy of transcendental naturalism: The opposability of transcendental to dogmatic naturalism, on the one hand, and the priority of thinking over being, on the other. Since these theses are opposable, transcendental ontology is dogmatic by criterion (1), above. Nevertheless, the core problem of the identity of reason and nature remains open. As for all dogmatisms, therefore, transcendentalism is a naturalism concerned not with the determination of mind by nature, but with that of nature by free

---

64. C. F. Kielmeyer, *Natur und Kraft. Gesammelte Schriften*, ed. F.H. Köhler (Berlin: Kieper, 1938), 236.

65. 'The transcendental idealist […] must have the courage to assert the strongest idealism that has ever been taught, and not even to fear the charge of speculative egoism' (F.H. Jacobi, 'Realism and Idealism', in B.Sassen (ed.), *Kant's Early Critics: the Empiricist Critique of the Theoretical Philosophy* (Cambridge: Cambridge University Press, 2000), 175.

causes supported by necessary contingency. We will now examine both the Hegelian and the Cuverian antinomies of transcendental naturalism in turn.

3. THE ANTINOMIES OF TRANSCENDENTAL NATURALISM

I. THE HEGELIAN ANTINOMY

Hegel presents an antinomy of transcendental naturalism in *The Difference between Fichte's and Schelling's System of Philosophy*, through Fichte's transcendental deduction of nature. The deduction is transcendental insofar as its starting point is the absolute *Ich*'s oppositing of nature to the empirical *Ich*, or the 'self-limitation of free activity'.[66] In other words, the differential between the absolute and the finite *Ich*s, or the degree to which the latter approximates the absolute identity of the former, provides the necessary conditions for thinking nature in accordance with the programme of the *Science of Knowledge*. Hegel[67] cites Fichte postulating that nature

> is characterised by its antithesis to freedom. 'Nature determines itself' must [accordingly] be translated into 'nature *is* determined by its essence, *formaliter*, to determine itself'; nature can never be indeterminate, as a free being can very well be; and *materialiter* too, nature is determined just in one way and no other; unlike a free being, it does not have the choice between a certain determination and its opposite.[68]

---

66. Hegel, *The Difference Between Fichte's and Schelling's System of Philosophy*, op. cit., 136.

67. Ibid., 137-8.

68. Fichte, *Werke* IV, 112-3; *The System of Ethics*, op. cit., 108.

Fichte here makes explicit the necessary indeterminacy of being that is merely implicit in Kant, and applies this to the production of a nature as formal and material *being-determined*. Accordingly, nature *is* formal and material determinability. The determinable is never possibly not-determined, so that the empirical *Ich* can never not be determined in turn by determinacies it posits as its own limits. Empirical or living self-consciousness therefore sets itself as its task an unlimited striving to overcome these limits and increase the indeterminacy of or in being.

Because striving takes *time*, and because it must be *unlimited* if it is a free striving rather than a determined and therefore merely natural drive, Hegel complains that rather than resolving the antithesis of nature and freedom, Fichte replaces it with an antithesis between 'a limited present and an infinity extraneous to it'.[69] Replacing an 'absolute object' with an absolute subject merely produces, notes Hegel, a 'dogmatic idealism';[70] antinomising it by way of a living self-consciousness generates no solution, therefore, to the antithesis of nature and freedom, but transposes the ground of this antithesis outside itself, a subjectivity as objective and absolute as the object of dogmatic materialisms. This is borne out by Fichte's concept of 'drive', drawn from physiological researches into the nature of living beings. Thus, he writes:

> The highest exhibition of intelligence outside itself, in nature, is the drive.[71]

---

69. Hegel, *The Difference Between Fichte's and Schelling's System of Philosophy*, op. cit., 139.

70. Ibid., 127.

71. Fichte, *Werke* XI, 363.

Positing the drive as the highest exhibition of intelligence in nature – rather than, for example, the closest nature gets to exhibiting intelligence – therefore clearly exhibits transcendental dogmatism's maintenance of the dichotomy, while at the same time demonstrating the site of the struggle over determinacy versus purpose, between physics and ideality. Fichte reconstructs ethics as the direct conflict of matter and ideality, as the infinitely unresolvable struggle of embodied determinacy for absolute indetermination, and thus posits 'Nature [as] something essentially determined and lifeless'.[72] Nothing demonstrates more concretely this antinomy of transcendental naturalism than the 'shock of the objective world',[73] or nature determined as absolute object.

Hegel's own solution follows from a view of Kant's transcendentalism he shares with Schelling. That is, when reason takes itself as its own object, transcendental philosophy is the investigation of the nature proper to reason. Accordingly, the Hegelian solution to the antinomy concerns the latter's provocation of the need of philosophy to overcome dichotomy. Yet Reason *by its own nature* is driven to maintain the dichotomy in and as its identity with the Absolute. The 'speculative proposition' that satisfies this need always and necessarily asserts identity with the Absolute (Frege's Hegelianism), but never equivalence to it, so that the 'identity of identity and dichotomy' resolves the antinomy of finitude and extrinsic infinity.

Therefore it is a condition of Reason's nature that it is *both* unconditioned by the dichotomy of freedom and

72. Hegel, *The Difference Between Fichte's and Schelling's System of Philosophy*, op. cit., 139.

73. Schelling, *Werke* I, 337.

nature, *and* maintains it. This is an important solution in three ways. Firstly, Hegel's is a species of *naturalised epistemogenesis* in accordance, as both the Greater *Logic* and the *Phenomenology* show, with living reason. Secondly, it is a largely forgotten solution to a problem that remains unresolved: namely, the relation of reason to nature, on the one hand, given the nature of reason on the other. Speculative idealism, in this regard, shares its concerns with philosophical inquiries regarding naturalised epistemology, neurophilosophy, and dialethism,[74] amongst others. Thirdly, Hegel's proposals do not resolve but amplify antinomy, making his a hyperdogmatism that remains undetermined with regard to nature or reason.

II. THE CUVERIAN ANTINOMY

Let us then return to the indeterminacy of being thesis common to transcendentalism in general. If what is at stake, for Fichte, is the relative determinability of the *Ich* and its opposed 'nature'; and if, for Hegel, it is the determinability of all dichotomy by Reason's nature that matters, then transcendental philosophy has, in the 'positing' principle considered above, a naturalistic means for accounting for determination. We will first investigate this before pursuing the Cuverian antinomy of transcendental naturalism.

---

74. For naturalised epistemology, see W. V. O. Quine 'Epistemology naturalized' in *Ontological Relativity and Other Essays* (New York: Columbia University Press, 1969). For neurophilosophy, see P. M. Churchland, *Neurophilosophy* (Cambridge: MIT, 1986), 482: 'so it is that the brain investigates the brain, theorizing about what brains do when they theorize'. Graham Priest, in *Beyond the Limits of Thought* (Oxford: Oxford University Press, 2002), defines dialethism as a transcendental investigation into the nature of true contradictions.

445

Positing is an *act*, the actualisation of a power in the world, subject to resistances and limitations. If nature or being is able to impose resistances and limitations upon subjectivity, philosophy returns to pre-Copernican dogmatic naturalism. Thus the antidogmatic critique of causation consists in a refutation of its capacity to determine reason. To be so capable, a thing or cause (*causa*) would have to be ascribed powers; without a thing-in-itself as their possessor or vehicle, there remains only a set of powers. If a powers ontology is generalised, and if determination is a power of reason, then reason acts in one and the same world as do other powers. As Warnke notes,

> *Actions* are conceived by traditional metaphysics as the *expressions of things*. [Transcendentalism] stands this common view on its head [and] determines *things as expressions of actions, objects* as products of *relations*, *being* as a reified, objectified *doing*, exhausted in its product.[75]

Considered along these lines, the powers or *Vermögen* of the first *Critique*, held responsible as they are for the existence or actuality of determinations, constitute a step towards supplanting bodies with forces in fundamental physics. This, for example, is how the medical scientist Andreas Röschlaub read Fichte, rendering the latter capable of a philosophy of medicine,[76] and how the natural

---

75. C. Warnke, 'Schellings Idee und Theorie des Organismus und der Paradigmawechsel der Biologie um die Wende zum 19. Jahrhundert' in *Jarhrbuch für Geschichte und Theorie der Biologie* 5, 1998: 187-234: 200.

76. Developing the theme of Idealist influences in their contemporaneous sciences, Tsouyopoulos (1978: 90) cites Röschlaub's assessment of transcendental naturalism from the latter's *Magazine for the Improvement of Medicine* vol.8, part 3 (1805): 473: 'The philosophemes of a Kant, a Fichte and a Schelling have given the labours of the physician and the natural scientist a manifest and proper direction in our own day, just as the philosophemes of Empedocles, Democritus, Heraclitus and Aristotle did earlier'.

historian Carl Friedrich Kielmeyer reports the substance of Kant's Copernican revolution to Cuvier:

> This experiment of Kant's is astute, and it recommends itself in that in this way, the necessary, the universal and the certain in our knowledge remains subjective in our mind, while the contingent and the particular will be attributed to objective nature, which is unknown in itself. [77]

As for Kant, then, although he allows no naïve knowledge of nature 'in itself', Kielmeyer's ontology is modal, consisting of what necessarily and what contingently is. Objective nature is not nature-as-objects but as *matter* and, as matter, is subject to further determination by forces. Here Kielmeyer joins Hegel in asserting that Kant does not go far enough (although for different reasons). For to turn matter, as the *Metaphysical Foundations of Natural Science* attempts to, solely into the product of attractive and repulsive forces, would have satisfied naturalistic demands on the first *Critique* without sacrificing transcendentalism. According to Kielmeyer, however,

> Kant neither achieved this, and nor, although he ought to, would he want to; the proof is still wanting that all qualititative differences in matter are simply and immediately differences in the quantitative relations between the attractive and repulsive forces. I would very much like to see this proof undertaken and the qualities of matter explained from these two forces without the intervention of a *tertium*, whether this be God, atoms, or some third force. [78]

---

77. Kielmeyer, *Natur und Kraft*, op. cit., 243.

78. Ibid., 245.

So Kielmeyer demands that the powers hypothesis become an objective ontology. What we are left with now, however, are two accounts of transcendental naturalism: in one, the necessary indeterminacy of being is maintained at the cost of anything other than the subjective determination of actuality; in the other, forces supply a unified and speculative ontogenetic account of the material of knowledge, or objectivity. However, to complete this as an account of transcendental naturalism, an additional element must be added to the powers thesis: namely, the ontological thesis regarding the necessary indeterminacy – and therefore determinability – of being. It is with this in mind that we turn finally to the Cuverian Antinomy.

The Cuverian Antinomy is also Schelling's, and concerns priority and posteriority in relations of determination. Where Cuvier asks whether external nature can be deduced according to principles of mind prior to experience, Schelling asserts that being precedes thinking and not the converse. Since the implicit antinomic contrary in Cuvier's question raises precisely this prospect, we will restate the substance of Schelling's account of it:

THESIS	ANTITHESIS
Nature precedes	Thinking
the thinking it	precedes the
spawns	Nature it thinks

A transcendental naturalism based on powers may be held to supplant the problem of logical and real priority with that of reciprocity – powers are reciprocally, rather than mechanically or efficiently, determined. Since, however, reciprocity is simply a time-cancelling version of Husserl's co-natality thesis, this strand of transcendental naturalism is clearly dogmatic, in that it asserts a perfected equilibrium or static eternity of forces against the time-based antithesis of that view, as stated in the above antinomy.

If being is necessarily indeterminate, then this indeterminacy must precede its determination, since the converse would entail that being is determinate in advance of its determination, thus defeating the transcendental gambit from the outset. From this, once Kielmeyer's Kant-derived powers ontology is added to it, it follows *not* that being is inert and only acted upon by powers-possessors – since this would amount to a dogmatic reversion to things in themselves – but rather, that being itself is determinability in accordance with powers. It is this, then, that gives Schelling his conviction concerning the priority of being over thinking, and Cuvier his scepticism concerning the priority of thinking over nature: Being is therefore potentiality for determinate being, *Seynkönnen*, rather than the object over which transcendental subjects struggle.

The Schelling-Cuvier antinomy thus results, its transcendental condition-giving notwithstanding, in a dogmatic naturalism premised on the multiple determinability of being. Finally, therefore, transcendental naturalism is either a dogmatic naturalism of the Cuvier-Schelling-Kielmeyer type – that is, simply naturalism – or it is not a naturalism at all, like those of Fichte, Heidegger and Husserl. Copernicanism does not eliminate dogmatism, but continues it in new forms – a dogmatism of appearance as opposed to that of essence, as has been recently made crystal clear by Béatrice Longuenesse:

449

It is a fact that we live in a world of things. Still, we must understand that these things are our fact, our doing – not in the sense that a philosophy of praxis would give to this statement [...] but in the sense of a metaphysical account of the world as constituted by a process of thinking.[79]

Just as this dogmatism of appearances resulted from Kant's experiment in thought, it remains true of transcendentalism now, and prompts a challenge to those who pursue transcendental philosophy – to demonstrate that theirs is not simply a dogmatic anti-naturalism.

In conclusion, the ontology of powers, with its modal determinations (necessity, contingency, possibility, actuality), can only be regarded as a reducibly metaphysical problem if the physical dimensions of its actuality are ignored. Field ontology entered physics and philosophy at the same time, although its philosophical pedigree is perhaps longer, stretching back at least to Plato's *Sophist* and the topics and interlocutors addressed therein. Accordingly, I will conclude by drawing out some implications of powers ontologies.

Firstly, powers necessarily involve modal concepts. Against Hegel's denial that the Categories of Modality determine anything objective, objectality is nothing other than a set of potentials for actualisation, as Plato insisted. Powers make contingency into an ontology, a metaphysics and a physics.

Secondly, and again emphasising contingency, powers necessarily involve time determination, not as the

79. Béatrice Longuenesse, *Hegel's Critique of Metaphysics* (Cambridge: Cambridge University Press, 2007), 6.

transcendental form of inner sense, but, as Johann Heinrich Lambert noted, as determining change: 'If changes are real, then time is real [...]. If time is unreal, then no change can be real'.[80] Of course, this does not mean that the *nature* of time is given in advance as linear, as again physicists remind us.

Thirdly, powers do constitute a dogmatically assertible transcendental field insofar as they are both necessary to determination and in and of themselves indeterminate.

Fourthly and finally, the prospects for dogmatism are raised wherever the certainties of transcendental reflection are revealed not as another species of reason, but rather as dogmatism parochialised:

Being is necessarily indeterminate if actuality is determinable.

Or, in practical terms:

The necessity of contingency is necessary for the determinability of the actual.

---

80. Lambert to Kant, October 13th 1770, in Kant *Ak*. X, 107.

A Throw of the Quantum Dice Will Never Abolish the Copernican Revolution[1]

Gabriel Catren
Illustrations by Cristian Turdera

I. THE PTOLEMAIC REDUCTION OF QUANTUM MECHANICS

One of Kant's seminal contributions to modern science is the injunction according to which the Copernican reflection on the spatiotemporal localisation of the subject of science has to be radicalised into an inquiry regarding its transcendental localisation. If the Copernican revolution allowed the development of a rigorous scientific astronomy delivered of the limits imposed by the contingent localisation of the earth, Kant's critique opens up for the first time the possibility of performing a transcendental deanthropomorphisation of science. Instead of imposing juridical limits on science, such a transcendental self-consciousness should allow a progressive emancipation of the scientific comprehension of nature from the limitations imposed by the a priori structures of scientific knowledge (such as human

1. I would like to thank Damian Veal for his insightful criticisms and comments on a first draft of the manuscript. Of course, I take sole responsibility for the final result.

physiology, categories of human understanding, scales accessible to human experience, technological possibilities, imaginary and ideological representations, limitations imposed by the anthropic principle, particular linguistic structures, sociological, political and economical preconditions of research, and so on).

Alas, instead of exponentiating to a transcendental power the projective dehumanisation of science, most proponents of the critical philosophy instead attempted to stitch up the narcissistic wound opened by the Copernican revolution. Even Kant, far from pushing the transcendental revolution to its ultimate, inhuman denouement, instead used his critique to demonstrate that science would never be able to sublate its humanity. In this way, the required transcendental reflection on the preconditions of scientific experience did not lead to the announced transcendental Copernican revolution. On the contrary, the ultimate sense of the Copernican revolution was, as Meillassoux clearly shows in *After Finitude*,[2] completely distorted. A narcissistic reaction aims to counteract the Copernican decentring of the planet earth – and tries to heal what Freud called the 'cosmological humiliation'– by re-situating human existence on a transcendental 'unmoving *Ur*-earth' (Husserl). In the last instance, it does not matter whether humanity dwells on an orbiting earth; the transcendental ego is the ultimate centred source of the objective consistency that science naïvely believes itself to discover in nature.

---

2. See Chapter Five, 'Ptolemy's Revenge', of Q. Meillassoux, *After Finitude: An Essay on the Necessity of Contingency*, trans. R. Brassier (London: Continuum, 2008).

In particular, quantum mechanics is a privileged target of what Meillassoux has notably called the transcendental 'Ptolemaic counter-revolution'. Indeed, many interpretations of quantum mechanics could be translated – to differing extents – in transcendental terms. In what follows, we will use the term 'transcendental' to characterise any interpretation according to which quantum mechanics can be considered a scientific formalisation of certain impassable limits to the knowledge of physical nature. We could say that a transcendental interpretation of quantum mechanics states that the conditions of possibility of scientific experience restrict the amount of accessible information that can be predicted of (or extracted from) physical systems.[3] This transcendental interpretative framework could thus be summarised in the following terms:

> [...] it now proves quite easy to justify transcendentally a large part of the structure of Quantum Mechanics. One can for instance derive a crucial part of the quantum formalism from assumptions about the limits of accessible experimental information; or from assumptions about contextuality of phenomena [...] This means that one is no longer compelled to understand quantum theories as a representation of the 'external', 'independent' world, with all the strangeness and paradoxes that are associated with such a representation. Rather, quantum theories can very naturally be understood

---

3. The forthcoming book *Constituting Objectivity: Transcendental Approaches of Modern Physics,* M. Bitbol, P. Kerszberg and J. Petitot (eds) The Western Ontario Series in the Philosophy of Science, Vol. 74 (Berlin: Springer Verlag, forthcoming February 2009) is entirely devoted to the relationship between transcendental philosophy and modern physics. Some of the most interesting and far-reaching transcendental analysis of the quantum formalism can be found in the works of S. Y. Auyang, M. Bitbol, E. Cassirer, B. Falkenburg, G. Hermann and P. Mittelstaedt. We address the reader to the aforementioned work for all the relevant references.

as expressing the constraints and bounds of (experimental) knowledge. This is very much in the spirit of Kant, if not in the letter of his original texts.[4]

In classical mechanics, the exact position and the exact momentum (roughly speaking, the velocity) of a particle can be simultaneously predicted for all times from a given set of initial conditions. In quantum mechanics, on the contrary, we cannot predict the momentum of a particle characterised by a well-defined position (and vice versa). More generally, Heisenberg's uncertainty principle states that certain pairs of variables can be simultaneously predicted only up to some inversely-correlated uncertainties. It is therefore tempting to try to localise the transcendental a priori structures (instrumental, pragmatic, cognitive, linguistic, etc.) that are at the origin of this supposed limitation. According to this 'Kantian' strategy, quantum mechanics seems to show that it is impossible to go through the 'transcendental' looking-glass towards a hypothetical 'nature-in-itself' inhabited by systems with intrinsic properties. Rather, quantum mechanics seems to provide a mathematical account of the correlations between the 'observed' systems and their (not necessarily human) 'observers'.[5]

---

4. M. Bitbol et al., *Introduction to Constituting Objectivity: Transcendental Approaches of Modern Physics*, op.cit, 17-18.

5. It is worth remarking that the thesis according to which quantum mechanics only describes correlations between physical systems does not necessarily entail that there exist impassable limits to the knowledge of nature. For example, the so-called 'relational' interpretations of quantum mechanics maintain that the notion of an isolated system with 'absolute' properties is meaningless. We could say that this strategy amounts – in a Hegelian style – to avoiding anthropomorphic interpretations of the quantum 'limitations' by ontologizing the correlations and doing away with any phantomatic 'thing-in-itself'. Hence, relational quantum mechanics cannot be considered a transcendental interpretation of the theory. These relational interpretations could be summarised by means of the following claims:

In this way, physicists seem forced to accept that they cannot abstract from the *constitutive* role that their measuring instruments play in experimental inquiry. This means that quantum systems seem to be inherently *contextual*, that is to say we cannot separate their properties from the experimental contexts that constitute them as systems. The quantum realm that underlies our everyday object-oriented macroscopic experience is a kind of uncanny domain peopled with weird, shadowy entities that assume definite properties only when they are observed, that 'decide' to behave like waves or particles depending on the experimental setup, and so on. In Kantian terms, we could say that quantum systems seem to conform to our faculty of experimental intuition. If classical mechanics is supposed to rely on a classical ontology of observer-independent physical objects endowed with intrinsic objective properties, quantum formalism seems to forbid any ontological extrapolation in terms of decontextualised physical objects. Employing Popper's characterisation of the so-called Copenhagen interpretation of quantum mechanics, we might say 'that quantum mechanics does not represent [physical systems], but rather our knowledge, our observations, or our consciousness, of [physical systems]'.[6] Instead of pushing our comprehension of nature's rational structure further than

---

'Properties of quantum systems have no absolute meaning. Rather, they must be always characterised with respect to other physical systems. Correlations between the properties of quantum systems are more basic that the properties themselves.' C. Rovelli, 'Relational quantum mechanics', *International Journal of Theoretical Physics* 35, 1996, 1675. See also F. Laudisa & C. Rovelli, 'Relational Quantum Mechanics', in Edward N. Zalta (ed.) *The Stanford Encyclopedia of Philosophy* (Fall 2008 Edition), at http://plato.stanford.edu/archives/fall2008/entries/qmrelational/.

6. K. Popper, *Quantum Theory and the Schism in Physics* (Cambridge: Unwin Hyman, 1982), 35. (Popper writes of 'particles' rather than 'physical systems').

classical mechanics, quantum physics forces us to withdraw from noumenal nature and to place ourselves at the centre of a transcendentally-constituted experience. In doing so, quantum mechanics, far from positively extending physical knowledge, only allows us to recognise the transcendental illusions of classical mechanics and to set out the juridical limits of the precritical dream.

In this article, we will argue that in order to construct a satisfactory interpretation of the quantum formalism it might be necessary to advocate what we could call a 'precritical realism', that is to say, to put aside any kind of transcendental considerations. Far from denying the importance and the necessity of a transcendental reflection – and of the consequent transcendental deanthropomorphisation of scientific knowledge – we only mean to suggest that the theoretical scope of quantum mechanics might be strictly physical rather than transcendental. If this were indeed the case, then we would have to accept that, from the point of view of a transcendental critique of scientific knowledge, quantum mechanics is just as 'precritical' as classical mechanics.

When confronted with the paradoxes of quantum mechanics, Einstein adopted what we could call a 'naïve', 'precritical' attitude. Indeed, he was not willing to accept 'transcendental' limits to physical knowledge; he continued to long for a physical theory capable of describing physical reality in *realistic* (i.e. observer-independent) and *complete* terms. Regarding the supposed limitations imposed by Heisenberg's uncertainty principle, Einstein expected the advance of physics to lead to a more complete theory that would describe *all* the 'elements of physical reality' – that is, both the position and the momentum of quantum systems.[7] In this article we claim that Einstein was completely right in demanding, in spite of the critical attempts to interpret quantum mechanics in a 'transcendental' framework, that a physical theory has to be 'realistic' and 'complete'. According to the position that we will advocate, he only failed in not recognizing that quantum mechanics itself provides, *unlike classical mechanics*, a 'realistic' and 'complete' description of physical reality. The main objective of this article is to support this last claim in purely conceptual terms.[8]

II. SPECULATIVE PHYSICS

Before presenting such a 'precritical' interpretation of the quantum formalism, we want to make some remarks concerning the motivations and the methodology of this ongoing project. We could say that the discussion that we shall propose belongs to a particular mode of physical thinking that we shall call, in the wake of Schelling, *speculative physics*. We shall now give a succinct description of what we mean by this term.

In general, the substitution of one physical theory by another one is not a consequence of the mathematical inconsistency of the former. In particular, both classical and quantum mechanics are mathematically-consistent theories.

7. A. Einstein, B. Podolsky and N. Rosen, 'Can Quantum-Mechanical Description of Physical Reality be Considered Complete?', *Phys. Rev.* 47, 1935, 777-80.

8. More technical justifications of the proposed arguments, as well as an extended bibliography, can be found in the following articles: G. Catren, 'On Classical and Quantum Objectivity', *Foundations of Physics* Vol. 38, No. 5, 2008, 470-87 (available from http://philsci-archive.pitt.edu/archive/00004298/); G. Catren, 'Can Classical Description of Physical Reality be Considered Complete?', in M. Bitbol, P. Kerszberg and J. Petitot (eds.), *Constituting Objectivity: Transcendental Approaches of Modern Physics*, op. cit. (available from http://philsciarchive.pitt.edu/archive/00004295/).

Hence, mathematical constraints do not seem to suffice for explaining the a priori necessity of physical theories. The heuristic postulate of speculative physics asserts that physical theories are endowed with a rational necessity that stems *neither* from their mathematical consistency, *nor* from the transcendental preconditions of human experience. If physics formulates laws that describe the consistency of natural phenomena, speculative physics aims to understand why *these* particular laws or theories, instead of others, describe nature. In other words, speculative physics aims to raise what seem to be empirical (or contingent) laws of nature to the status of rational necessities. In order to do so, speculative physics has to establish demarcation lines between mathematical necessity, transcendental structures, and other kinds of a priori principles. Using Kantian rhetoric, we could say that we apply the term 'speculative' to all knowledge that is not so much occupied with discovering the laws of physical nature as with ascertaining their a priori (neither mathematical nor transcendental) rational necessity. In other words, speculative physics aims to reduce as far as possible the contingency of natural laws, that is, to deduce their empirical validity from a priori principles. For the fact that empirical experience provides very important clues for the seeking of more satisfactory physical theories, for their effective construction and for their a posteriori (provisional) corroboration, does not necessarily mean that it is impossible to unveil retrospectively their own rational necessity. As Schelling writes, 'it is *not, therefore*, that WE KNOW Nature as a priori, but Nature *IS* a priori [...] But if Nature *is* a priori, then it must be possible to recognise it as something that is a priori [...]'.[9] Such a recognition is the main task of speculative physics. Even if the hypothetical limits of human understanding prevented scientists from absolving physics of its experimental basis in empirical experience, this fact cannot be used as a proof of the *essentially* contingent character of the laws of nature. As Hegel clearly states, 'the course of a science's origin and the preliminaries of its construction are one thing, while the science itself is another. In the latter, the former can no longer appear as the foundation of the science; here, the foundation must be the necessity of the Notion.'[10] We can thus state that speculative physics tries to consider the laws of nature in their 'own immanent necessity in accordance with the self-determination of the Notion.'[11] If physics depends upon empirical data, speculative physics aims to unveil the inherent rational necessity of physical theories independently of any experimental justification or corroboration. In this way, speculative physics challenges the unquestioned presupposition according to which physics is *de jure* an empirical science. We could thus say about physical theories what Schelling says about the 'judgements of experience', namely that these theories '[...] become a priori [...] when we become conscious of them as necessary [...]'.[12] The very possibility of ascertaining the rational necessity

9. F. W. J. Schelling, *First Outline of a System of the Philosophy of Nature*, trans. K.R. Peterson (Albany: State University of New York Press, 2004), 198-9.

10. G. W. F. Hegel, *Hegel's Philosophy of Nature. Part two of the Encyclopaedia of the Philosophical Sciences* (1830), trans. A.V. Miller (New York: Oxford University Press, 2004), § 246, 6.

11. Ibid., 6.

12. Schelling, op.cit., 198-9.

of physical theories stems from the postulate according to which '[...] the distinction between a priori and a posteriori judgements is not at all, as many people may have imagined, one originally cleaving to the judgements themselves, but is a distinction made solely with respect to our knowing, and the kind of our knowledge of these judgements, so that every judgement which is merely historical for me – i.e., a judgement of experience – becomes, notwithstanding, an a priori principle as soon as I arrive, whether directly or indirectly, at insight into its internal necessity.'[13]

The very terms of this project go against the main claim of Meillassoux's *After Finitude*, namely that it is possible to demonstrate the necessary contingency of physical laws. The essential point for the present discussion is that Meillassoux simply disqualifies the possibility of *deducing* the laws of nature. Following Hume, he assumes that ('unless we are Hegel')[14] we are unable to discover such a necessity. Consequently, he says, we can only *describe* the *contingent* structural order that we *empirically* find in nature. To justify these claims, Meillassoux identifies natural laws with inductive inferences, obviating in this way the fact that inductive reasoning does not play any role in con-temporary physics. The lack of any logical justification for inductive inferences leads Meillassoux to conclude that the nomological constancy of nature is not grounded on any a priori necessity. We might say that Meillassoux elicits the implicit 'metaphysical' content of the standard thesis according to which the undecidability between two

---

13. Ibid., 198-9.

14. Q. Meillassoux (with R. Brassier, I. H. Grant and G. Harman), 'Speculative Realism' in R. Mackay (ed.), COLLAPSE III (Falmouth: Urbanomic, 2007), 441.

mathematically consistent theories can only be settled by appealing to empirical experience. The physicist's job would be to choose the most accurate mathematical model for describing a completely contingent empirical order. If for Rutherford 'all science is either physics or stamp collecting', according to Meillassoux we must accept that even physics is mere (mathematised) stamp collecting.

The only argument that Meillassoux seems to give, besides the simplistic reduction of physics to inductive inferences, is that the project of demonstrating the necessity of natural laws supposes an infinite regress of reasons that could only be interrupted by a 'metaphysical ' first cause capable of positing itself in virtue of its mere notion (an 'ontological argument'). In other words, since the project of (absolute) knowledge seems to be either an 'infinite task' (Husserl) or a 'metaphysical ' project (Hegel), we must accept the absolute validity of the 'abstract negation' according to which it is simply not possible to understand why nature is regulated by certain laws instead of others. With regard to this second argument, it is worth noting that Meillassoux seems to conflate the formal ontology of possible worlds with the problem of understanding the hypothetical necessity (or contingency) of existence, that is to say of the effective *givenness* of ontic reality. But even if we rejected the possibility of an ontological argument capable of deducing existence from the concept, this would not prevent us from tackling the problem of understanding the rational necessity of physical theories. We could say that a physical theory provides a particular provisional solution to a certain problem. For instance, quantum mechanics is, as we shall argue below, the best solution that we have at the moment to the problem of explaining the objective consistency of nature. In order to understand the rational necessity of quantum mechanics, speculative physics must (among other things) evaluate the unicity of this solution. Are there other possible solutions to the problem of constructing a theory of generic physical objects besides quantum mechanics? To what extent could the physics of a possible world differ from the physics of our world? Even if we could prove the impossibility of an ontological argument, this 'no-go theorem' would not entail that we cannot analyse in rational terms the physical constraints of a possible world and their range of variability. It is also worth remarking that the project of understanding the rational necessity of physical theories defines local problems of scientific knowledge like any other. The answers that speculative physics can provide are of course – as is always the case in science – conditional and partial answers that will evolve within the rhythm of physics and mathematics. It is difficult, then, to understand why the supposed impossibility of providing a satisfactory rational global model for the 'topology' of absolute knowledge (an infinite regress of reasons, an 'axiomatic' well-founded system, a Hegelian suspended circle, etc.) would imply the futility of such a local project.

Far from providing stronger arguments for showing that natural laws do *in fact* lack any rational necessity, Meillassoux's addresses his efforts to the demonstration that this supposed contingency cannot be an epistemological limitation of human understanding, but must rather be an absolute principle. Therefore, Meillassoux's attempt to demonstrate the *absolute* (i.e. non-epistemological) contingency of physical laws relies on the unquestioned presupposition that *in fact* it is not possible to discover any rational necessity. Even if we can decide legitimately to explore the consequences of the *hypothesis* according to which the laws of nature lack any rational a priori necessity, we cannot pretend that we are rationally forced to accept the validity of such an hypothesis, nor that the principle of reason must be abandoned.

Moreover, even if it were true that we are unable to determine the rational necessity of natural laws, this supposed *empirical* fact could not be used as proof of their absolute contingency. If we assume that we cannot discover any rational necessity in physical laws, we have to decide whether this incapability results from the limits of human understanding or from the fact that physical laws are intrinsically contingent. We shall call this alternative Dilemma I. Nevertheless, instead of addressing this dilemma, Meillassoux tries to decide whether the contingency of physical laws is a correlate of human thought or rather an absolute contingency. We shall call this alternative Dilemma II. In order to solve this second dilemma, he argues that facticity cannot be consistently considered a correlate of thought. In this way, he concludes that facticity could only be an 'absolute' facticity. However, the crucial step for passing from the pertinent Dilemma I to the fictive Dilemma II is the deliberate confusion between epistemological criticism (according to which we cannot discover any rational necessity in natural laws because we are not clever enough) and ontological idealism (according to which facticity is a correlate of thought). But the hypothetical existence of impassable limits of human understanding cannot be legitimately identified with the thesis according to which 'to be is to be a correlate of human thought'. In short, to say that an ant will never be able to understand general relativity does not mean that one believes that nature is nothing but a correlate of the ant's 'thought'. If we restore this essential difference between Kant and Berkeley, the inference that leads from our alleged inability to discover any natural necessity to the absolutisation of facticity remains groundless. Indeed, the first step for pushing further the Copernican deanthropomorphisation of science is to reduce the narcissistic illusion of converting a conjectural limit into an absolute principle. We must avoid at all costs being like a congenitally deaf person trying to demonstrate the absolute impossibility of music. Indeed, Hume and Kant were perfectly right to reject any kind of ontological extrapolation of epistemological limitations. Just as Hegel, in turn, was right to deny the unavoidable character of these limitations.

To summarise, we can say that Meillassoux's 'proof' ('for it is indeed a proof', as Badiou tells us)[15] begins with an unquestioned (and probably false) presupposition (namely, that physics cannot discover any rational necessity in physical laws), and proceeds by means of an illegitimate 'deductive' inference (namely, that of absolutising a supposed limitation). Far from defending science from the Ptolemaic counter-revolution that Meillassoux describes so admirably, this narcissistic absolutisation of an inexistent limitation bolsters a certain form of philosophical contempt for scientific rationality. Indeed, the shift from a

15. A. Badiou, 'Preface' in Q. Meillassoux, *After Finitude*, op. cit., vii.

gnoseological statement to a speculative one only serves to absolutise the critical reduction of science. Meillassoux rehearses a paradigmatic gesture of 'Kantian' critique, namely that of 'proving', in purely philosophical terms, what physicists will never be able to do – in this case, understand the rational necessity (or the corresponding ranges of variability) of their own theories. Moreover, this is consistently done without any consideration of physics itself – after all, why should the philosopher consider in detail scientific (ontical) descriptions lacking any rational necessity if he can produce philosophical (ontological) demonstrations? Why would he analyse in accurate terms that of which he speaks – namely, physical theories – if he knows in advance that physics is only a collection of contingent laws that can change without any reason? Why should he try to understand the rational structure of particular physical theories, if the latter will surely be superseded by other theories, as has always been the case in the history of science … ?

It is worth noting that, if speculative physics aims to force as far as possible the conversion of physics into an a priori discipline, the progressive comprehension of the rational necessity of natural laws is already a constitutive part of theoretical physics itself. For example, we could say that, at least to a certain extent, Einstein 'deduced' general relativity by means of purely theoretical reasoning lacking any empirical motivation. Moreover, we can now provide a priori arguments that show why general relativity is a more satisfactory theory than the Newtonian theory of gravity. Indeed, we could say that one of the great lessons of general relativity is that it is necessary to absolve physics from the

467

presupposition of any kind of metaphysical or transcendental (back)ground. More precisely, general relativity permitted scientists to free the description of gravitational phenomena from some of the geometrical 'absolute objects' (as Anderson calls them) presupposed by the Newtonian theory.[16] The replacement of a *metaphysical 'God-given' ground* – the spatiotemporal background – by new physical degrees of freedom – the gravitational field – produced what we could call a *suspended (cor)relational nature*. As a result, the relativity of motion could be generalised beyond uniform motion: Accelerated motion, far from being defined with respect to a presupposed fixed geometrical stage-set, is 'relative' to the gravitational field (which defines the geodesics of space-time). Hence, the dynamics of the resulting extended set of interacting degrees of freedom is relative to nothing but itself. In this sense, general relativity established from within physics a 'speculative' disjunction between the correlational *absolute* and the metaphysical (or transcendental) *ground*. In Hegelian terms, we could say that the absolute absolves itself from any ultimate ground, that is to say from any last unmoving instance subtracted from the immanent mediation conveyed by physical interactions. It is then necessary to establish a sheer distinction between the *principle of reason* and the *principle of the ground* (*Der Satz vom Grund*). The history of physics clearly shows that the principle of reason – that is to say, the practical imperative

16. See J. L. Anderson, *Principles of Relativity Physics* (New York: Academic Press Inc., 1967); M. Friedman, *Foundations of Space-Time Theories. Relativistic Physics and Philosophy of Science* (Princeton: Princeton University Press, 1983); C. Rovelli, *Quantum Gravity* (Cambridge: Cambridge University Press, 2004); and G. Catren, 'Geometric foundations of classical Yang-Mills Theory', *Studies in History and Philosophy of Modern Physics* 39, 2008, 511-31.

of pushing the rational comprehension of the real as far as possible – requires us to abandon the metaphysical principle of the ground. Science does not progress by trying to found itself on a last self-posited metaphysical or transcendental reason, but rather by trying to absolve itself from any kind of presupposed background. At the antipodes of Meillassoux's stance concerning the metaphysical scope of 'correlationism', we can say that general relativity taught us that an absolution with respect to any metaphysical background whatsoever requires us to understand nature in (non-anthropomorphic) correlational terms.

To summarise, let us admit that we now understand the intrinsic theoretical limitations of the Newtonian theory of gravity for explaining gravitational phenomena. This means that it is not contingent that nature is better described by general relativity than by Newtonian mechanics, nor that general relativity has the particular formal structure that it has. This comprehension of the rational necessity of general relativity is not incompatible with the fact that this theory will surely be superseded by a more satisfactory one, in this case a quantum theory of gravity. Such a substitution will probably not be a 'scientific revolution' that will condemn general relativity to death, but rather a kind of dialectical overcoming that will deepen the main lesson of general relativity; namely, that physics has to absolve itself from any kind of metaphysically or transcendentally presupposed background. More generally, we could say that the main task of speculative physics is to elicit the conceptual continuity and the rational necessity that bridges the historical discontinuities opened up by so-called 'scientific revolutions'.

If Meillassoux is right in asserting that the attempt to demonstrate the necessity of laws of nature is basically the Hegelian project, he presupposes dogmatically that such a project cannot be legitimately reactivated. Hegel's (as well as Schelling's) philosophy of nature depends on a *heuristic* (not dogmatic) raising of the principle of reason to a higher power: If physics explains the nomological consistency of nature, we should try to explain in purely rational terms why physical laws have the particular form they have. Such a task cannot be effectively developed by trying to demonstrate general statements about the global validity of the principle of reason, but only by trying to apply it locally to particular scientific theories. If in the end such a project could not be effectively accomplished, it would at least permit us to localise and characterise in rigorous and precise terms the corresponding kernels of irreducible facticity. Hence, we could say that speculative physics aims to discriminate between what is *essentially* contingent and what stems from an a priori necessity. In other words, the speculative conversion of empirical determinations into a priori principles should permit us to identify what is essentially empirical. Indeed, the effective possible obstructions to the principle of reason can only be identified by remaining faithful to this principle as far as possible. As is usually the case in mathematics, the most interesting theoretical configurations emerge as obstacles to the realisation of a certain programme. In other words, it is necessary to be programmatically ambitious in order to fail in a productive way. On the contrary, the a priori general 'proof' that the program is condemned to failure is simply unfruitful. In our particular case, this means that

470

we shouldn't give up on our desire to understand the a priori principles that guarantee the rational consistency of nature. Paraphrasing Badiou, we could adopt the following methodological prescription: 'Méfions-nous des gens trop pressés de consentir [à l'irraison]. [...] J'aime qu'on abdique [le principe de raison] seulement contraint et forcé.'[17]

The proposed definition of speculative physics entails the following methodological consequence: in order to understand the rational necessity of a physical theory it is necessary to comprehend 1) the inherent theoretical deadlock of the preceding theory and 2) how the new theory bypasses this impasse. In other words, the *speculative deduction* of a physical theory aims to identify what we could call its *theoretical surplus value*. This means that speculative physics does not try to demonstrate the *unconditional* rational necessity of a physical theory, but rather to localise its *differential* theoretical superiority. In particular, even if – undoubtedly – quantum mechanics is not the final satisfactory formulation of mechanics, it should be possible to understand *in purely conceptual terms* why it is a more satisfactory theory than classical mechanics. This apparently banal prescription has important consequences. In particular, it challenges the prevailing idea that the difficulties in understanding quantum mechanics contrast with our satisfactory comprehension of classical mechanics. Indeed, our definition of speculative physics implies that our lack of

---

17. In the original quotation Badiou writes 'mi-dit ' (literally 'half-said', but the sense is 'half-hearted' or 'half-measure') and 'Tout' ('Whole') instead of 'irraison' and 'principe de raison' respectively. See A. Badiou, *Théorie du sujet*, (Paris: Editions du Seuil, 1982), 138. ('Let us be wary of those too keen to consent [to 'unreason']. I would rather one abjure [the principle of reason] only when constrained and forced to do so'. *Theory of the Subject*, trans. B. Bosteels [London: Continuum, forthcoming 2009]. Translation modified).

a conceptual understanding of quantum mechanics is a direct consequence of our unsatisfactory comprehension of classical mechanics. More precisely, we have not yet understood precisely what internal theoretical deadlocks in classical mechanics make its quantum sublation necessary. In other words, we do not understand why it is not a contingent empirical fact that the objective consistency of nature is better formalised by quantum mechanics than by classical mechanics. Hence, in order to comprehend the rational necessity of quantum mechanics we must go back to classical mechanics and try to identify its theoretical flaws. According to this perspective, quantum mechanics, instead of inaugurating a radically new non-classical 'paradigm', should be understood as deepening a programme initiated by classical mechanics. In other words, the astonishing success of quantum mechanics shows retrospectively that Newton, Galileo and Kepler were in fact on the right path.

This is the effective methodological prescription we have followed in arriving at the conclusions described below. That is to say, we tried to localise the intrinsic deadlocks of classical mechanics and the corresponding theoretical surplus value of quantum mechanics. Very briefly, in classical mechanics there exists a certain correspondence between each physical quantity of physical systems (such as the position, the momentum or the energy) and the so-called *classical operators*.[18] The important point is that this classical correspondence between physical quantities and classical operators is not entirely satisfactory because it

18. Roughly speaking, an operator is a mathematical entity that generates transformations of other mathematical entities. For example, a derivative is a mathematical operator that transforms functions into other functions.

does not associate *distinct* physical quantities with distinct classical operators (i.e. the classical correspondence is not an isomorphism).[19] It is possible to show that the mathematical formalism of quantum mechanics emerges when one forces this isomorphism. To do so, it is necessary to substitute quantum operators for the classical operators.[20] Hence, the heuristic questions of speculative physics, in the case of quantum mechanics, are the following: Why do operators play such a fundamental role in mechanics? What is the conceptual content of the correspondence between physical quantities and operators? And why should this correspondence be isomorphic?

In order to answer these questions we have to take into account that physics could be defined as a *theory of objects*. Such a theory consists of two parts. In the first place, physics depends on a general formalism, called *mechanics*, for treating any kind of physical objects, that is to say for studying their properties, their symmetries, their temporal evolution, and so on. Secondly, there are different particular kinds of objects (particles, fields, molecules, waves, astrophysical systems, etc.) that can be treated by means of this general formalism. The different branches of physics

19. In technical terms, physical quantities are given by functions on the phase space, whereas classical operators are given by so-called Hamiltonian vector fields: See R. Abraham and J. E. Marsden, *Foundations of Mechanics*, Second Ed., (Cambridge: Addison-Wesley Publishing Company, 1978).

20. It is worth noting that this characterisation of the relationship between classical and quantum mechanics is not the usual one. In fact the proposed interpretation of quantum mechanics stems from an analysis of the so-called geometric quantisation formalism, due mainly to the seminal works of J.-M. Souriau and B. Kostant in the early seventies (see J.-M. Souriau, *Structure of Dynamical Systems. A Symplectic View of Physics* [Cambridge: Birkhäuser Boston, 1997] and J.-L. Brylinski, *Loop Spaces, Characteristic Classes and Geometric Quantisation, Progr. Math.* 107 [Boston: Birkhäuser Boston Inc., 1993]).

result from the application of the general formalism to the study of these different particular systems. If mechanics is a general formalism that can be used to study *any* kind of physical system, it could be tempting to define mechanics as a formal ontology of generic physical objects. By *formal ontology* we mean the study of generic determinations that do not depend on the particular properties of any particular (kind of) object. In Kantian terms, we could say that mechanics is a formalisation of the structure of the (non-transcendental) generic object = X. The important point is that, contrary to a widespread idea, classical mechanics does not provide a satisfactory definition of physical objects. It is then possible to show that quantum mechanics permits an overcoming of the classical obstacles to the formulation of such a definition. As we shall see, the definition of physical objects depends essentially on the correspondence between physical quantities and operators. Therefore, the complete claim is that quantum mechanics, *unlike classical mechanics*, is a consistent formal ontology of generic physical objects. Indeed, and as we shall see, quantum mechanics seems to provide a possible physical solution to a transcendental problem, namely the problem of understanding the constitution of physical objects by means of a synthesis of the manifold of sensible (or experimental) intuition. As opposed to Kant's or Husserl's solution, quantum mechanics shows that the intrinsic consistency of physical objects does not require any transcendental – i.e. (inter)subjective – constitution. As we shall see, this solution pushes the Copernican deanthropomorphisation of physics to a further limit: rather than the transcendental subject, it is the object itself that generates the synthetic operations which unify the phenomenological manifold of its aspects or profiles. In Kantian terms, one might say that quantum mechanics demonstrates how to make physics conform to the quantum nature of self-constituted objects, and not the objects to our (all too human) faculty of classical intuition.

III. Phenomenology of a Quantum Elephant

Physical experience is not a chaotic swarm of disconnected empirical data. As Whitehead cleverly observed: 'Sometimes we see an elephant, and sometimes we do not'.[21] In other words, physical reality decomposes itself in different objective configurations that can be identified and recognised. We should add that properly speaking we can only see particular phases, aspects or profiles of the elephant. As Lacan says, 'l'être se présente, se présente toujours, de par-être'.[22] By turning the elephant around an axis (or, equivalently, by moving around the elephant ourselves) we can observe *different* phases of the *same* elephant. This means that there is a defining kernel (that we could call the elephant's *quiddity*) that remains invariant through the modifications of its modes of phenomenological presentation. We can thus define an object as a physical configuration characterised by a certain set of *objective properties* that allow virtual observers to recognise the object in spite of the variations of its phases. As Badiou says: '[...] par «objet» il faut entendre ce qui compte pour un dans l'apparaître, ou

---

21. A. N. Whitehead, *Process and Reality* (New York: The Free Press, 1978), 4.

22. J. Lacan, *Le Séminaire*, livre XX (Paris: Editions du Seuil, 1975), 44 ('being presents itself, always presents itself, by para-being.' J. Lacan, J.-A. Miller (ed.), *On Feminine Sexuality, The Limits of Love and Knowledge, 1972-3*, trans. B. Fink [New York: Norton, 1998], 45. Note that the English translation does not preserve Lacan's play on words 'par-être'/'paraître' ['para-being'/'to appear']).

ce qui autorise à parler de cet être-là comme étant inflexible-
ment «lui-même».'[23] This means that the objective properties
that define the object cannot change under the transformations that permit observation of its different phases (for
instance, turning the elephant around an axis). Henceforth
we shall call such transformations *phase transformations* of
the object. Hence, we can assert that objective properties
must be *invariant* under phase transformations. We can thus
redefine an object as a set of invariant objective properties
that manifests itself through a phenomenological multiplicity of phases. This means that there is no entity without
identity (Quine), nor without different phases (Husserl).
In Frege's terms, we could say that the same reference
(*Bedeutung*) can have different senses (*Sinn*), that is to say
different modes of presentation. For example, the morning
star and the evening star are nothing but different modes of
presentation of the same object.

In this way, the manifold of sensible intuition
decomposes itself in sheaves of aspects orbiting around
sets of invariant objective properties. As Kant and Husserl
noted, the objective consistency of nature requires an
operational function capable of synthesizing the multiplicity of phases of a given object. Therefore, a satisfactory
theory of physical objects should be able to explain the relationships between the *invariant objective properties* that define
the *quiddity* of the object, the *phenomenological multiplicity of its
phases*, and the *synthetic operations* that guarantee its objective
unity. According to the transcendental tradition, the

---

23. A. Badiou, *Logiques des mondes*. (Paris: Seuil, 2006), 205 (' [...] by "object" we must
understand that which counts as one within appearing, or that which authorises us to
speak of this being-there as inflexibly being "itself"', A. Badiou, *Logics of Worlds*, trans.
A. Toscano [London/New York: Continuum, forthcoming 2009], 193).

unifying synthesis is performed by the subjective faculties. In Husserl's terms, the 'hyletic' multiplicity of sensible intuition becomes a 'noematic' objective unity thanks to the 'noetic' functions of synthesis carried out by the transcendental ego. In other words, the subjective functions of synthesis posit, on the basis of bundles of sense data lacking any intrinsic consistency, the ideal objective unities that compose human experience.

The main task of what we could call a speculative theory of physical objects is to explain the objective consistency of nature without appealing to a transcendental synthesis. As Whitehead says: 'We are concerned only with Nature [...] and not with the synthesis of the knower with the known. [...] Accordingly none of our perplexities as to Nature will be solved by having recourse to the consideration that there is a mind knowing it. Our theme is the coherence of the known [...]'.[24] Our main claim is that, according to quantum mechanics, it is the object itself that generates the synthetic operations that unify its different phases. In other words, we shall transfer the constitutive capabilities from the subject to the object. As we shall see, the utilisation of operators in mechanics is a direct consequence of the necessity of (self-)synthesizing the multiplicity of the object's phases. Hence, operators play a central role in mechanics because mechanics is nothing but a formal theory of generic physical objects, that is to say a theory that explains how the multiple phases of an object are mutually related by means of certain synthetic operations that leave its objective properties invariant. The important point is that a satisfactory

---

24. A. N. Whitehead, *An Enquiry Concerning the Principles of Natural Knowledge* (New York: Dover, 1919), vii.

interpretation of mechanics as a theory of generic physical objects is only possible within the framework of quantum mechanics. The theoretical surplus value of quantum mechanics relies on the fact that the classical definition of operators does not permit a satisfactory definition of physical objects.

We shall now present in conceptual terms the ontology of generic physical objects that can be extracted from the formalism of quantum mechanics. As we said before, an object is a kind of 'projector' (or 'radiator') of phases, aspects or profiles whose essential *quiddity* is given by a persisting kernel of invariant objective properties. The set of invariant objective properties of an object will be called from now on the *eidos* ε of the object. In general, it is possible to perform different kinds of phase transformations in order to observe the multiple phases of an object. Borrowing Husserl's terminology, we could also call the phase transformations 'eidetic variations'. A set of phases connected by means of a given kind of phase transformation (such as, for instance, rotations around a given axis) will be called an *orbit of phases*. In Figure 1, the different lateral phases of the elephant (whose name is Colin) can be observed by rotating Colin around a vertical axis. By definition, these different lateral phases belong to the same orbit of phases. Equivalently, let's suppose that the phenomenological observer Jean-Sol Partre is orbiting around Colin in a plane perpendicular to the vertical axis. By doing so, Jean-Sol Partre will observe the phases of Colin that belong to the orbit of lateral phases.

Phase transformations are 'phantasmatic' acts that do not produce any *objective* effect. Therefore, phase transformations

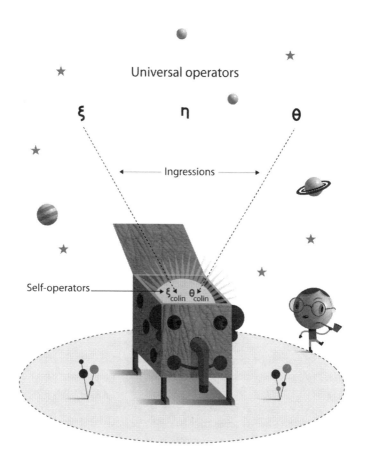

Figure 1. Jean-Sol Partre observes elephant

have to be distinguished from transformations that change the object *objectively*, that is to say that change the object into *another* object. For instance, the transformation that breaks an object into two objects is not a phase transformation of the former. These kinds of transformation will be called *objective transformations*. In this way, there are two kinds of transformations that can be performed on an object, namely the *objective transformations* that objectively transform the object into another object, and the *phase transformations* (or 'eidetic variations') that interchange the different phases of the object without modifying it objectively.

Since phase transformations only interchange the different phases of an object, the objective properties that define the object are necessarily invariant under phase transformations. In Husserl's terms, the object's *eidos* is composed of the invariants under eidetic variations. In order to stress that phase transformations transform the object into itself, they will also be called *automorphisms* of the object. With this terminology, we recover Weyl's well-known characterisation: 'objectivity means invariance with respect to the group of automorphisms.'[25] It is worth stressing that *phase transformations* (that interchange the phases of the object), *eidetic variations* (that permit the definition of the invariant objective *eidos*) and *automorphisms* (that transform the object into itself) are interchangeable terms. These three terms, however, emphasise different aspects of the same notion. The fundamental distinction is the distinction between phase transformations on the one hand and objective transformations on the other.

---

25. H. Weyl, *Symmetry* (Princeton: Princeton University Press, 1952), 132. An analysis of the relationship between group theory and perception can be found in E. Cassirer, 'The Concept of Group and the Theory of Perception', *Philosophy and Phenomenological Research* Vol. 5, No. 1 (1944), 1-36.

It is now necessary to specify more precisely what we understand by objective properties. To do so, we have to take into account that the characterisation of objective properties as *invariants* under eidetic variations does not suffice for providing a satisfactory definition of objective properties. The problem has been clearly stated by Nozick in the following terms: 'The notion of invariance under transformations cannot (without further supplementation) be a complete criterion of the objectivity of facts, for its application depends upon a selection of *which* transformations something is to be invariant under.'[26] In other words, there is no general prescription for determining which transformations are needed in order to define the invariant objective properties of a physical object. Therefore, the eidetic invariants depend on the election of a certain group of eidetic variations.[27] If we consider too many transformations as eidetic variations, the 'object' will have no eidetic invariants. Every property of the object will be nothing but a phase with no objective value. Hence, the 'object' will be a phenomenological set of phases without any invariant identity. If, on the contrary, we consider too few transformations as eidetic variations, the object will have no phases. This means that every property of the object will be an objective invariant. Hence, the 'object' will be an identity without phases.

26. R. Nozick, 'Invariance and Objectivity', *Proceedings and Addresses of the American Philosophical Association* Vol. 72, No. 2 (1998), 21-48. In Weyl's terms, 'Reality may not always give a clear answer to the question what the actual group of automorphisms is [...]', H. Weyl, op.cit., 132.

27. Evidently, we cannot solve this problem in a circular way by stating that the automorphisms of an object are the transformations that leave the objective properties invariant.

In fact, quantum mechanics provides a very elegant solution to this indetermination. As we shall see, the quantum definition of physical objects furnishes the required 'further supplementation' by stating that the object's automorphisms are induced by the very objective properties of the object. In other words, each objective property defines a particular kind of phase transformation. Hence, not only is an objective property invariant under all of the object's automorphisms; it also induces a particular kind of automorphism. Far from being a circular characterisation, we shall show that Heisenberg's uncertainty principle is a direct consequence of this definition.

In order to formalise this idea, we shall propose a definition of physical objects by means of two fundamental postulates. But first we must introduce some terminology. In Platonic terms, we shall say that a physical object realises (or participates in) a certain number of universal operators (or 'ideas') in a way that depends on the object. Or we may alternatively say, in Whiteheadian terms, that a universal operator (or 'eternal object') makes *ingression* into the object in an *object-dependent way*. The ingression of a universal operator into an object defines what we shall call a *self-operator* of the object.[28] As we shall see below, the self-operators of an object perform the self-synthesis of its

---

28. It is worth noting that the language of universal entities (and their multiple possible ingressions) is borrowed from category theory (see S. Mac Lane, *Categories for the Working Mathematician* [New York: Springer-Verlag, 1997]). For example, an element a of a set M can be redefined in terms of the so-called *characteristic function* χa from the singleton $\{*\}$ (which is a terminal object of the category of sets) to the set M. By definition, the characteristic function χa sends the singleton $\{*\}$ to the element a (i.e. $\chi a : \{*\} \rightarrow a$). In other words, any element x of M can be defined by means of a particular 'ingression' χx of the 'universal element' $\{*\}$. In our case, the universal operators are given by elements of a Lie algebra, whereas the self-operators that result from their ingression are the so-called quantum operators.

phenomenological multiplicity of phases. In Figure 1, Colin participates in the universal operators ξ and θ. The ingressions of these universal operators define the self-operators ξ_{colin} and θ_{colin}. On the contrary, Colin does not participate in the 'idea' η. By means of this Platonic terminology, we want to convey the idea that an object can be characterised by the way in which it participates in a certain number of universal ideas. Hence, in order to define the *quiddity* of an object we have to specify (1) which are the universal ideas realised by the object and (2) how these ideas make ingression into the object. The important point is that two different objects can realise different universal ideas and/or realise differently the same universal idea. In figurative terms, we could say that an elephant and a giraffe are different because they realise different ideas, and that two elephants are different because they realise differently the same idea. For example, in Figure 2, Colin and the giraffe (whose name is Chloé) participate differently in the same universal operator ξ. This means that the self-operators ξ_{colin} and ξ_{chloe} that result from the corresponding ingressions are different. On the other hand, Colin realises a universal operator that is not realised by Chloé, namely the operator θ. In turn, Chloé realises a universal operator that is not realised by Colin, namely the operator η.

We have thus far proposed two alternative ways of characterizing the *quiddity* of an object, namely (1) by means of its invariant objective properties (the 'Husserlian' definition) and (2) by specifying how the object participates in a certain number of universal 'ideas" (the 'Platonic' definition). The first postulate of the quantum theory of physical objects unifies these two ways of defining the *quiddity* of an object:

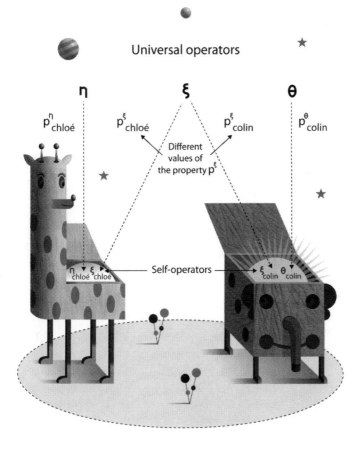

Figure 2. Elephant meets giraffe

Postulate ♠: an objective property of an object is a particular numerical value that specifies how the object realises a certain universal operator.

For example, two objects that differ in the value of their energy realise differently the same universal operator. In Figure 2, Colin and Chloé realise differently the idea ξ. According to postulate ♠, there exists a property p^ξ such that each possible numerical value of p^ξ defines a different ingression of the universal operator ξ. In turn, these different ingressions define different self-operators. Since both Colin and Chloé realise the universal operator ξ, the quantity p^ξ defines objective properties of both of them. Since Colin and Chloé realise differently the universal operator ξ, they are characterised by different values of the quantity p^ξ (namely p^ξ_{colin} and p^ξ_{chloe} respectively).

We could say that postulate ♠ articulates and formalises the relationship between the 'Platonic' universal *ideas* and the 'Husserlian' *eidos* of particular objects. Indeed, the object's *eidos* (i.e. the set of numerical values of its objective properties) specifies how the object participates in a certain number of universal 'ideas'. Reciprocally, the ingression of certain universal ideas defines the *eidos* of the object. More precisely, the ingression of the universal ideas (ξ, θ, ...) into an object like Colin defines a set of particular numerical values (p^ξ_{colin}, p^θ_{colin}, ...) of the quantities (p^ξ, p^θ, ...). These particular values constitute the objective properties of Colin. Hence, the set of these values defines Colin's *eidos*, that is to say the essential *quiddity* that allows us to identify and to recognise Colin through its different modes of presentation.

According to our terminology, the ingression of an universal operator ξ into Colin defines a self-operator ξ_{colin} of Colin. By definition, an operator is a mathematical entity that generates transformations. In particular, the self-operator ξ_{colin} generates transformations of Colin. The second postulate of the quantum theory of physical objects specifies the nature of these transformations:

Postulate ♣: The transformations generated by a self-operator of an object are phase transformations (or automorphisms) of the object.

In other words, a transformation generated by one of the object's self-operators is not an *objective* transformation of the object into another object, but rather a phase transformation that does not modify the object's *quiddity*. This means that the self-operators of an object generate all the possible phantasmatic transformations of the object into itself, that is to say all the different non-trivial declinations of its identity. The self-operators unfold the transformations which, without modifying the object's *quiddity*, permit the observation of its different phases. We could thus say that the self-operators of an object are the generators of its phenomenological presentation.

In order to fix ideas, let's consider again the case of Colin. Let's suppose that, as in Figure 1, Colin participates in the universal operator ξ. According to postulate ♠, there exists a quantity p^ξ whose particular numerical value p^ξ_{colin} specifies how the universal operator ξ makes ingression into Colin. This ingression defines the self-operator ξ_{colin}. Let's suppose now that the self-operator ξ_{colin} generates rotations around the vertical axis. According to postulate ♣, these virtual rotations around the vertical axis are nothing but phase transformations of Colin. This means that the self-operator ξ_{colin} generates the sequence of Colin's phases that Jean-Sol Partre will observe if he orbits around Colin as in Figure 1. In other words, the phase transformations generated by the self-operator ξ_{colin} unfold the orbit of *lateral* phases of Colin. In this way, the numerical value p^{ξ}_{colin} of the objective property p^{ξ} defines the self-operator ξ_{colin} (postulate ♠), this self-operator being the generator of one kind of phase transformation of Colin (postulate ♣). We shall sometimes summarise these two postulates by saying that the objective property p^{ξ}_{colin} induces a certain kind of phase transformations of Colin. In particular, the objective property p^{ξ}_{colin} specifies how Colin will appear when he rotates around the vertical axis (or when Jean-Sol Partre rotates around him). In this way, each objective property induces an orbit of phases corresponding to a particular mode of presentation of Colin (such as, for instance, rotations around an axis, translations along an axis, temporal evolutions, etc.).

We can now summarise the two proposed postulates by means of the following definition of physical objects:

Definition: An object is a physical configuration that can be completely characterised by specifying the numerical values of the objective properties that induce all the object's automorphisms.

According to this definition, the object's *eidos* (i.e. the set of its objective properties) plays a twofold role, namely it defines the invariant *quiddity* of the object and it induces the object's automorphisms. These automorphisms unfold the different orbits of phases of the object, that is to say the multiple sets of aspects that the object offers to all possible virtual observers. Hence, the imbrication between these two roles can be summarised by stating that *the object's invariant* quiddity *generates its phenomenalisation*. We can also describe this sort of 'speculative theorem' in the following terms: On the one hand, the identification of an object requires an invariant eidetic kernel. On the other hand, the phenomenalisation of an object requires phantasmatic acts, that is to say phase transformations that permit the observation of its different phases without producing any objective effect. Quantum mechanics establishes a link between the 'essence' and the 'appearance' by stating that the *eidos* of an object is the inducer of its phantasmatic acts.

In order to provide an imaginary schematisation of the relationship between the invariant *eidos* and the object's phenomenalisation, we could also appeal to Brion Gysin's *dream machine*. For, in fact, the following stroboscopic experience is at the origin of Partre's persisting hallucinations. Let's consider for instance the orbit of Colin's lateral phases. As we said before, this orbit of phases is generated by the self-operator ξ_{colin}. Let's represent this self-operator as an inner source of yellow light. Let's suppose now that each lateral phase is translucent and that ξ_{colin} is the unique source of light. Thanks to this 'eidetic' generator of light, Jean-Sol Partre can observe the markings on Colin's skin. If Jean-Sol Partre orbits around Colin, he will observe the different patterns of markings of each lateral phase. However, the light that passes through each translucent phase will always be yellow. Hence, the colour of the eidetic radiator that allows Jean-Sol Partre to observe the orbit of lateral phases is invariant under the corresponding eidetic variations. In other words, the colour of the eidetic source that generates the lateral phenomenalisation of Colin is an invariant objective property.

Auyang has already remarked that the 'representation-transformation-invariance structure' that allows the definition of objective properties as invariants under transformations between different representations of a physical system is still valid in quantum mechanics.[29] Nevertheless, the proposed definition of physical objects goes further than the usual characterisation of objective properties as group invariants. Indeed, this definition states *also* that the automorphisms that define the objective invariants are induced by the objective properties themselves. Therefore, we could say that quantum mechanics completes the usual characterisation of objectivity and provides for the first time a satisfactory definition of physical objects.

IV. PACHYDERMAL NOMADOLOGY

'[...] comment l'objet qui se meut serait-il en un point de son trajet?'

H. Bergson, *La pensée et le mouvant*[30]

We shall now try to establish more explicitly the relationship between the previous definition of physical objects and quantum mechanics. In fact, it is possible to show that none of the proposed postulates can be implemented in

---

29. See S.Y. Auyang, *How is Quantum Field Theory Possible?* (New York: Oxford University Press, 1995), Chapter Five.

30. Paris: PUF, 1938, 158 ('How could the moving object be in a point of its trajectory passage?', H. Bergson, *The Creative Mind: An Introduction to Metaphysics*, trans. M.L. Andison [New York: Dover, 2007], 143).

the framework of classical mechanics;[31] whereas, on the contrary, quantum mechanics can be considered a satisfactory formal implementation of the proposed definition of physical objects. In particular, we shall now show that Heisenberg's uncertainty principle is a direct consequence of this definition. Roughly speaking, we could say that Heisenberg's uncertainty principle is a formalisation of the virtuous circle that results from the intertwining of objective and non-objective properties.

According to the proposed definition, an objective property is an invariant quantity that induces a particular kind of phase transformation of the object. In turn, a property is objective (i.e. invariant) if it does not change when the object is acted upon by a phase transformation. Hence, objective properties satisfy two conditions, namely (1) they are invariant under all the phase transformations of the object and (2) they induce a particular kind of phase transformations of the object. We can thus conclude that an objective property of an object has to be invariant under the phase transformations *induced by all the objective properties of the same object*. If a property is invariant under the phase transformations induced by another property, we shall say that these properties are *commensurable*. Let's consider for example an object defined by the *eidos* $\varepsilon = \{p, l\}$, where by definition p and l are objective properties of the object. This means that the numerical values p and l characterise completely the object's invariant *quiddity*. The standard definition of objectivity requires that the value of each objective property be invariant under a

---

31. A technical presentation can be found in G. Catren, 'On Classical and Quantum Objectivity', *Foundations of Physics* 38, 5, 2008 470-87.

certain group of eidetic variations. Nevertheless – as we have explained above – this standard definition does not specify *which* group of transformations are to be used for defining the objective invariants. The proposed definition of physical objects bypasses this flaw by stating that the eidetic variations are induced by the objective properties themselves. Therefore, each objective property has to be invariant under the eidetic variations induced by the other objective properties of the same object. The phase transformations induced by an objective property p will be denoted δ_p. In particular, if p and l are objective properties of an object, then they have to satisfy $\delta_p l = 0$ (i.e. l has to be invariant under the phase transformations induced by p) and $\delta_l p = 0$ (i.e. p has to be invariant under the phase transformations induced by l).[32] In general, the phase transformations induced by an objective property of an object cannot modify the other objective properties of the same object. This fact imposes a restrictive condition on the *eidos* of an object. Indeed, the *eidos* cannot be an arbitrary collection of objective properties. Each objective property has to satisfy the condition of being invariant under the phase transformations induced by all the others. This requirement constitutes what we shall call the *clause of self-consistency of the eidos*. This clause states that the *eidos* of an object can only be composed of commensurable properties.

---

32. Of course, the objective properties p and l have to be also invariant under the phase transformations induced by themselves. In other terms, they have to satisfy $\delta_p p = 0$ and $\delta_l l = 0$. Nevertheless, it can be shown that these conditions are trivially satisfied by any property. The non-trivial conditions stem from the invariance of an objective property under the phase transformations induced by the other objective properties of the same object.

In particular, if a certain property is modified by the phase transformations induced by an objective property belonging to the object's *eidos*, then the former cannot also be an objective property of the same object. This statement can be considered the conceptual translation of Heisenberg's uncertainty principle. In particular, it is possible to show that the momentum p is a property that induces transformations in the position q (and vice versa). Hence, if the momentum p is an objective property in the object's *eidos*, then the position q cannot also be an objective property of the same object. The position q is rather a phase of the object that changes when the object is acted upon by the phase transformations induced by p. In other words, since the position q and the momentum p are incommensurable, they cannot be both objective properties of the same object.[33]

We could say that Einstein was literally right in thinking about quantum objects in terms of dice. Indeed, what God would obtain if he threw a die is not an objective property of the die, but rather one of its faces. And the important point is that a die's face is a die's *phase*. Asking after the objective position q of a quantum elephant with an objective momentum p is as nonsensical as looking for the objective (or privileged) face of a die. Nevertheless, even if a die has

---

33. For the sake of simplicity we have only considered the case of an object with a well-defined momentum p and a completely undetermined position q. The reciprocal case – a well-defined position with an undetermined momentum– is completely analogous. In the general case, both the position and the momentum are subject to certain indeterminacies. In fact, the flexibility of quantum mechanics' formalism makes it possible to define physical objects characterised by properties which are neither objective properties nor phases, but rather a mixture of both. In these cases, both q and p are unsharp objective properties of the object. The resulting subtle equilibrium between unsharp objective properties and unsharp non-objective phases is formally governed by Heisenberg's uncertainty principle.

no objective face, it will show a particular face when thrown. Obviously, this does not mean that the result obtained was the objective but unknown face of the die. Analogously, even if a quantum elephant with an objective momentum p has no objective position q, it will appear in a particular position q_1 if a measurement of the position is performed. This does not mean that q_1 was the objective but unknown position of the elephant. Neither does it mean that the garden where Colin carelessly wanders splits in parallel paths, such that in each path Colin is in a well-defined position. In any case, a stampede of elephants in a quantum casino will never crush the Copernican revolution: Colin's delocalisation is intrinsic. It cannot be bypassed by appealing to the supposed limitations stemming from a transcendental constitution of objectivity, nor by forking the paths of his garden. Like the faces of a die, the different possible positions q_i of Colin are mere phases with no objective value. In this way, even a single quantum elephant has '[...] une onde [or a die – GC] associée comme flux qui définit l'espace coexistant de ses présences.'[34] We might say that Colin is a deterritorialized quantum elephant with no objective position. Dispersed across the garden, Colin's 'method of resistance [is] always just to keep moving – seeking, not a place to hide out, secure and fixed, but a state of dynamic ambiguity about where [he] might be any given moment, along the lines of Heisenberg's uncertainty principle.'[35]

34. G. Deleuze and F. Guattari, *L'Anti-Œdipe (Capitalisme et schizophrénie 1)* (Paris: Minuit, 1972), 333 ('[...] an associated wave as a flow that defines the coexisting space of its presences.', G. Deleuze and F. Guattari, *Anti-Oedipus*, trans. R. Hurley, M. Seem and H.R.Lane [Minneapolis: Minnesota University Press, 1983], 280).

35. T. Pynchon, Introduction to Jim Dodge's *Stone Junction* (New York: Grove Press, 1998).

V. QUANTUM CASINO

According to the proposed definition of physical objects, the measurement of a quantum object can be understood as a throw of a die. This means that in general the obtained result will not be an objective property of the object, but rather one of its non-objective phases. Nevertheless, there is a crucial difference between quantum objects and ordinary dice, namely that the former can be superposed.[36] According to our interpretational framework, quantum superposition stems from the intuitive fact that an object is a superposition of phases, aspects or profiles. The important difference is that in quantum mechanics the superposed phases of an object are in turn quantum objects. As in set theory, where a set is a collection of sets, a quantum object is a superposition of phases that are in turn quantum objects. Hence, the superposition of quantum objects produces a new quantum object such that each term of the superposition is one of its phases.

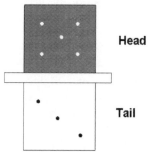

Figure 3. Quantum coin

36. Another significant difference is that the only phenomenological access to a quantum object is by 'throwing' it. In other terms, a quantum object is like a die whose phases can only be observed if one throws the die.

This difference between ordinary dice and quantum objects opens new phenomenological (or experimental) possibilities. For example, we could schematise a particular quantum object as a coin $\bigcirc$ such that each of its two phases is in turn a die (see Figure 3). Let's denote these two dice as the die-head $\blacksquare_{head}$ and the die-tail $\square_{tail}$. The object $\bigcirc$, then, is a superposition of the objects $\blacksquare_{head}$ and $\square_{tail}$. Let's write this superposition as $\bigcirc = \blacksquare_{head} + \square_{tail}$.

Let's suppose now that in our casino there are two tables, namely a table for playing with coins and a table for playing with dice. So, what can we do with the object $\bigcirc = \blacksquare_{head} + \square_{tail}$ in such a casino? First, we can play heads or tails in the table for coins. Let's suppose that, by doing so, we obtain the phase $\blacksquare_{head}$. Since the obtained phase is in turn a die, we can go on playing and throw the die $\blacksquare_{head}$ on the table for dice. By doing so, we will obtain a number between 1 and 6. The important question is now the following: Can we play with the object $\bigcirc = \blacksquare_{head} + \square_{tail}$ *directly* on the table for dice, that is to say without having initially played heads or tails? The formalism of quantum mechanics shows that this is in fact possible. In order to visualise such a possibility, we have to modify the imaginary representation of the object $\bigcirc$. Instead of considering it as a coin with a die in each phase, we can represent it as a sort of 'hyperdie': We can literally superpose the two dice by putting the die $\blacksquare_{head}$ within the die $\square_{tail}$, such that their vertices are rigidly linked (see Figure 4). If we now throw the hyperdie $\bigcirc$ directly onto the table for dice, the quantum formalism shows that the probability for obtaining a given number between 1 and 6 depends on the relative orientation (or 'relative phase') between the two dice. For example, the two phases with the

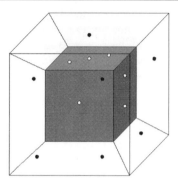

Figure 4. Hyperdie

number 1 might be (among other possibilities) 'in phase' (i.e. aligned) or 'out of phase' (i.e. opposed). If they are in phase, then the number 1 is a possible result of the throw of the hyperdie ('constructive interference'). If they are out of phase, then the number 1 is not a possible result of the throw of the hyperdie ('destructive interference'). In any case, it is meaningless to ask from which die the obtained number comes from.

It is worth noting that a rotation of the hyperdie as a whole (i.e. without modifying the relative orientation between the two dice) is a phase transformation of the hyperdie. Whereas if we modify the relative orientation between the two dice that compose the hyperdie, we will obtain a new hyperdie characterised by another probability distribution. For example, phases that were out of phase might be in phase after the transformation. Hence, a change in the 'relative phase' is not a phase transformation, but rather an objective transformation.

We have only considered thus far the superposition of quantum objects. Nevertheless, in *quantum design*, the construction of objects depends on two fundamental operations, namely the superposition '+' and the tensor product '⊗'. As we have explained above, the superposition '+' permits the construction of a new object by superposing different phases (which are in turn quantum objects). Hence, the terms of the superposition constitute the different 'phenomenological' profiles of the new object. On the other hand, the tensor product '⊗' permits the construction of a single phase by 'pasting' different objects. Whereas the superposition '+' combines two objects as different phases of another object, the tensor product '⊗' combines them as different parts of the same phase.[37]

VI. THE QUANTUM ESSENCE OF MANIFESTATION

This quantum theory of physical objects allows us to resist to the Ptolemaic counter-revolution on two different fronts: First, it shows that quantum mechanics provides a *realistic* and *complete* description of physical objects. The fact that the position q and the momentum p cannot be both objective properties of the same object does not mean that the very *quiddity* of the object depends on the observing subject, on the measurement device or on the experimental context. This means that it is no longer necessary to appeal to a 'transcendental' argument to explain why it is not possible to gain access to all the objective information that defines an object. Hence, quantum mechanics cannot be considered an intra-scientific formalisation of a

---

37. The mixing of these two operations is at the origin of so-called quantum entanglement. For example, the object $\psi = \alpha \otimes \phi + \beta \otimes \phi$ results from the superposition of two phases, namely $\alpha \otimes \phi$ and $\beta \otimes \phi$. These phases are obtained by 'pasting' the objects α and ϕ on the one hand and β and ϕ on the other one.

transcendental limitation of physical knowledge. As
Žižek says, the uncertainty principle 'is thus profoundly
"Hegelian": what first appeared to be an epistemological
obstacle turns out to be a property of the thing itself.'[38]
Indeed, the uncertainty principle is nothing but a signature
of the intertwining between the invariant *eidos* that defines
an object and its experimental phenomenalisation. If the
momentum p is an objective property of an object, then the
position q is necessarily, like the face of a die, a phase with
no objective value. In consequence, the classical description
of physical objects, which includes both q and p, is over-
determined. This means that in classical mechanics non-
objective properties are wrongly considered objective. We
can thus conclude that, *unlike classical mechanics*, quantum
mechanics describes all the intrinsic objective properties of
observer-independent objects.[39]

But not only does this interpretation allow us to contest
the Ptolemaic reductions of quantum mechanics, but also
suggests, secondly, a possible intra-physical solution to a
transcendental problem, namely the problem of explaining
the constitution of physical objects from the manifold of
sensible (i.e. experimental) intuition. In Kantian terms,
we can say that the unification in the representations of a

38. S. Žižek, *The Indivisible Remainder* (London: Verso, 1996), 211.

39. It is worth remarking that this point was recognised by Deleuze and Guattari in
very accurate terms: '[...] even in quantum physics, Heisenberg's demon does not
express the impossibility of measuring both the speed and the position of a particle
on the grounds of a subjective interference of the measure with the measured, but
it measures exactly an objective state of affairs [...] Subjectivist interpretations of
thermodynamics, relativity, and quantum physics manifest the same inadequacies.
Perspectivism, or scientific relativism, is never relative to a subject: it constitutes not
a relativity of truth, but, on the contrary, a truth of the relative [...] Of course, a well-
defined observer extracts everything that it can, everything that can be extracted in
the corresponding system.', G. Deleuze and F. Guattari, *What is Philosophy?*, trans. G.
Burchell and H. Tomlinson [London: Verso, 1994], 129-30.

physical object no longer requires the unity of transcendental apperception in the synthesis of these representations. The quantum theory of objects shows that the 'counting-as-one' of the phenomenological multiplicity of the object's phases is provided by the very *eidos* of the object. Thus the function of synthesis is anchored in the eidetic kernel that defines the *quiddity* of the object. More precisely, the self-synthesis of an object is performed by its self-operators. Each self-operator generates one kind of automorphisms of the object, that is to say a particular sequence of non-trivial 'phantasmatic' transformations of the object into itself. Each sequence of automorphisms connects the different phases belonging to the same orbit of phases. In turn, the self-operators are defined by the objective properties that constitute the object's *eidos*. In this way, the *eidos* that defines the invariant 'essence' of the object induces at the same time the synthetic functions that guarantee the objective consistency of its phenomenological manifold of aspects. In Hegelian terms, we could say that it is the essence of the essence to generate the manifestation of the object. The *essence* of the object is the projector of its *appearance*. Thus the objective consistency of the manifold of experimental intuition is not noetically constituted by the transcendental subject (or the experimental context), but rather induced by the 'eternal objects' that make ingression into nature.

Errancies of the Human:
French Philosophies of Nature and the
Overturning of the Copernican Revolution

Alberto Gualandi

1. THE 'FRENCH ANOMALY' AND THE RADICALISATION OF THE COPERNICAN REVOLUTION

It is customarily maintained that the Copernican revolution dealt a sort of originary blow to the narcissistic human self-image that had endured for two thousand years. According to Freud, after Copernicus man would have ceased to position himself at the centre of the universe; after Darwin, to position himself at the centre of living nature; and after the psychoanalytic revolution, to position himself at the centre of himself.[1] Within the horizon of contemporary philosophy, it is perhaps the French philosophies of the sixties which radicalised, in a materialist direction, this critique of the anthropocentrism cosubstantial with the Western metaphysical tradition, supplementing Freud's interpretation of the Copernican revolution with the lessons drawn from the other 'masters of suspicion', Marx and Nietzsche.

---

1. 'A Difficulty in the Path of Psychoanalysis' in *Introductory Lectures on Psychoanalysis* (London: Penguin Books, 1991), 325-6.

The radicality of this critique surpassed that of other national traditions of thought, for it did not stop at recognising the marginal position of the 'human' in the cosmos, living nature and the unconscious psychic system. Rather, it sought to weed out everything that still remained anthropocentric in the Western tradition after Copernicus; beginning with Cartesian dualism, which reserved for the human spirit alone the characteristics of finality and liberty, in an infinite Galilean cosmos, albeit one reduced to a mechanical system (endowed with movement and extension); and reaching as far as the transcendental forms and principles of Kant, who had continued to place the consciousness of man at the centre of the system of knowledge, morality and art.

This radical attitude on the part of French philosophers was not gratuitous, however. For it could be claimed that a number of philosophies which, in the second half of the twentieth century, claimed to draw the consequences of the lessons of Darwin, Marx, Freud, or of the great scientific revolutions of the past century, continued nonetheless to construct their systems upon some form of methodological dualism or linguistic transcendentalism which ended up reserving a privileged place in the system of knowledge for critical reflection on the human – its actions and cognitions, its possibilities and conditions. The French philosophers of the sixties attempted something more audacious: According to them, man and his thought would be but finite forms among others, all engendered on the basis of an obscure and infinite ground that one might call Being or Nature. The most extreme consequence of the Copernican revolution would therefore not be the death of God, but rather the disappearance of Man and of his 'face'.[2]

2. M. Foucault, *The Order of Things* (NY: Vintage Books, 1973), 387.

Now, although the radical character of this enterprise placed French philosophy in an anomalous and solitary position in relation to other traditions of thought, today it must be noted that it anticipated a tendency internal to many contemporary philosophical and scientific approaches whose stated goal is the naturalisation of the human and cognitive sciences. Comparing it with this contemporary tendency, at work in a number of disciplines – from neuroscience to human ethology, via cybernetics and evolutionary psychology – one might even affirm that the French anomaly harboured something more profound. Although the developments of modern science represented a privileged source of inspiration for them, the French philosophies of the sixties believed themselves capable of refusing those determinist and mechanist presuppositions that they attributed, above all, to their predecessor Descartes. For according to them, determinism and mechanism would be but anthropomorphic residues, models of thought that were still too humanist – the result of projecting human schemata of action upon an external nature deprived of its depth[3] – and which every properly materialist thought must rid itself of, if it would think the whole of Life and of Nature. As I shall try to demonstrate in what follows, the pertinence and the richness of this critical attitude, singularly characteristic of French philosophies of nature of the sixties, finds itself confirmed by the epistemological debate, presently in progress in the contemporary life sciences,

3. G. Canguilhem, *La connaissance de la vie* (Paris: Vrin, 1965), 182; Eng. trans. S. Geroulanos, D. Ginsburg as 'Knowledge of Life' (New York: Fordham University Press, forthcoming 2008); G. Deleuze, *Différence et répétition*, (Paris: Minuit, 1968), 360; Eng. trans. P. Patton as *Difference and Repetition* (London: Athlone, 1994); *Spinoza et le problème de l'expression* (Paris: Minuit, 1968) 207; Eng. trans. M. Joughin as *Expressionism in Philosophy: Spinoza* (New York: Zone Books, 1992).

which turns around problems of ontogenesis and 'actualisation'.

However, my objective in the following pages will not be to sketch an apologia for an intellectual movement which tried to liquidate its Cartesian heritage by pushing to the maximum the materialist and anti-anthropocentric stance that had animated Western reflexion from Copernicus onward. What I shall try to show is only that this tendency, although legitimate, cannot succeed. It cannot succeed because the critical question raised by the *other* Copernican revolution that shook Western thought – *Kant's Copernican revolution* – continues to represent its unabsolved debt to thought. In the light of this second revolution, anthropomorphism can never be completely liquidated, since the question of the human is always ready to resurge qua transcendental question rooted not in immutable and eternal *a priori* forms and principles, but in the incontrovertible fact that man is indeed the being that interrogates nature, poses its questions to nature.[4]

How to escape this epochal dilemma which tears Western thought in two? Must one follow to the very end the direction indicated by Copernicus' scientific revolution, and end up dissolving the face of man in the 'waves' of an infinite nature?[5] Or must one instead follow the opposite tendency and, radicalising Kant's Copernican revolution, end up affirming, with Husserl, that 'the earth does not move'?[6] In other words, how are we to reconcile the

4. E. Straus, 'Der Mensch als ein fragendes Wesen', in *Jahrbuch für Psychologie und Psychotherapie* 1, 1953: 139-153.

5. Foucault, *The Order of Things*, op. cit.

6. E. Husserl, 'Umsturz der kopernikanischen Lehre in der gewöhnlichen

equally legitimate stances of what appear today as the most opposed 'factions': That of philosophers (and scientists) of nature, and that of phenomenologists? And more generally, how are we to articulate the relation between science and philosophy in an epoch where everything seems to point to their mutual and radical exclusion?

Even if it must be brief, our analysis of the 'French anomaly', represented emblematically by the philosophies of nature of the sixties (an analysis to be developed further in part 2, below), and the reconstruction of the ways in which the question of the human resurges in them (and despite them) – at their very heart, in their (analogical) theories of individuation (part 3) – will allow us to foresee a solution which I shall outline in the final part of this text (parts 4 and 5). To place oneself at the centre of the cosmos and from there 'to pose questions to it'; or to displace oneself from this centre, to occupy, through an *eccentric* thought, the point of view of galaxies, of quarks or of neurons; returning to occupy once again the centre of one's own animal body, sensible and self-developing: These are activities accessible exclusively to a rather singular living being. A being which – beyond all suspicion of anthropocentrism or finalism, and in line with the most recent findings of evolutionism – one might also define as that being 'capable of error. A human error which is probably as one with errancy [...]

weltanschaulichen Interpretation', in M. Faber (ed.), *Philosophical Essays in Memory of Edmund Husserl* (Cambridge, Mass.: Harvard University Press, 1940), 307-25. Eng. trans. Fred Kersten as 'Foundational Investigations of the Phenomenological Origin of the Spatiality of Nature' in P. McCormick and F. Elliston (eds), *Husserl: Shorter Works* (Notre Dame, Indiana: University of Notre Dame Press, 1981): 222-237; revised trans. Leonard Lawlor in L. Lawlor (ed.), *Husserl at the Limits of Phenomenology* (Evanston: Northwestern University Press, 2002), 117-131.

and dissatisfaction'.[7] To try to understand more clearly the quasi-biological conditions of possibility of this character-istically human *errancy* – an errancy which, through the proxies of our senses and our bodies (and not despite them, as has often been said) leads us from the earth to the sun and from the sun to our brain – such is the task with which this text ultimately engages.

2. THE WORLD 'IS' AN EGG: PHILOSOPHIES OF NATURE, BIOLOGICAL ONTOGENESIS AND HUMAN INDIVIDUATION

I would like to begin this journey through what I have called the 'French anomaly' with a provisional response to the following question: At the level of philosophical reflection on the natural and life sciences, what happened in France in the sixties that was novel in relation to what had been going on in the preceding decades? I would say that the most apparent change was as follows: In the sixties, epistemological reflection on science gave way to a renaissance of *philosophies of nature*. This renaissance is a new and significant fact, for reasons that I will try briefly to enumerate.

Above all, for reasons internal to the French tradition of reflection on science: In the epistemological tradition of the preceding decades, philosophies of nature had been considered as the lowest degree of reflection on science. Brunschvicg, for example, identified philosophies of nature with the romantic and idealist philosophies of Schelling and Hegel. According to Brunschvicg, the latter took a dangerous step backwards in relation to Kantian epistemology, because not only did their post-Kantian philosophies of nature aim

---

7. G. Canguilhem, *Etudes d'histoire et de philosophie des sciences* (Paris: Vrin, 1970), 364.

to grasp, in atemporal fashion, the *a priori* principles at work in the science of their time, they claimed to step beyond the methods and results of the different scientific disciplines by identifying ontological laws presiding over the historical genesis of scientific reason.[8]

A second notable reason: In my view, this movement of the renaissance of philosophies of nature relates to a tendency that belongs exclusively to French philosophy and which, during this epoch, is absent from other traditions of thought. Outside France, philosophical reflection on science is dominated by critical revisions of the neo-positivist paradigm put forward by authors such as Popper, Kuhn and Lakatos; or, on the German side, by authors such as Habermas. Reflection on science is above all a reflection on the *language* of science, and the Wittgensteinian distinction between the causal domain and the rational domain, the Popperian demarcation between context of discovery and context of justification, or the hermeneutic distinction between explanation and reconstruction, seem to prohibit any contamination between the object of science and the subject of reason, between the human mind and the nature of the objects and bodies studied by physics or biology. In short, outside France, epistemological reflection remains fundamentally Kantian, because it remains a reflection on the logical and discursive structures of the mind and of scientific reason. It is only in the last two decades that things have begun to change, in both England and the United States (and this in spite of the resistance of certain analytic philosophers, who tried to reterritorialize the Kantian transcendental problematic upon language). This change of

8. L. Brunschvicg, *L'expérience humaine et la causalité physique* (Paris: Alcan, 1922).

direction is usually referred to as the programme of the *naturalisation* of the sciences of man and of culture. Everyone today has some idea of what this programme means and what it entails. The only thing I would like to note here is that this programme of naturalisation surely presupposes a certain philosophy of nature and of life, but the authors who put forward the programme do not consider that this conception of nature and of life has anything whatsoever to do with metaphysics, because they believe it possible to draw their conceptual tools from science itself, and in particular from the Darwinian conception of evolution. With the aid of several examples, I would like to show that the current partisans of this programme of naturalisation nevertheless find themselves confronted by problems fairly similar to those posed by the French thinkers who gave life to this renaissance of philosophies of nature.

Who are these French authors? I would like to name three: Gilbert Simondon, Gilles Deleuze, and Michel Serres. Which are the works to which I would attribute this turn toward philosophies of nature? *The Individual and its Physico-Biological Genesis*, written at the end of the fifties but published in 1964; *Difference and Repetition*; and *The System of Leibniz* and the two first volumes of *Hermes*. As far as Serres is concerned, I shall limit myself to a few citations through which I believe one can confirm the above claims about the rupture that took place between philosophies of nature in the sixties and Brunschvicg and Bachelard's historical epistemology. From Serres: 'The term "cut" is the mathe-mateme of discontinuity', but it is also the sign of a 'history that is normalised', 'ideal', 'based on a mathematical model', which rests in turn 'on an ethics': the ethics 'of reform' and of 'the founders of the University'.[9] 'Now, there exists no cut between science and philosophy. [...] epistemology is more the *sign* of divorce than the possibility of an agreement, it designates the dehiscence, in trying to reduce it.'[10] This dehiscence can only be surpassed by a 'new scientific spirit' which decrees the 'end of idealist theories of knowledge' and of historical epistemologies,[11] and which 'leads us towards a philosophy of nature', where the information-structure is 'inscribed' in 'the thing itself', and where one could affirm that 'there does indeed exist an objective transcendental'.[12]

As for Simondon, I shall limit myself to certain notions that are essential for understanding the rest of my argument. The central notion in Simondon's system of nature is certainly that which gives the title to his masterwork: The notion of the process of individuation. Simondon's philosophy of nature is without any doubt a philosophy of 'univocal being', since for Simondon a crystal, a drosophila fruitfly, a pig, or a philosopher, are all 'individuals'. What makes a human being more individual than any other, however, is the fact that the process of actualisation through which a human individual is determined as such does not end at the moment of his death. I shall come back directly to this Simondonian way of posing the question of the human.

9. M. Serres, *Hermès II. L'interférence* (Paris: Minuit, 1972), 15, 213-4.

10. M. Serres, *Le système de Leibniz et ses modèles mathématiques* (Paris: PUF, 1968), 64-5.

11. M. Serres, *Hermès I. La communication* (Paris: Minuit, 1968), 66-7.

12. M. Serres, *La naissance de la physique dans le texte de Lucrèce* (Paris: Minuit, 1972).

Let us turn now to Deleuze. In a certain sense, Deleuze's philosophy of nature seems the most distant from any possible epistemological interpretation.[13] However, I myself believe that every philosophy must demonstrate a certain comportment in relation to science, and I believe that Deleuze's philosophy of nature is capable of doing so – even that it was capable of doing something more. I said above that, for Brunschvicg, the major failing of philosophies of nature lay in their pretention to overstep science, in a deductive and *a priori* fashion. I am not sure that Deleuze actually made such a claim (extravagant for any historical epistemology). But his philosophy of nature was able to sketch out, according to a method that was neither deductive nor inductive, neither *a priori* nor *a posteriori*, the lines of the evolution or development of science, which were only virtually prefigured in the science of his times, but around which the science of our times is in the process of constructing a new scientific paradigm. To show this, I would like to take the example of biology and, in particular, to return to a celebrated page where Deleuze proposes to us an ontological model of the egg; or, better, the egg as model of the world:

> The world is an egg. Moreover, the egg, in effect, provides us with a model for the order of reasons: differentiation-individuation-dramatisation-(specific and organic) differenciation. We

---

13. In the Introduction of *Difference and Repetition*, Deleuze puts us on guard against any over-strict epistemological interpretation of his 'metaphysics'. 'A book of philosophy', Deleuze maintains, 'must be in part a very particular type of detective novel'; and 'on the other hand a type of science fiction', whose author knows very well that the usage he makes of science 'is not scientific' (ibid., xx-xxi). Twenty years later, in *Negotiations*, he recalls explicitly that epistemology was never his thing, and that he never considered it necessary to pass through epistemology in order to do philosophy.

think that difference in intensity, such as it is implicated in the egg, expresses first the differential relations as virtual matter to be actualised. This intensive field of individuation determines the relations that it expresses to be incarnated in spatio-temporal dynamisms [...] Individuation always governs actualisation [...] Notions such as 'morphogenetic potential', 'field-gradient-threshold', put forward by Dalcq [...] take account of this complex ensemble. This is why the question of the comparative role of the nucleus and the cytoplasm, in the egg as in the world, is not easily solved. The nucleus and the genes designate only the differentiated matter – in other words, the differential relations which constitute the pre-individual field to be actualised; but their actualisation is determined only by the cytoplasm, with its gradients and fields of individuation.[14]

This page is most significant, for many reasons. First of all, because it sums up the Deleuzian conception of structuralism, the problem of the relation between structure and genesis, ideal and real, virtual and actual; but also because of its reinterpration of the Kantian problem of the schematism and the transcendental. Secondly, it allows us to bring to light Deleuze's discursive strategies, his way of working with the science of his times, of putting into communication different theories and authors: in this case Simondon's theory of individuation and Dalcq's morphogenetic embryology. Re-read in the light of the great tradition of the philosophies of nature of Spinoza, Leibniz, Nietzsche and Bergson, the Simondonian theory of individuation allows us to see *in the egg a great metaphor of the world*.[15] Here is our

---

14. Deleuze, *Difference and Repetition*, op. cit., 323 (translation modified).

15. According to Canguilhem, one can in fact maintain that the vitalist is someone driven to reflect on the problems of life through the contemplation of an egg rather

provisional hypothesis: Deleuze's philosophy of nature, like every great philosophy of nature, allowed us to go beyond science because it succeeded in identifying the metaphors which underly the conceptualisations of science, its paradigmatic changes, its epistemic ruptures.[16] In what follows, I shall try to clarify further what should be understood by *metaphor*. For now let us try to confirm this hypothesis by returning to the example of the egg.

What problem is Deleuze coming to grips with by means of this complex set of concepts, in which Simondon's concept of individuation plays an important role? Deleuze, as we know, is an anti-Platonist. As such, he holds that what exists in the immanence of the world is not a copy of a model that would constitute the ideal mould of real individuals. What is real is not *the one* or *the transcendent*, but rather singularities and differences. Now, which concepts in contemporary biology fulfill the function of the transcendent model? Quite obviously, the concepts of biological code and of the gene. For an extremist geneticist such as Richard Dawkins, for example, we are nothing other than the vehicle of our genes, the corporeal envelopes of an information-model which exploits us as much as possible so as to transmit itself from generation to generation. For this ultra-geneticist conception, 'all the various complex aspects of being an organism, being a person, are merely ways in

---

than through the use of a capstan and bellows (Canguilhem, *La connaissance de la vie*, Paris : Vrin, 1965).

16. In discussing the relations between mechanism and vitalism, Canguilhem reminds us, among other things, that, paradoxically, philosophy can also indicate to science a position which the latter should still occupy, rather than occupy tardily, as Bachelard would have it, an already outdated position (Canguilhem *La Connaissance de la vie*, op. cit.,149).

which our selfish genes program the lumbering robots which constitute us, to serve their, that is the genes', interest.'[17] The most apt and high-performing are those which pass the test of selection. In this model, as can be imagined, there is not a great deal of room for differences. Differences are produced at the source, thanks to the copying mechanisms which Jacques Monod compared to a roulette wheel or a lottery. But once differences are produced, they are selected or eliminated as a function of the unique imperative of the survival of the fittest and best-adapted. In which case, the good news of the 'eternal return of the different' would afford us little hope. In other words, where there is nothing but chance and necessity, there is no longer any space for the virtual and for creation: Everything depends on the matrix, that is to say on the code in which the great book of the world is written.

But in that case, in the light of current biology, what validity can we grant the ontological model put forward by Deleuze in *Difference and Repetition*? I would like to respond to this question with the following citation:

Living organisms exist in four dimensions, the three of space and one of time, and cannot be 'read off' from the single dimension that constitutes the strand of DNA. Organisms are not empty phenotypes, related one-to-one to particular patterns of genes. Our lives form a developmental trajectory, or lifeline, stabilized by the operation of homeodynamic principles. This trajectory is not determined by our genes nor partitioned into neatly dichotomous categories called nature and nurture.

17. S. Pinker, S. Rose, 'Pinker vs Rose: A Debate', at http://www.edge.org/3rd_culture/pinker_rose/pinker_rose_p4.html

Rather, it is an autopoietic process, shaped by the interplay of specificity and plasticity. In so far as any aspect of life can be said to be 'in the genes', our genes provide the capacity for both specificity – a lifeline relatively impervious to developmental and environmental buffeting – and plasticity – the ability to respond appropriately to unpredictable environmental contingency, that is, to experience.[18]

I believe this citation suggests a perspective very close to that proposed by the metaphor of the egg. Above all, it tells us that the genotype is not a mould which univocally determines the individual. Between the genotype and the phenotype there intervenes a process of epigenetic development in which the role of the temporal variable is as important as that of the topologico-spatial. Structure is actualised by a process of development which introduces factors of stochastic and temporal variability that singularise the individual phenotype. In other words, organisms 'create themselves through the dynamic interplay of DNA and the cellular orchestra in which it's embedded, and the cells, with their external environment'.[19]

The above citations are not from Deleuze; they are taken from the books and articles of contemporary neurobiologist Steven Rose. They allow us to understand that the problems raised by Deleuze in the sixties are once more at the centre of the contemporary biological discussion. For they touch on the problems, today known as 'evo-devo', concerning the relation between development and evolution, epigenesis and the genetic code, neurobiological

18. S. Rose, *Lifelines: Life Beyond the Gene* (NY: Oxford University Press, 2003), 306.

19. Pinker and Rose, 'Pinker vs Rose: A Debate', op. cit.

plasticity and cerebral modularity. But they touch also on larger questions concerning philosophies of nature and of life, ontology and gnoseology. According to Rose, the rigidly geneticist conception of a theorist such as Dawkins or Pinker – a conception Rose calls 'ultra-Darwinist' – is too static and mechanical, incapable of giving an account of the true becomings of nature. It freezes life and loses its becoming. It transforms 'processes into reified objects'. According to such a conception, true organisms, individual phenotypes, are simply copies of ideal models, which need expend no effort in order to actualise themselves in the concrete world, in the *here* and *now* of natural becoming:

> The crucial thing is this. All living organisms have simultaneously both to be and to become. [...] And it's that dynamic, that self-construction, which is completely lost in the abstract understanding of genes and the behaviors they control.[20]

So as to deepen this comparison and to show that the relation between the Deleuzian concepts and those of contemporary biology is not a vague and pseudo-poetic one, we could construct an argument which, starting with Deleuze's proposed genetic reactualisation of Geoffroy de Saint Hilaire's concept of the plane of organisation,[21] sought to demonstrate that Deleuze attempts to *mathematicise* either the architechtonico-spatial components of genetic structure, or the temporal becomings through which they are actualised. In fact, it seems to me that the Deleuzian enterprise of employing both differential analysis and the topological mathematics of algebraic transformations to

---

20. Ibid.

21. Deleuze *Difference and Repetition*, op.cit.,185.

think genetic structure and its process of actualisation is close to that of contemporary biology, becoming concrete in the concepts of development genes – concerned with the architectonic structure, the organic *Bauplan* – and regulative genes, which determine the rhythms of its actualisation.[22] For with these two concepts, contemporary biologists try to describe the play of interaction between the spatial and temporal components of genetic structure in the domain of ontogenetic development as well as in that of macro-evolution.[23] As we shall see, these two concepts also have very important implications in relation to the individua-tive deceleration which characterises the human species as compared to that twin-species with which we share 98.6 percent of our genes – that is, the chimpanzee. Having insufficient space to enter into the details of this somewhat technical argument, I must come straight away to my conclusions.

Deleuze's philosophy of nature is not a vague metaphor in the sense that someone like Alain Sokal might suppose it to be. If it is a metaphor, it is so in a more noble sense, perhaps even in the sense that it grasps theoretical problems of science – problems which even the latter has itself not yet clearly perceived – and systematises them. It is a metaphor in the sense that one could say that every creative intellectual procedure proceeds via metaphor and analogy. For, following Lakoff and Johnson, metaphors and analogies can be defined not as mere rhetorical figures, but as heuristic strategies

22. A. Prochiantz, *Les anatomies de la pensée* (Paris: Odile Jacob, 1997); G. Marcus, *The Birth of the Mind* (NY: Basic Books, 2004).

23. S. J. Gould, *The Structure of Evolutionary Theory* (Cambridge, Mass.: The Belknap Press of Harvard University Press, 2002), 1322ff.

which allow the conceptualisation of new domains of being and of experience, by transposing structures, schemata or models from one domain of knowledge to another, from a well-known domain to a lesser-known one.[24] Once again, I would like to use some citations to express this idea more effectively. The first is drawn from Stephen Jay Gould who, in posing the problem of the authentically creative method of science, and in particular the method which led Darwin to the formulation of the theory of evolution by selection, states that he has often been impressed by the fact that the theoretical contributions most decisive for the elaboration of the Darwinian theory did not come from biology, but rather from sociology (Comte), from economics (Smith) and from population statistics (Malthus). From this fact, Gould concludes as follows:

> If, on this basis, I might advance an hypothesis on what constitutes the common denominator of genius, I would conclude that it is characterised by vast interests and by the capacity to construct fruitful analogies between different domains of knowledge.[25]

According to Gould, in other words, the inventive method of science is 'neither deduction', 'nor induction', but 'what is given in the middle': that is to say, *analogy*. If this is so for science, one might well think that it is even more so for philosophy. And I would say that it is qua faculty of grasping reflexively the metaphors and analogies common to different domains of knowledge that philosophy, even

24. G. Lakoff and M. Johnson, *Metaphors We Live By* (Chicago: University of Chicago Press, 1980).

25. S. J. Gould, *The Panda's Thumb* (London: Penguin, 1980), 57.

today, can boast of an advantage in relation to science. I also think that it is to the systematic employment of this faculty of tracing passages and analogies[26] that we owe a good part of the theoretical charm exerted by that crafty genius who was Gilles Deleuze. But let us try to be more precise, and to redefine metaphors and analogies through the medium of a more technical concept, that of *transduction* – a metaphorical term itself (originally drawn from bacteriology), which allows us to displace these concepts into the context of the theory of individuation. Simondon writes:

> Transduction can be a vital operation; in particular, it expresses the sense of organic individuation; it can be a psychic operation and an effective logical procedure, even if it is in no way limited to logical thought. In the domain of knowledge, it defines the very nature of invention, which is neither inductive nor deductive, but transductive, that is to say corresponding to a discovery of dimensions according to which a problematic can be defined; it is that which is valid in the analogical operation. This notion can be employed to think the different domains of individuation [...] Objectively, it allows us to understand the systematic conditions of individuation, internal resonance, the physical problematic. Logically it can be employed as the foundation of a new type of analogical paradigm, to pass from physical to organic individuation, from organic individuation to psychic individuation, and from psychic individuation to subjective and objective transindividuation, a passage which defines the plan of this research.[27]

---

26. The faculty of tracing passages and analogies to arrive at models and structures which remain invariant in different domains of knowledge, for example from the mathematical and physical domain to the biological and socio-economic (Deleuze, *Difference and Repetition*, op. cit., 184-6).

27. G. Simondon, *L'individuation psychique et collective* (Paris : Aubier, 1989), 25-6.

The only objection I would put to Simondon is that this research plan can only be carried to completion in bringing to light the singular place and the crucial communicative role played by that domain of being through which analogical transduction effectively becomes a logical procedure and an heuristic method. In other words, the project that animates philosophies of nature can only succeed on condition of recognising in the human the source and the condition of all metaphorical transduction.

3. ERRANCIES OF THE ULTRA-NEOTENIC ANIMAL

I thus come to the central part of my argument concerning the place which the question of the human holds in the French philosophies of nature. To avoid all sterile polemic on the question of the humanism or anti-humanism of the philosophy of the sixties, I would like to tackle the question from a biological point of view: What place do the philosophies of nature of the sixties reserve for the human animal, within their system of nature or of life? I say the human *animal*, since all the authors I am speaking of would probably agree 'that one cannot remove man from the vital' and that 'the notion of anthropology already includes the implicit affirmation of the specificity of Man, separated from the vital'.[28]

Man, however, is a symbolic animal, and one must therefore take account of the way in which symbolic structures of sense and signification, whether linguistic or pre-linguistic, are rooted in the living body. For the ambition of every philosophy of nature is to retrace a

28. Ibid., 181.

genesis of thought, by retracing the path of the emergence of thought and culture on the basis of nature. The question that must be asked is this: Do these authors succeed in identifying the precise place where the symbolic is rooted in the biological nature of the human animal? Have they not, rather, simply juxtaposed or superposed, in a sort of onto-epistemological parallelism, the question of the symbolic onto that of the living and of animality? And does not this superposition lead these authors to treat the great problems of the sciences and of culture – language, history, society – as simple structural effects, like the products of a spatio-temporal process of individuation that follows the same morphogenetic laws, or the same mathemes, as are in play in the production of nature? And because of this, don't they end up seeing in language, history and society the effects of a machinic calculus that subtracts from human symbolic acts what I would like to call their metaphoric and communicative intentionality?

In posing these questions I do not want to maintain a dualist position according to which culture and thought would be the effect of an irreducible irruption. Just as biologists and palaeo-anthropologists such as Gould, Tattersall or Corballis have recently shown, I hold that language, culture and history take to their extreme consequences a logic of restructuring *exaptation* already at work everywhere in the living world. For this logic of *exaptation* or, as Lévy-Strauss and Jacob called it, this strategy of *bricolage*, represents a process of functional displacement or cognitive *transduction* by virtue of which an anatomical, perceptive, symbolic or institutional structure comes to be used for ends different to those which it had at its origin.[29]

However, what remains to be explained is the reason why the *exaptive* bricolage assumes in man a far more important cognitive and heuristic role than in every other animal. Now, the sole response I know to this question is the following: This cognitive transfer is motivated by the fact that man is an animal which, to live, is obliged to establish between itself and the world an analogical and communicative relation. It is because of this originary communicative relation that a symbolic structure must not be considered as the simple result of a 'connectionist calculation'.[30] I am of the view that every symbolic structure, in fact, attempts to resolve a typically human problem, the problem posed by the fact that every process of symbolic individuation can only be accomplished in man in an indirect fashion, that is to say by virtue of the mediation of the *Other*. We might underline the philosophical consequences of this thesis in familiar terms, in the following way: Every process of cognitive individuation of external reality is metaphorised by a process of subjective individuation, just as every process of individuation of the structures of reason and of mind is

---

29. According to a neurobiologist such as Vilayanur Ramachandran, or a cognitive linguist such as George Lakoff, the basis of this heuristic transfer is to be found in the diffused hyper-connectivity of the human brain which permits the establishment, in the course of the process of human ontogenesis and phylogenesis, of synaesthetic and symbolic relations between the different sensori-motor modalities, between cerebral regions which preside over the elaboration of the data of hearing and sight, and those which preside over the control of the hand and voice. The hypothesis that the process of anthropogenesis could have passed by way of the liberation of the hand and the restructuring exaptation of the phono-auditive apparatus would find here a neurobiological confirmation.

30. P. Maniglier 'Il calcolo delle culture. Lo "strutturalismo" nella storia dell'intelligenza artificiale' in *Discipline filosofiche*, XII, 1, 2007.

mediatised[31] by processes of individuation taking place in external reality. Simondon once more: 'The individuation of the real external to the subject is grasped by the subject by virtue of the analogical individuation of knowledge in the subject [...] This grasp is therefore [...] an analogy between two operations, which amounts to a certain mode of communication'.[32] Now, to what is owed this analogical mode of communication which is at the basis of all animist and anthropomorphic, totemistic, religious and transcendent phenomena,[33] but which is also at the foundation of the fact that man is the only living thing that has a need to identify itself metaphorically with the Other – another animal, a machine or even a God – to know what he is and how he should act in the world?

To respond to this question, we must once more turn to biology, reformulating the question as follows: If we remove from man the faculty of understanding and elaborating that group of more or less abstract and conventional information which are symbols and signs, must we then consider man an animal like all the others? For ultra-Darwinist biologists and psychologists such as Dawkins and Pinker, man is very simply an overendowed ape, to which a surplus of 900 cubic centimetres of cerebral matter furnishes cognitive modules, genetically predetermined, which allow it to accede to the dimension of language and other cultural significations. For a biologist such as Gould, but also for neurobiologists such as Ramachandran, Gary Marcus or Alain

---

31. See for example Simondon's critique of the hylomorphic model of Aristotle and Kant, and Serres's metaphorological analyses.

32. Simondon, *L'individuation psychique et collective*, op.cit., 30.

33. Serres, *La naissance de la physique dans le texte de Lucrèce*, op. cit.,150-1.

Prochiantz, however, this response risks attributing to man *too many* qualities, in making him the contrary of what he is.[34] Man is not a hyperadapted animal, but rather a *neotenic ape*, with a delayed ontogenetic development, which natural selection favoured at a time of great climatic change[35] because of its maladapted and 'infantile' character, because of its quasi-fœtal cerebral plasticity, which permitted it to specialise in (territorial) non-specialisation, in communication and in sociality.[36]

It may be noted that this neotenic conception of man is close to the Simondonian conception of individuative retardation which opens the human being onto the transindividual, psychic and social dimension of the symbolic. But it also comes close to the Deleuzian conception of man as the essentially deterritorialized being, and Canguilhem's thesis according to which man is distinguished from every other living thing by that anxious errancy which pushes him continually to modify his conceptual *a prioris*. For, let us recall in passing, this conception had already been known in France since the beginning of the thirties, above all thanks to Gawin de Beer's work *Embryologie et évolution*. In his major work, Simondon also cites Lodewijk Bolk, as well as the concept of neoteny,[37] and one of the categorial couples used

34. A. Prochiantz, *La construction du cerveau* (Paris: Hachette, 1989); G. Marcus, *The Birth of the Mind* (NY: Basic Books, 2004); V. Ramachandran, *The Emerging Mind* (London: Profile Books, 2004).

35. S.M. Stanley, *Children of the Ice Age* (NY: Freeman, 1996); J. Gribbin and J. Cherfas, *The First Chimpanzee* (London: Penguin, 2001).

36. S. J. Gould, *Ontogeny and Phylogeny* (Cambridge, Mass.: The Belknap Press of Harvard University Press), 402; *Ever Since Darwin* (London: Penguin, 1978); A. Prochiantz, *La philosophie dans le boudoir* (Paris : Odile Jacob, 1995), 143.

37. G. Simondon, *L'individu et sa genèse physico-biologique* (Paris : PUF, 1964), 280.

by De Beer's embryology is that of virtual and actual, later to be reprised by Simondon and Deleuze. In reprising the thesis formulated by Bolk in 1926, De Beer, in this little book, proposes a heterochronic conception of development and evolution, emphasising the concept of human indi-viduative retardation or neoteny.[38] This conception would later be taken up again by Gould, who would show (after Portmann), how human temporality must in reality be characterised by a double heterochronic phase, defined by certain authors as ultraneoteny.[39] In human ontogenesis, the individuative retardation – expressed above all in the almost disproportionate prolongation of the condition of neonatal and infantile dependence (and then in adolescence and in a period of post-reproductive old age), but also, at the morphological level, by the conservation of fœtal characteristics (concerning the reduced size of the mandible and the ocular cavities, or the advanced position of the *foramen magnum* and the vagina) – is preceded by a phase of intra-uterine acceleration.[40] This phase of intra-uterine acceleration is characterised by an increased rate of brain growth whose consequence is a premature birth (around ten months early).[41] This birth is rendered necessary by

38. G. De Beer, *Embriologie et évolution* (Paris: Amédée Legrand 1930), Ch. VIII.

39. M. Mazzeo, 'Il tempo del tatto' in Contessi, Mazzeo, Russo (eds.), *Linguaggio e percezione* (Rome: Carocci, 2002), 67; *Tatto e linguaggio* (Rome: Laterza, 2005); *Storia naturale della sinestesia. Dalla questione Molyneux a Jakobson* (Macerata: Quodlibet, 2005).

40. A. Gehlen, *Man: His Nature and Place in the World*, trans C. McMillan and K. Pillemer (NY: Columbia University Press, 1988); Gould, *Ontogeny and Phylogeny*, 369-370.

41. Considered in terms of the relation between the neonatal and adult size in other species.

the form of the pelvis in the female biped, but also by the cognitive and behavioural advantages that the human species received from the fact of its possessing a quasi-fœtal brain which is exposed to the conditioning of the familial and natural milieu in a premature and still very plastic state. This brain, which comes into the world 23 percent developed – as opposed to the roughly 40.5 percent of the chimpanzee[42] – would however be completely inapt to face the world, and to make sense of the profusion of *meaningless stimuli* to which it finds itself exposed, if it was not in a position to transpose into all sensorial modalities the communicative structure which links the infant to its mother and which the auditory modality had already begun to exercise in the darkness of the uterine night.[43] This communicative structure is what allows different sensory modalities to maintain synaesthetic and meta-phorical relationships which distinguish the brain of the human animal from that of every other animal. In conclusion, *man is a symbolic animal because its ultra-neotenic condition imposes upon it the maintenance of a communicative relation with the Other in order that it might begin, and pursue in a sufficiently successful fashion, its process of cognitive, emotional, social and linguistic individuation.*

---

42. Gould, *Ontogeny and Phylogeny*, op. cit., 366-7, 371-2; *Ever Since Darwin*, op. cit., 59-60.

43. Gehlen, *Man*; A. Tomatis, *L'oreille et le langage* (Paris: Seuil, 51); D. Meltzer, *Explorations in Autism* (London: The Ronald Harris Educational Trust, 1975); M. C. Corballis, *The Lopsided Ape* (Oxford: Oxford University Press, 1991), 213; T. J. Crow, 'Auditory hallucinations as primary disorders of syntax: An evolutionary theory of the origins of language' in S. Spence and A. David (eds) *Voices in the Brain: The Cognitive Neuropsychiatry of Auditory Verbal Hallucinations* (Hove, East Sussex: Psychology Press, 2004), 124-46.

Now, I believe that this neotenic conception of the human animal has most significant consequences for philosophy – or, better, for the relation between the natural and biological sciences and the human sciences, such as cultural anthropology, psychoanalysis, linguistics and sociology. On the other hand, I believe that this problem allows us to identify a true difficulty with structuralism, because if one does not take account of this communicative structure which orients human anthropogenesis, then the onto-epistemological isomorphism or parallelism between natural structures and psychic, social and cultural processes of individuation becomes merely what Aristotle would call a *metabasis eis allo genos*, that is to say a categorial transgression or 'category mistake' which, to cite Serres or Simondon once more, could also be defined as a 'bad analogy'.[44] It is an analogy behind which one might also recognise the transcendental illusion which leads to the presumption of a new absolute knowledge and to the scientistic suppression of that effort of critical reflection concerning human knowledge and its history, which – beyond every legitimate aspiration to a rebirth of (anti-finalist) metaphysics of nature and of life – is also philosophy.

4. THE MÖBIUS BAND OF BEING AND THOUGHT

Let us try now to systematise the analyses presented above in a critical fashion. At the heart of these analyses we saw emerge forcefully the 'fundamental thesis, without which human experience in general would remain incomprehensible: the thesis of the *communicative character* of this

44. Simondon, *L'individu et sa genèse physico-biologique*, op. cit., 280.

experience'.[45] In its most general signification this thesis denotes a set of dynamics singularly characteristic of human experience: metaphorical and synaesthetic translations, functional restructurings and 'cognitive mappings', sensori-motoric exaptations and inferential invariances which permit a circulation among different domains of experience. These dynamics are essentially characteristic of human experience because it is thanks to them that a communicative and circular relation is established between the internal and external world, between individual consciousness and the social milieu, between the human world and natural reality.[46] Although propositional language represents the principal vector of this experiential dynamic, the roots of the communicative structure of experience go deep into a sensory and pre-linguistic dimension, a dimension which furnishes the 'embodied' foundation of the syntactic, semantic and pragmatic structures of 'audio-vocal' language. This thesis has a crucial importance for the horizon of contemporary philosophy. In fact, to describe this set of communicative dynamics means, on one hand, to stay close to the task which phenomenology assigned to philosophy.[47] On the other hand, this task is perhaps also compatible

---

45. Gehlen, *Man.* op. cit.

46. Gehlen, *Man*, op. cit.; J. Jayne, *The Origin of Consciousness in the Breakdown of the Bicameral Mind* (Boston: Houghton Mifflin, 1990); G. Lakoff and N.E. Núñez, *Where Mathematics Comes From. How the Embodied Mind Brings Mathematics into Being* (NY: Basic Books, 2000); V. Ramachandran 'Hearing Colors, Tasting Shapes', in *Scientific American* 288, 5, 2003: 42-9.

47. This task might be described effectively as follows: 'To explore human experience, revealing its depth and wealth, instead of reducing it, […] and to resist the temptation to take [the data of experience] for coded signs which reveal their true meaning only after an intricate process of deciphering' (E. Straus, in H. Spiegelberg, *Phenomenology in Psychology and Psychiatry* (Evanston: Northwestern University Press, 1972), 263, 267.

with that proper to an epistemology which, in transgressing the indications of phenomenology, refuses to resign itself to accepting the antinomies which our epoch imposes upon philosophy: The antinomy between sensory experience and propositional language (and, consequently, mathematical symbolism); the antinomy between Kant's 'Copernican revolution' and Copernicus' own. In what way might these antinomies be surpassed?

If we are today to sketch out an adequate image of the human being and its singular mode of experience, we must try to construct a sort of *theoretical interface* capable of establishing a *circular* and *communicative* relationship between science and philosophy. It is firstly a question of avoiding the imprisonment of theory between the aprioristic schemata of philosophy, but also one of avoiding forcing it into a scientific empiricism insufficiently elucidated in terms of a comprehension of its own conceptual foundations. The word 'theory' should therefore not be understood here uniquely as 'a *static* set of propositions in accord with the facts', but also as an interpretative *dynamic* in a state of circulation 'from below to above'; and, inversely, from 'above to below': from concepts to experience, and vice versa. It is a question here of putting into communication the customarily separated dimensions of 'subjective intentional sense' and 'objective empirical facts', without falling back into the rigid separation between *Naturwissenschaften* and *Geisteswissenschaften*. This rigid distinction is inapplicable in the present context, since the object and the subject of investigation are 'the same':[48] man in his unity and his corporeal

---

48. E. Husserl, *Crisis of European Sciences and Transcendental Phenomenology* (Evanston: Northwestern University Press, 1970), §53.

and spiritual determinations. In other words, it is a question of giving an account of human experience in the duplicity of its *natural* and *cultural* determinations. On one hand, an experience rooted in a *biological, natural body*, in its singular physiology and sensoriality; on the other, an intentional experience which is constructed and developed in a communicative relation with the *Other*, which is structured and stabilised by virtue of the institutionalised forms of *cultural* intersubjectivity.

In the light of these methodological presuppositions, the central thesis animating this new image of the human could well be reformulated in the following way: Since the human body is an ultra-neotenic body – organically non-specialised and cognitively speaking not 'pre-wired' for any specific determinate milieu – human experience is coordinated and structured in a communicative relation with the Other, compensating for its extra-specific instinctive deficit through communicative, intra-specific and quasi-instinctive 'circuits', which 'from our origins' (phylogenetic and ontogenetic) have favoured in a determinative fashion the survival of the species. In other words, the alterity towards which the *erfahrende Bewusstsein* intentionally transcends is not originarily that of the object or of the external world (the *Allon*), but rather that of other human beings: the *Heteros*.[49] Or, in still other words, the relation with the object is 'intentioned' in a metaphorical and mediated fashion by the relation with the *Other*. To affirm this does not mean, however, rushing headlong into an 'intersubjective idealism', denying that the 'external

49. E. Straus, 'Psychiatrie und Philosophie', in H.W. Gruhle, R. Jung, (eds), *Psychiatrie der Gegenwart*, Band I/2, (Berlin: Springer, 1963), 969.

object' possesses an 'ontological' existence 'already', or that it has a (physical, chemical, biological) structure *in itself*. It means, rather, affirming that this object is not yet endowed with a sense *for us* and *for itself*. The fundamental theoretical kernels of the two antithetical conceptions of the movement of auto-constitution of the human spirit – phenomenology in its Hegelian and Husserlian guises – are thus superposed, their features now agreeing.

What there is of truth in transcendental philosophy and in phenomenology – that is to say, in the fact that human consciousness is self-constituted in the course of an historical and intersubjective genesis whose sense is not predetermined in advance and which, opening onto the future, is thus always exposed to the risk of falling back into the past – must not, however, make us forget that the foundations of this genesis project their roots back into *Nature*. As was shown by the French philosophers of the sixties, along with the contemporary biologists which we have met along our way, man is only one living form amongst others: A form which has detached itself, during an infinitely short time, and 'by way of an hereditary error', from the obscure and chaotic ground of a nature which ceaselessly actualises itself by bricolaging '*a priori*' structures and forms (which we share with all the other animals), and upon which are founded our cognitive strategies for the capture of information which, in large part, is already inscribed in things.[50] In this sense, human 'knowledge' cannot be anything other than the 'anxious search for the greatest quantity and the greatest variety of information. Consequently, to be a [human] subject of knowledge, if the *a priori* is within things, if the

---

50. Canguilhem, *Etudes d'histoire et de philosophie des sciences*, op. cit., 364.

concept is in life, is only to be unsatisfied with the sense that is found. Subjectivity is thus nothing but dissatisfaction. But perhaps this is life itself.'[51] From this point of view, contemporary biology thus harbours a 'philosophy of life'[52] whose aspirations would be no less totalising than those (opposed to it) advanced by the philosophies of history and of consciousness. But, after all that we have said about the neotenic nature of man – and the interactive (stochastic and temporal) play between information and milieu, between structure and actualisation, strongly amplified by the human brain – can we stop there? To accept in their ultimate consequences the stances taken by these philosophies of nature and life seems to project us into a profoundly contradictory situation, where the specific pertinence of 'human errancy' in the 'metaphorico-transductive' process of knowledge – a pertinence which we have tried to bring to light throughout the above – becomes 'erased' by the great current of life. Can we be satisfied with this dazzling short-circuit between being and thought; or, in other words, with this unsurpassable antinomy between philosophies of being or nature and philosophies of consciousness or culture?

Let us try first of all to take the measure of this apparently contradictory situation by conceptualising it symbolically, which means assuming this situation in all seriousness by pushing to the maximum the circular dynamic which it ceaselessly engages. The appropriate symbol is that of the Möbius band, where it is always possible to reverse the relation of foundation between 'that which founds and that

---

51. Ibid.

52. Ibid.

which is founded': between subject and object, theory and experience, intentions and causes, science and philosophy. This possibility of reversal is owed in the last instance to a fact that is at once banal and paradoxical, and whose meaning we have not yet completely grasped. On the one hand, man is an infinitely small part, an infinitesimal element, of a nature which surpasses him spatio-temporally on every side and which envelopes him as an All; on the other, this idea of 'Nature', just like the Kantian idea of the 'world', 'is neither object nor concept'. For it is founded and constituted by virtue of a mental activity which is necessarily rooted in a body and which is necessarily 'centred' on sensory and cognitive structures which belong inalienably to it. Its mental activity – including scientific activity – can never be emancipated or completely abstracted from these structures. This is why all those who, from Bachelard onwards, considered that the Copernican revolution, just like every other scientific revolution after it, determined a complete and definitive rupture with the body and its sensory modality of knowledge, are seriously mistaken. In my view, the whole problem is rather to comprehend how there can exist an animal that is capable of causing its thought to 'get out' of its body, and from the relation that every animal maintains with its milieu,[53] so as to install this thought in the place of God, of the sun, of the proton, the neuron, and from this point of view – errant and anxious, taken up in an unsatisfied and incessant movement – to watch itself live, know, and think.

Returning for now to the Möbius band and to this unsurpassable circularity: If, from the point of view of science, it

53. A. Prochiantz, *Machine-Esprit* (Paris : Odile Jacob, 2001), 154.

is natural causes and processes that produce an individual
body and engender consciousness, from the point of view
of modern philosophy, the causal concepts of science are
but theoretical abstractions progressively constructed in the
course of a genesis whose point of departure must be the
'intuitions' of sense and the *a priori* structures of consciousness. Let us represent the first 'side' of the band as a sort of
eccentric dimension in relation to the human, to its body and
its consciousness, a sort of *Copernican vector* typical of modern
science (and paradoxically, of ancient science).[54] From this
point of view, Kant's Copernican revolution – the continuation and deepening of Descartes' 'subjectivist' revolution,
and the anticipation of Husserl's 'phenomenological
revolution' – is not completely symmetrical, in the domain
of philosophy, with the scientific revolution unleashed by
Copernicus, but rather precisely its *reversal*. This gives the
impression of a complete opposition, a radical divergence
between science (centred on the category of causality) and
philosophy (centred on the category of intentionality). For,
whereas science identifies in finalist anthropocentrism the
insupportable evil of philosophy,[55] philosophy accuses
science of objectifying man and of dehumanising the world
and the life upon which all scientific enterprise is founded.[56]
Whereas science tries to mobilise our reflection ever more
by pushing it to adopt the point of view of the solar system,
the universe, the subatomic particle or the neuron, modern
philosophical consciousness arrives at the scientifically

54. E. Straus, 'The Expression of Thinking' in J.M. Edie (ed.), *An Invitation to
Phenomenology* (Chicago: Quadrangle, 1965).

55. J. Monod, *Chance and Necessity* (London: Fontana, 1974).

56. Husserl, *Crisis*, op. cit., §2.

scandalous affirmation according to which the Earth, qua originary soil of all quotidian and scientific knowledge, 'does not move'.[57] Hence the exigency of defining a new circular and communicative relation between science and philosophy, fit to take account of the necessary complementarity between the *critical* and *eccentric* dimension of man[58] and his singular place in the All of Being or of Nature.[59] This exigency nevertheless finds in our perspective, a collocation different from that which philosophy usually assigns it: The pivot of this communicative relation is not represented by the 'transcendental ego', a self-evident object or a self-conscious subject of thought, but rather by a body that senses and develops in relation to its milieu according to intentional modalities of a particular type. An ultra-neotenic body that, in the course of the anthropogenic process, has discovered strategies that have permitted it not only to see, touch and move in a singular fashion, but also to speak of the Other and, ultimately, to *hear* itself *think*.

5. EMBODIED TRANSCENDENTAL PHILOSOPHY

The methodological hypothesis orienting our research is that the 'eye' and the 'ear', the 'hand' and the 'voice' represent corporeal-mental structures around which pivot the communicative relation between the 'eccentric' vector of

57. Husserl, 'Umsturz der kopernikanischen Lehre in der gewöhnlichen weltanschaulichen Interpretation', op. cit.

58. H. Plessner, *Die Stufen des Organischen und der Mensch*, in *Gesammelte Schriften* (Frankfurt: Suhrkamp, 1980-1985); *Die Frage nach der Conditio Humana*, in *Propyläen-Weltgeschichte* (Frankfurt/Berlin: Verlag Ullstein, 1961).

59. M. Scheler, *Die Stellung des Menschen im Kosmos* (Darmstadt: Otto Reichl-Verlag 1928); H. Jonas, *The Phenomenon of Life. Toward a Philosophical Biology* (NY: Harper and Row, 1966).

science and the 'centric' vector of philosophy. Organs and functions of objective and biological bodies and, at the same time, *a priori* structures of phenomenological consciousness, the human senses can only be described in their function as 'interfaces' between mind and world by reconciling an objective 'third-person' description with a subjective 'first-person' modality. If no-one can know what seeing, touching or hearing means without being afforded the possibility to accede directly and in the 'first person' to the different modalities of sensory feeling; no-one can say what effect proves one is a 'human being' without situating oneself at the 'centre' of a singular body that, even before it 'thinks' in objective fashion, must be lived, in the first person and subjectively, according to the synaesthetic and metaphorical modalities unavailable to any other animal. Although for man, as for other animals, the senses represent those *material a prioris* that function as 'categorial axes' around which turn the relation of mutual implication between consciousness and milieu, human beings seem capable of constructing a scaffold of intrasensorial schemata, ever more exempt and abstracted from the corporeal *hic et nunc*, and which find their highest expression in audio-vocal language.[60] My suggestion is that our experience of our own 'mute thought' or interior dialogue – an experience upon which, in large part, our feeling of self-consciousness and self-determination is founded – is in reality closely linked to the function of silent self-hearing which the ear gradually assumes in the course of the phylogenetic process of anthropogenesis (*hominisation*). If we must therefore maintain – just as the partisans of the 'linguistic turn' do – that it is in language that the

60. A. Clark, *Being There* (Cambridge, Mass.: The MIT Press, 1997).

question introduced by the 'what' ('What is man?') changes sign, being transformed into the question concerning the 'who' ('Who is man?') of he who asks the question; it is also true that the mute and silent thought which we identify with our interior 'I' is rooted in the terrain of a sensory activity already endowed with its own intentionality.

As Helmuth Plessner and Erwin Straus have shown, this originary sensory intentionality can only be grasped by carrying out a reversal of direction in every objective description – physiological, neurobiological, behavioural – of sensory activity, a reversal which results in replacing the third person with the first. And so it is that, at the precise point where this replacement happens, the fundamental philosophical question concerning the conditions of possibility of experience is reintroduced, through a sort of reversal or epistemological *Umkehrung* internal to the eccentric and objective descriptions of science and the philosophies of Nature. In a certain sense, this reversal of perspective, which is also a reversal of the Copernican revolution, is not new. Plessner calls it 'critique of sense' or 'aesthesiology', and maintains that every biological science or philosophy of nature and of life which claims to assign man his place in the order ('vertical' and of growing complexity) of living nature, absolutely cannot pass from this ('horizontal') dimension which, in their 'heterogeneous unity', the senses half-open to the 'transcendental I' of consciousness. This aesthesiological reversal was then radicalised by Straus in a phenomenological direction, by showing, on one hand, that only the activity of sensing allows us to accede in the first person to that which is *real*; and on the other, that the aesthesiological analysis of diverse sensory modalities allows us to avoid all recourse to an intentional consciousness which – as is still the case in certain analyses of contemporary neurobiologists who wish to explain in purely causal and objective fashion the engendering of consciousness on the basis of bodies and emotions – *contemplates* sensory contents from without, like a spectator who *watches* a 'film' that passes before the mental *eye* of *its* consciousness.[61] In conclusion, according to our hypothesis the paradigm of the ear and the voice would allow us to surpass the tactile and ocular dichotomies which are still at the basis of contemporary science, as well as transcendental philosophy.

Qua sensing and self-developing organism, the living body is already endowed with an intentionality in relation to its milieu. In being incarnated, however, in a multiplicity of sensory modalities, this intentional structure is split into a plurality of *a priori* forms concerning space and time, the possible and the real, the extensive and the intensive, distance and direction, passive and active character, pleasure and pain.[62] These categorial structures, incarnated in different sensory modalities, pose the problem of their order and their integration into a unitary structure, of which the 'transcendental I' is a *result* rather than a *condition*. In Straus, Plessner and Gehlen's aesthesiological perspective, the 'Mind's I' is the product of intrasensorial schemata capable

---

61. A. Damasio, *The Feeling of What Happens. Body and Emotion in the Making of Consciousness* (NY: Vintage, 2000), 24. For a deconstruction of this ocular metaphor employed by Damasio, see J.-P. Petit's general introduction in J.-P. Petit (ed.), *Les neurosciences et la philosophie de l'action* (Paris : Vrin, 1997), and J.-P. Changeaux and P. Ricoeur, *Ce qui nous fait penser: La nature et la règle* (Paris: Odile Jacob, 1998), Eng. trans. M. B. DeBevoise, *What Makes us Think?* (Princeton and Oxford: Princeton University Press, 2000).

62. E. Straus, 'Aesthesiology and Hallucinations' in R. May, E. Angel, H.F. Ellenberger (eds), *Existence* (New York: Simon & Schuster, 1958).

of surmounting this modal difference by transcending the dimension of the corporeal *hic et nunc* through contents of experience ever more abstracted from direct sensory contact with reality. Visual data are thus allowed to symbolically take the place of tactile data, the phono-auditive gesture to replace visual data, and ultimately the ear comes to relieve the voice, by becoming silent discourse or mute thought. This aesthesiological redefinition of the Kantian problem of the schematism of the imagination plays a crucial role in our attempt to establish a communicative relation between contemporary science and philosophy. On the neurobiological side, this aesthesiological hypothesis today finds corroboration in those theories that try to explain the emergence of consciousness without reference to any central instance assigned in advance the task of integrating information coming from different cortical regions. On the palaeo-anthropological side, it finds confirmation in those theories of cultural phylogenesis which identify in the processes of anatomical and cerebral exaptation, in the strategies of motor and sensory exemption, and in the synaesthetics and the metaphors between different cortical regions, the very vector of the process of anthropogenesis (*hominisation*). In light of these theories, internal self-consciousness now appears as a sort of 'refolding' or 'circumvolution' of a 'phenomic surface' – deprived of all topological distinction between interior and exterior, since it lacks all 'thickness' – which is incarnated in the aesthesiological structures of sense and perception. It is this absolute phenomenological surface[63] which might be considered as the veritable matrix of sense, the Möbius band of which we spoke above.

---

63. E. Melandri, *La linea e il circolo* (Bologna: Il Mulino, 2004).

But the model of the Möbius band can also be developed in the other direction, that is to say in the direction of a 'critique' of the structure of experience which science presupposes as ontologically already given at the foundation of its action of knowing. If everything that is determined by language, by science, or by any other type of theoretical abstraction, presupposes the originary and uncircumventable ground of 'sensing',[64] aesthesiology might then assume the role formerly occupied by transcendental epistemology. In other works, we have, for example, tried to indicate the consequences that might be drawn from this transcendental aesthesiology at the level of mathematical philosophy.[65] The problem of the relation between the finite and the infinite, the continuous and the discrete, can only be conceived dynamically by a living being for which it is necessary, from its birth, to harmonise the fundamental phenomenological difference which separates the aesthesiological structure of haptic touch (an active, discrete, repetitive and algorithmically finite structure) from the heterogeneous and nuanced structure of vision (a passive, continual and virtually infinite structure) through invariant relational structures constructed in large part through analogy.[66] Similar consequences could also be drawn at

---

64. E. Straus, *Vom Sinn der Sinne* (Berlin: Springer, 1935, second expanded edition 1956).

65. A. Gualandi 'Brunschvicg, Kant e le metafore del giudizio matematico' in *Discipline filosofiche* XVI (2), 2006.

66. A project very close to the present one, critically analysing the 'embodied' transcendental foundations which underly mathematical construction, is that of F. Bailly and G. Longo, *Mathématiques et sciences de la nature. La singularité physique du vivant*, Paris : Hermann, 2006 – see esp. 41-3. Longo and Bailly's approach shows us, amongst other things, that in contemporary French philosophy the question of the human is far from having been definitively liquidated.

the level of the epistemology of physics; in demonstrating, for example, that the concepts of cause and of natural law necessarily contain metaphorical elements derived from the feeling of necessity that humans feel when faced with the 'conventions' of language and other laws which regulate their social action;[67] and, more profoundly, from the feeling of vital auto-affirmation which we derive from our intentional movements and acts.[68] These analyses might, however, also be deepened in relation to that ontological terrain, common to scientific knowledge and traditional philosophy, which is constituted at the crossroads of a well-determined intrasensorial schematism: The objective properties or primary qualities of the real, upon which Western science has founded its ontology since Galileo and Descartes, up to the great rupture of quantum physics; for what are they if not the product of a common tactile-ocular sense of which humanity had already had a first intuition beginning from Aristotle and Democritus? And how to explain the 'substance-accident' syntax of experience which, from Aristotle onward, has been recognised as lending its basis to propositional language, without reference to the tactile-ocular schematism from which the linguistic imaginary of scientific knowledge still struggles to free itself today?

These are only a few examples which cannot, in the present text, be translated into an sufficiently articulated epistemological analysis. To acquire a sufficient theoretical coherence, these examples would have also to integrate the question of the conceptual foundations of contemporary

---

67. Lakoff and Núñez, *Where Mathematics Comes From*, op. cit.

68. H. Jonas, *The Phenomenon of Life*, op. cit.

biological knowledge, from which this article has drawn many of its arguments. This question is not, however, no stranger to our approach, since the critique of the 'machine' model, which serves as the foundation for the classic cognitivist theories of the elaboration of information, and which even governs the functioning of a number of contemporary theories of the genetic code and its informational structure, represents a prime example of it.[69]

In order for the Möbius band to successfully develop in the right direction, we must however return once more to the analysis of the modalities through which the living being incarnates in itself the forms which serve to interpret the real for it.[70] The theory of spatial structures incorporated in the genetic *Bauplan* of an organism, as in the aesthesiological structures which permit a living body to relate itself to its milieu, surely furnish us with a powerful model of description.[71] From this point of view, human experience might distinguish itself from that of other animals by its capacity to translate the aesthesiological structures of different sensory modalities one into another according to plastic and flexible dynamisms that contrast with the strongly hierarchised organisation of other animals.[72] This strongly metaphorico-analogical modality of intrasensorial

---

69. This epistemological critique which, with philosophical intelligence, contemporary biology addresses to its supposed precedents, is today confirmed also by mathematicians who work on the *incorporated* foundations of their discipline (see, for example, Bailly and Longo, *Mathématiques et sciences de la nature.* op. cit.).

70. Canguilhem, *Etudes d'histoire et de philosophie des sciences.* op. cit.

71. Prochiantz, *Les anatomies de la pensée*, op. cit.

72. Ramachandran, *The Emerging Mind*; M. Mazzeo, *Storia naturale della sinestesia. Dalla questione Molyneux a Jakobson* (Macerata: Quodlibet, 2005).

translation[73] – a modality that is not rigidly predetermined by the species (nor determined *a priori* by a univocally digital code, as Artificial Intelligence would have it) – leads us once more to the fundamental anthropobiological condition which makes it possible: The ultra-neoteny of the human body and brain. In thus elevating ourselves to the anthropobiological condition of possibility for our specific modality of making experience from reality, the status of this ultra-neotenic character of human nature is thus transformed from a scientific hypothesis into an uncircumventable phenomenological fact; into a sort of *material a priori* whose signs can be seen in the way, the errant and anxious way, in which our experience unfolds in every domain of its expression – beginning with that centrico-eccentric dynamic of experience that is at the base of Kant's Copernican revolution, but also that of Copernicus himself.

6. The Reversal of the Copernican Revolution and the Metaphorical Errancies of Thought

Let us return now to Copernicus, so as to draw a philosophical conclusion appropriate to his scientific revolution. According to a now canonical interpretation, the revolutionary character of Copernicus' system determined a clear and definitive rupture between sensory experience and scientific reason, and imposed a drastic reduction of philosophical anthropocentrism. I would like briefly to try to show that this interpretation is false, or at least only partly true. As far as the question of meaning is concerned,

73. A. Berthoz *Le sens du mouvement* (Paris: Odile Jacob, 1997); G. Longo, *Mouvement, espace et géométrie*, in *Intellectica*, n. 25., 1997; Bailly and Longo, *Mathématiques et sciences de la nature*.

we must first of all note that the contrast between sensory experience and Copernicus' theory 'is much more radical than the difference between a correct and an erroneous judgement'.[74] Following Straus and Husserl, in fact, it can be maintained that Copernicus did not simply replace a false sensory judgment ('the earth does not move') with a true judgment ('the earth moves'), but that he left the primary dimension of sensory experience so as to accede to a conceptual dimension, abstract and exempt, by virtue of which scientific thought apparently disengaged itself from all anchorage to our earth and to every living, sensing and self-moving body alike. Scientific thought thus *imagines* seeing the earth, the sun and the stars from an 'excarnate' and eccentric point of view which had not been possible for any human being before Copernicus: an 'intellectual vision' so powerful that it could be compared to the vision of God.[75] But is this scientific vision as *absolute* as we would like to believe it is?

---

74. Straus. 'The Expression of Thinking', op. cit., 281.

75. 'When Copernicus conceived and elaborated the heliocentric system, he did not watch the skies; neither did he wait for the night to observe Jupiter, Mars and Venus; nor for the day to see the sun rising and setting. He thought about cycles and epicycles. While in his thoughts he was concerned with the constellation of the stars in their continually changing positions, he was not bound to any particular place or time in his thinking. He used, of course, all the observations made on this globe by astronomers before him. But the heliocentric system deals with the relation of sun and star, envisioned as if it were from a point outside of the solar system and certainly from a position removed – in thought – from the earth, which Copernicus had cut loose from its moorings and enlisted in the company of the other planets. The Copernican system discussing the revolutions of the celestial bodies comprehends, in one view as partners in one relation, the sun and the stars, which are actually never seen together by a terrestrial observer. In this and in many other aspects, Copernicus' thoughts firmly contradict, or at least seem to contradict, the testimony of the senses. Western man knows that the sun is at rest; nevertheless, all of us – the astronomers not excepted – see that the sun moves, rises and sets. But this is not sufficient reason to condemn sensory experience as deceptive, for the contrast between seeing and thinking is much more radical than the difference between a correct and an erroneous judgement.' (Ibid., 280-1).

543

In the first place, it must be noted that this powerful theoretical vision bequeathed us by Copernicus does not furnish a sufficient reason 'to condemn sensory experience'.[76] As Straus and Husserl remind us, the construction of the mathematical imagination which a scientific theory is, must above all be in a position to rediscover the way that permits it to 'come back down', more or less mediately, to the level of 'centric' experience as delivered by the senses and the body.[77] If this were not to happen (neither today, nor tomorrow) the theory could be judged neither true nor false, but only as incapable of entertaining any relation whatsoever with the *reality* of this world.

Secondly, we must consider as one of the great lessons of the relativist and quantum revolutions of the twentieth century, as of the 'embodied' reflections on the foundations of mathematics and physics, that contemporary science is less excarnated and 'absolute' than its classic image claimed to be. In fact it does not seem able to progress along the generalising path of theoretical abstraction without enveloping in its mathematical symbolism the reference system or the concrete 'point of view' from which the subject of knowledge localises, measures, and marks out the reality of the world. But if, on one hand, this fact demonstrates the theoretical power and the philosophical profundity of contemporary science; it also shows, on the other, that at the heart of this science is implicated a metatheoretical Möbius band – analogous to that which we identified above – which can only be neutralised by returning to the absolute 'Earth

---

76. Ibid.

77. 'Whether I walk or I stop, I have my body [*Leib*] as centre and around me bodies [*Körper*] at rest or in movement, and a ground without mobility' (Husserl, *Umsturz der kopernikanischen Lehre*, op.cit, 7).

as ground' and to 'my body as centre' of all experience.[78]

As far as the question of anthropocentrism is concerned, it must first be noted that the eccentric dimension of experience conquered by Copernicus' revolution surely subtracts from the earth its privileged place within the cosmos, but that this effort is not sufficient to eliminate all anthropomorphism, the latter simply being pushed back to the confines of the universe in a sort of imaginary *absolute*, 'of the human body and face'. The Newtonian conception of absolute space as *sensorium dei* furnishes a proof of this marginal and phantasmatic persistence of the human form.[79] The most furious enemy of all anthropomorphism, Spinoza, offers another when he claims to ontologise an historical product of human reason – the deductive system of Euclidean geometry – in the eternal substance of divine Nature. Laplace's omniscient demon, who foresees the behaviour of the universe as if it were a Turing machine pre-programmed by a great evil engineer, represents a

---

78. 'If I now think of the Earth as of a body in motion, in order to so think it or, more generally, in order to think it as a body [...] I need a ground to which to refer every experience of the body and thus also all experience of the being which remains at rest or in movement' (Husserl, *Umsturz der kopernikanischen Lehre,* op. cit., 6-7). But since science can never rejoin this new absolute ground – because every new ground will be but an extension of that originary ground which is, for humanity, the Earth: 'the Earth can just as little lose its sense of *primordial enduring*, the arche of the world, as my body [*Leib*] can lose its most singular sense of being a proper primordial body [*Urleib*] from which every body derives a part of its sense of being.' (Ibid., 15).

79. This phenomena could be explained as follows: Since every relative movement comes to be seen as such in relation to an absolute – that is to say, in relation 'to a "body-ground", perceived as in a state of rest, a "body-ground" with which my corporeal soma is as one' (Husserl, *Umsturz der kopernikanischen Lehre*, op.cit., 5-6) – the (Copernican) subtraction of that originary ground which is the Earth provokes the theoretical production of new absolutes which necessarily function as phantasmatic 'body-grounds'.

third.[80] In sum, it is as if anthropocentrism was only progressively eliminated from the contents of knowledge – or,
more precisely, from the topologico-spatial structure of the
universe – whereas it is reborn in a reinforced fashion in the
specific form of the act of knowing. Why?

To understand this point, we must first of all recall
that the eccentric dimension of experience marks a radical
rupture between the human modality of human experience
and that of every other animal. The sensory experience
of the sun which moves against an immobile terrestrial
background is shared by human and animal alike.[81] On
the contrary, what remains inaccessible to every other
animal is the capacity to *transfer* its thought of the sensory
and corporeal here-and-now into a time and a space which
have not 'taken place'. In other words, qua exaptive and
metaphorical being, obliged to pass through a series of

80. This metaphorical displacement of the originary 'body-ground' might also
be produced in a purely 'subjective' dimension. Kant's transcendental I – which
claims to *unify* a shattered universe, which has lost its objective centre and which
refuses all interference of God in science – might offer an example. The difficulties
which contemporary neurobiological theories encounter in elaborating a theory of
consciousness which presupposes no preconstituted identitary instance – cerebral
homunculus or central processing unit – represent another. In short, once that
absolute that is the human body, perceiving and acting against the background of
the Earth, has been expelled from the system of reason and knowledge, it reappears
in a sublimated and metaphorised form as a central instance of consciousness, or as
a (quasi-intentional) sensor for information that is already inscribed – objectively as
metaphorically – in nature.

81. 'The gift of sensory experience is available only to motile creatures which, in
rising from the ground, establish a position opposite to the ground and thereby gain
a relation to objects qua objects within the open horizon of the world. In this truly
fundamental situation, the senses serve men and animals first of all in their basic task
of orienting them toward their environment. The primary frame of reference for our
moto-sensorium is the earth and the firmament, resting in their own weight. Against
this background, we actually see the sun, the moon, and the stars moving, and I
daresay we see it correctly as far as seeing is concerned.' (Straus, 'The Expression of
Thinking', op. cit., 282)

(intrasensorial) schemata and (linguistic) mediations ever more exempt from direct sensory contact with reality, man is in essence the eccentric animal; and it is indeed this eccentric dimension of experience which was conquered in systematic fashion by the Copernican revolution and the science that followed it.[82] Qua product of a specifically human modality of knowledge, science thus does not pursue a deanthropo-morphisation of reality, but rather a process of progressive humanisation, one whose price is a kind of ontological loss of the world. The price we pay for the eccentric character of our experience is, in fact, according to some, the effective loss of that originary dimension of experience which we share with all other animals; loss of the world to which we accede through our senses and our bodies.[83]

---

82. 'The Copernican system does not correct erroneous sensorial impressions; it transcends the realm of sensory experience. Though contemplated on earth, it is not visualized from the earth. The observer is transferred to Erehwon, to nowhere; he is removed from his terrestrial point of view and freed from its limitations. In sensory observation, bound to the actual situation, we are also limited by it; we see fragments only. The heliocentric system, however, puts together all the fragments. It considers not only sun, planets, and earth in one view of imagination; it comprehends the whole of their circuits. It comprises in one geometrical figure all the possible positions of the earth on its path around the sun, passed in the course of one full year. With the aid of a mathematical model, indifferent in its proportions to the natural conditions of place and time, size and weight, we break through the barriers of sensory experience.' (Ibid.)

83. 'In sensory experience we are in direct contact with things; they stand before us and we before them. In thinking the relation is an indirect one; the noema mediates between the thinker and the target of his imagination. Conceptual thinking requires a radical *ekbasis* from any particular position. We may as well say that because man can perform such an *ekbasis* from the social and the physical environment, and finally from his own corporeal existence, he is able to think. The characteristic attitude of the thinker expresses this 'excarnation' – the price man must pay for his intellectual and spiritual achievements' (Ibid., 282-3)

The objective of this text, however, was to show that there exists a path which leads from the human body to the eccentric thinking of science (passing through the hand, the eye, the voice, right up to the linguistic and mathematical schemata, exempt from any sensorial *hic et nunc*); and indeed, also an inverse path which leads back from eccentric thought to an animal body, to a singular ontogenetic development, a path which we discover in the necessity of transferring into the world its communicative structure, whose traces science will continue to carry up to the very (hypothetical) 'end' of its journey. As opposed to Straus and the other thinkers who conceive this path as a sort of leap, rupture or originary loss of infantile or animal paradise, I hope to have shown that the modality of experience that is at the foundation of the Copernican revolution and of all of modern science does not produce any void or irreversible loss, but only an anxious errancy which finds in a singular type of animal body its quasi-transcendental biological condition of possibility. An errancy which, from this point onward, cannot be infinitely diluted, but which does possess limits which coincide with the contours traced by an incessant oscillation between our body and its Other, imaginary or real; between our thought and a Nature from which thought emerged and detached itself as if it found itself faced with an alterity; between our nature and that of a reality with which we are obliged ceaselessly to conduct a dialogue. In conclusion, in this way human errancy could also be a metaphor for a singular animal condition to which Nature would oblige us, so as to both distance us from and bring us closer to it.

Thinking Outside the Brain

Paul Humphreys

Philosophy is a naturally sceptical discipline. Limits on what can be known, constant doubts about our most cherished beliefs, impossibility theorems – such is the gloomy lot of a philosopher. Fortunately for those of us with a more constructive outlook, not all philosophical results are so pessimistic. Were John Stuart Mill alive today, he may well have questioned our political wisdom, but he would surely be envious of the growth in our scientific epistemology. Yet there is a group of constraints on knowledge that has seemed insurmountable. This group contains the *egocentric predicament*, the Ralph Barton Perry claim that each human can experience and know the world only from his or her individual psychological and perceptual perspective; its generalization, which we can call *the anthropocentric predicament*, the apparent fact that we can only experience and know the world from a specifically human perspective, one that is fixed in part by our peculiar evolutionary history; and the *linguistic determinism* position, the idea that the limits of language are the limits of thought. All of this pessimism is natural, most of it is well argued, and a great deal of it will be rendered irrelevant by developments in science. This essay will explain why.

THE GREAT HALL OF MIRRORS

Perhaps because of these constraints, contemporary epistemology continues to be saturated with anthropocentric views. Its subject matter, almost without exception, is human epistemology, based on a tradition stretching from the pre-Socratics, on through Descartes, and affecting even the philosophy of artificial intelligence, within which human cognition still serves as the most significant reference point. Consider just a few famous titles: John Locke's *Essay Concerning Human Understanding,* George Berkeley's *A Treatise Concerning the Principles of Human Knowledge,* David Hume's *A Treatise of Human Knowledge,* Thomas Reid's *Essays on the Intellectual Powers of Man,* and Bertrand Russell's *Human Knowledge: Its Scope and Limits.* Despite their respect for science, the logical positivists emphasized the centrality of human sensory experiences, Thomas Kuhn's paradigms were rooted in communities of human scientists, and Willard Quine's pragmatism leans heavily on the choices made by human language users. We humans do like to admire ourselves in the mirror of nature.

Variations on these constraints place limits on knowledge whether one is a realist or an anti-realist, a human or another species altogether. Were you to be a solipsist, the boundaries of your lonely little existence would be set by the modes of thought peculiar to you as a self-conceived human. Chimps, extra-terrestrials, cognitively-aware computers; all have their own versions of the three predicaments just mentioned. Or so we are told.

Empiricism – the position that all legitimate knowledge must ultimately be justified in terms of evidence gained through human sensory experience – is one version of the anthropocentric predicament, for if empiricism is true, what we can know is essentially limited to what is accessible through a set of biologically contingent devices. Indeed, the supposed conflict between realism and empiricism makes sense only from the perspective of humans, simply because for an empiricist the limits of knowable reality are set by the cognitive limitations of humans. Realism thus acquires an anthropocentric taint in claiming that there are things lying beyond the reach of the human senses and that there exists a mind-independent reality, if only because the senses and the minds involved are those of humans. From the perspective of different kinds of knowledge producers, such as scientific instruments and computers, the division between what is accessible to the human senses or to the human mind, and what is not, is, ironically, an artificial division. It is for reasons such as this that traditional empiricism passed its expiration date long ago.

A famous version of the anthropocentric predicament is Kant's view that we are doomed to represent the world using fixed conceptual frameworks that form a part of the human cognitive apparatus. Kant's own choices for the frameworks – such as Euclidean spatial representations and deterministic cause-effect relations – turned out to be ill-advised, but the basic insight is striking.

Advances in science and mathematics, especially the development of formalism in the mid to late nineteenth century and the accompanying construction of non-Euclidean geometries, led to a liberalization of Kant's original position. Many non-Euclidean geometries are far more difficult, if not impossible, to imagine visually than is Euclidean geometry, but they can be developed and understood through the use of formal mathematical theories. This use of formal theories to generate new concepts shows that intuitionism as a philosophy of mathematics, with its emphasis on the human mind, is too confining, and that formal theories offer the possibility of taking an objective stand about mathematics without committing oneself to Platonism.

In fact, a formalist outlook has been present in some areas of science almost from the outset. Whatever the real motions of the planets are, for Ptolemy they were understandable only through their representations in mathematical astronomy;[1] for Galileo, the book of Nature was written in mathematics; and the struggle to understand inertia and gravitation in the seventeenth century was resolved only by conceding that one had to grasp those concepts through the role they played in mathematical physics. We should not forget that the modern idea of inertia, the idea that a body could continue to move forever without a force to maintain its motion, is deeply counterintuitive to a species that requires water and air to survive. Scientists who were born and thrived in a viscosity-free space would find inertial motion perfectly natural.

---

1. Although it must be said that Ptolemaic representations were driven primarily by Platonic concerns rather than by the attractions of formalism.

And so fixed psychological frameworks have been replaced by flexible theoretical frameworks. Yet humans still have to understand the concepts, such as sets, points, energy, and information, that are involved in these formal languages, and the ability to develop physical and mathematical intuitions about these concepts is highly prized. Moreover, sophisticated and profound as these theoretical frameworks are, the formal mathematical manipulations continued to be constrained by the a priori reasoning abilities of human mathematicians and scientists. It is within this context that linguistic determinism came to be seen as the new, inescapable, constraint. The languages remained languages of, by, and for the people.

THE INTERFACE PROBLEM

There are two things wrong with linguistic determinism. The first is that it is false. A famously pithy, *ex cathedra* statement of linguistic determinism is Wittgenstein's aphorism '*The limits of my language* mean the limits of my world'.[2] Empirical research has been cited both for and against linguistic determinism, but a recent study of two groups of Australian children speaking aboriginal languages shows that they can perform basic counting operations just as competently as English-speaking children, despite the indigenous languages lacking words for cardinal numbers.[3] For example, the children speaking only an aboriginal

2. *Tractatus Logico-Philosophicus*, trans. D. F. Pears & B.F. McGuinness (London: Routledge and Kegan Paul, 1961), §5.6.

3. B. Butterworth, R. Reeve, F. Reynolds, & D. Lloyd, 'Numerical thought with and without words: Evidence from indigenous Australian children', *Proceedings of the National Academy of Sciences* 105, 2008: 13179-13184.

language were able, as effectively as English speaking children, to select the correct number of beads matching the number of taps made by two wooden blocks. The most plausible explanation for this success is that the aboriginal children possess the mental concept of a one-to-one correspondence, even though they cannot express that idea, or the associated number concepts, in their languages. Results such as these are important because, even if lacking the appropriate vocabulary is an insurmountable barrier in some areas, the fact that it is not so in others shows that humans can develop terms for mental concepts for which they have no current vocabulary.

In the light of this, here is a little thought experiment: Much emphasis has been placed on computational accounts of the mind. Instead, imagine that non-computational biologically-based cognitive devices have been developed, perhaps modeled on human brains, perhaps on a different basis. It is entirely possible that such devices would possess innate concepts, just as human brains have developed such concepts through evolution, with the difference that the artifacts' concepts would probably be radically different from ours. The task would then be to have the artificial cognitive devices communicate their conceptual frameworks, firstly to each other, and secondly to us. The first goal is easily achieved by ensuring that the new devices have identical biological structures. The second goal is considerably more difficult – and not just because human brains and the newer devices would have different structures.

We can call the general problem of inventing effective intermediaries between artifacts and human cognition the *interface problem*. The interface problem is a generalization of the issues that underlie the difficulties in reconciling empiricism and realism and it is always present when we access the humanly unobservable realm using scientific instruments. It has two aspects – the interface between the instrument and its target, and the interface between the instrument and humans. Solutions to both aspects have been developed for traditional scientific instruments but we now have to develop interfaces for an even more powerful set of tools: those of a purely automated computational science.

THE SUBURBS OF THE SENSES

Precisely when humans first extended the range of their native perceptual abilities is not known. The first recorded mention of magnifying glasses is by the Arabic scientist Alhazen in 1021, although naturally occurring magnifiers such as rock crystal have been used for at least three thousand years. Microscopes were developed in Europe in the late sixteenth century, closely followed by refracting telescopes. Those early instruments have led to an astonishing array of devices that includes scanning tunnelling microscopes, nuclear magnetic resonance imaging devices, automated gene sequencing machines and many, many others. Until recently we required the output of these devices to be directly accessible to us in the form of visual images, numerical data arrays, and so on. But no longer. The computational revolution that began in the 1940s has led to an extension of our a priori representational abilities that is even more profound than the perceptual extension afforded by scientific instruments because it fosters the automation of knowledge. Computer assisted mathematics, computer simulations, the automated processing of data by computers – each of these has the ability to construct knowledge encoded in categories and processes that we cannot currently understand. The trick is to see whether, by extending our conceptual resources, we can appreciate what the science developed by such automata would be like – and, in turn, to gain access to realms of reality unimaginable by humans.

A Pair of Distinctions

I begin with two distinctions. Call the current situation within which humans have to understand science that is carried out in part by machines, in part by humans, the *hybrid scenario*. Call the more extreme situation of a completely automated science the *automated scenario*. The distinction is important because, in the hybrid scenario, we cannot completely abstract from human cognitive abilities when we discuss representational and computational issues. In the automated scenario human capabilities are irrelevant. The second distinction concerns shifts in scientific methods. Thomas Kuhn famously described as 'scientific revolutions' the discontinuities in concepts and methods that occur as a result of a change in scientific paradigms, such as the replacement of classical mechanics by modern quantum theory. We can usefully draw a distinction between *replacement revolutions* and *emplacement revolutions*. Replacement revolutions are then the familiar Kuhnian variety in which an established way of doing science is overthrown and a different set of methods takes over. Emplacement revolutions occur when a new way of doing science is introduced which largely leaves in place the existing scientific framework and supplements it with distinctively new methods. The introduction of laboratory experimentation was an emplacement revolution in the sense that it did not lead to the demise of theory or of observation. So too was the explicit development of statistics in the late nineteenth and early twentieth centuries.

In that sense, the rise and permanent establishment of computational science in the last half-century constitutes an emplacement revolution. This is not to say that theory and experiment remain unaffected by computational approaches, because certain theoretical methods that used to be carried out 'by hand' have now been taken over by computational methods and many experiments are now computer assisted, but theory and experiment have not been abandoned. They are not considered scientifically unacceptable in the way that the replacement revolutions of Copernican theory over Ptolemaic theory, Newtonian theory over Cartesian theory, or Darwinian theory over gradualism resulted in the previous approaches becoming untenable.

It is because we are currently in the hybrid scenario that computational science constitutes an emplacement revolution. If the automated scenario comes about, it is an open question whether we shall then have a replacement revolution. The question is open because we do not yet know whether a radically new non-representational apparatus will be used by the automated methods and existing methods of pursuing science will be abandoned by humans. My prediction is that automated experiments will continue but that automated theory and simulations will take on currently unrecognizable forms. Fortunately, in the hybrid scenario we can partially grasp a computer's world view. So let us start with that.

THE VIEW FROM INSIDE THE CAR

Thomas Nagel's famous article 'What Is It Like To Be a Bat?' argued that there was something that it was like to be a bat, but that we, as humans, could never know what that experience was like.[4] Nagel deliberately chose a species that was so different from humans in the way that it experienced and represented the world that we cannot analogically infer from our own experiences to what the bat's world is like.[5] Contemporary computers have no phenomenological experiences, so there is no phenomenology to account for, but there is such a thing as what it is like to represent the world in the way that a computer does. So let us see if we can imagine what it would be like to gather information about the world from the perspective of a computational device. One important feature is that such devices will often have only a local and not a global perspective on a situation. You can easily appreciate such local perspectives by imagining that you are sitting in a car in rush-hour traffic. You can see the car in front, the car behind, and the cars on either side, but no further. There are simple rules you obey, such as not colliding with another car, moving when and only when there is space in front or to the side, not reversing, and so on. The perspective you have on the traffic is purely local – you have no global understanding of the traffic jam as a whole. That's why drivers in traffic jams are always asking

4. See T. Nagel, 'What Is It Like to Be a Bat?', *Philosophical Review* 83 (1974), 435-50.

5. It is also possible that bats do not represent anything to themselves; they just do batty things without using representations of the world.

'What on earth is going on up there?' And indeed, this local perspective is exactly the perspective that an artificial agent has in a computer simulation of a traffic jam.

Contrast this with one of the most significant abilities that we humans possess, the ability to take an external, global perspective on many situations.[6] A helicopter pilot flying over a traffic jam has, of course, taken advantage of a third spatial dimension to view the jam, but the pilot also has the essential ability to conceptualize the traffic jam as a whole – here's a two mile clogged segment, there's a slowly moving segment near the on-ramp, and so on. Developing this global cognitive ability is one of the most important human intellectual achievements and one that computers often lack. Playing the board game of *Go* requires a global perspective, more so even than playing chess, in part because *Go* is a territorial game, in part because no human can consider the consequences of all possible moves at any given stage of a game – nor, for that matter, can any existing computer. In a different way, mathematical proofs require a global strategy as well as an understanding of the local rules governing individual steps in the proof. That is why someone can understand each step in a proof and not understand the proof as a whole.

We can catch another glimpse of what it is like to be a computer by using the device of a cellular automaton. This is a particular kind of computer which in its two-dimensional form consists in a square array of cells, each cell being coloured either black or white. Time-steps between states of the automaton are discrete and at the

---

6. From here on I shall use 'global' as a synonym for 'non-local'.

next time-step, the colour of any given cell depends on just two things, the current colour of that cell and the current colours of the neighbouring cells. Once a rule for the transition between the current state and the next state has been specified, the cellular automaton has been completely specified. For example, one cellular automaton runs on the rule 'If the current state of the cell is black, three of its neighbours are black and the rest white, then turn the cell white; otherwise the cell is black at the next time step'. It is possible to represent the behaviour of many important systems in physics using cellular automata, but our example will be philosophical. A traditional metaphysical problem has concerned whether the principle called the identity of indiscernibles has any possible exceptions. The principle states that if the names 'a' and 'b' pick out entities with *exactly* the same properties, then 'a' and 'b' are just different names for the same thing. Put another way, the principle says that there cannot be two things with exactly the same properties. Various clever or exotic counter-examples to this principle have been considered, going back at least as far as Kant. Indeed, the entire subject matter of quantum statistics is based on the violation of this principle by quantum entities such as electrons and photons. Many of these examples are difficult to imagine, but here is one that needs no fancy physics. Note that the rule defining a given cellular automaton does not mention which of the neighbours are in a given state, only how many of them are in that state. So imagine yourself as a black cell within a cellular automaton, equipped with our exemplary rule. As such, you do not have the ability to distinguish neighbouring cells by their location. All you know is that three otherwise indistinguish-able cells are black and five indistinguishable cells are white

and each falls into the class of things you need to consider.
So you need to dutifully change your state from black to
white.[7] In such ways we can imaginatively project ourselves
out of our familiar spatial world in which position distinguishes otherwise identical objects such as two mint copies
of *Harry Potter and the Deathly Hallows* and project ourselves
into a non-spatial, cellular automaton world within which
there are indistinguishable 'things'. So, at least to some
extent, we can project ourselves into the conceptual frame
of a computer. The point of these examples is to show that,
with the help of imagination – sometimes a little, sometimes
a great deal – humans can come to understand alien modes
of thought.

A different issue is whether a locally-situated observer
can have evidence for the global state of a system. This
move from a local to a global perspective is a special sort
of inductive inference, and an agent located on a cell of
a cellular automaton could not necessarily make that
inference. There are at least two reasons for this. First, his
cell may exhibit a limited variety of behaviour that does not
permit the inference of the global state of the automaton.
For example, his own cell and its neighbours may simply
alternate between two states, thereby not providing enough
information to infer how other cells are behaving. He
would also not have access to the global initial state, and
knowledge of this state is ordinarily required to predict
future states of the entire cellular automaton. The second
reason is that new predicates that apply to the global
states, and that cannot be defined in terms of individual

---

7. I am taking the neighbourhood to be the von Neumann neighbourhood, which
consists in the eight vertical, horizontal, and diagonal neighbours of a given cell.

states, may have to be invented in order to make effective predictions. Aggregate properties such as averages are no problem, but to reclassify the shape of a hanging chain as a catenary requires creative judgment. Just as we sometimes cannot understand the local perspective of computers, so they often cannot understand our global perspectives.

LIVING WITH INCOMPLETENESS

We have seen that humans can overcome the anthropocentric predicament. There is also evidence that we are not trapped inside a web of words. Freed of these constraints, we can gain glimpses of what kind of realism is tenable. Mathematical models extend our conceptual reach but neither Platonism nor formalism entails that humans should be able to grasp all of mathematics. There is precedent for that view in other areas: medieval discussions of the Ontological Argument held that claims to have a full understanding of God were necessarily false in addition to being blasphemous. So it is hardly news that formally identifiable concepts exist that lie forever beyond the reach of humans. Despite Gödel's famous insistence that the truth of certain mathematical results is directly accessible to humans even though not amenable to proof, the epistemology of Platonism has always been mysterious, and it requires a commitment to supernaturalism because abstract objects, in the sense in which Platonists take abstract objects, are not a part of the natural world. This is in contrast to the epistemology of formalism within which, even if humans cannot fully or even partially understand certain formal concepts, we can understand how a computer can construct those concepts and effectively use them to interact with an external world.

Clear-thinking realists recognize that knowledge of the external world will always be incomplete and that Kant bequeathed to us a chimera, an unattainable because unintelligible goal, that of knowing a thing-in-itself. The challenge that modern science presents to us is a different one, it is to develop methods by means of which we can grasp the extended realm of reality to which instrumentally based, computationally augmented science provides access.

BEYOND THE HUMAN PALE

Let me now put the principal philosophical novelty of these new scientific methods in the starkest possible way: Computational science introduces new issues into the philosophy of science because it uses methods that push humans away from the centre of the epistemological enterprise. In doing this, it is continuing a historical development that began with the use of clocks and compasses, as well as the optical telescope and microscope; but it is distinctively different in that it divorces reasoning, rather than perceptual tasks, from human cognitive capacities. There were historical ancestors of computational science, such as astrolabes and orreries, but their operations were essentially dependent upon human calculations.

For an increasing number of fields in science, an exclusively anthropocentric epistemology is inappropriate because there now exist superior, non-human epistemic authorities. We have been discussing a special case of the anthropocentric predicament, the problem of how we, as humans, can understand and evaluate computationally based scientific methods that transcend our own abilities and operate in ways that we cannot fully understand.

563

Once again, this predicament is not entirely new because many scientific instruments use representational intermediaries that must be tailored to human cognitive capacities. Within the hybrid scenario, the representational devices, which include simulations and computationally assisted instruments such as automated genome sequencing, are constructed to balance the needs of the computational tools and the human consumers.

And so I am interested in a question that is common to computational methods in science and to mathematics. Simply put, there are two parts to this question. The first and easier part is: Is it possible to legitimately expand the set of concepts used in these areas to include some that we as humans do not currently possess? The second, harder, part is: Could science or mathematics be carried out using concepts and techniques that are essentially beyond human understanding?

The first part is easy to answer because the expansion has already happened. As for the second question, the answer also seems obvious – science as an objective mode of inquiry transcends human limitations and there already exist instruments – radio telescopes, scanning tunneling microscopes, and many others – for which a human/instrument interface can be somewhat crudely constructed but is irrelevant to the operation of the instrument. In the computational realm, data-mining algorithms on massive data sets, the detailed computations underlying many condensed matter simulations, and many others – all proceed in realms far removed from human computational abilities. There are, of course, serious dangers associated with these methods such as flawed code, hidden logic errors, wrongly calibrated instruments, and a general inability to check the methods in detail. These are not fatal to the enterprise; rather, they require a thoughtful understanding of how these new methods work. It is with understanding the concepts involved that the most problematical aspect of the new science enters.

'IT'S A COMPUTATIONAL THING – YOU WOULDN'T UNDERSTAND.'

Science has a number of aims. Some of these, such as the prediction and control of natural events, have already been automated. Most of us have safely flown on aircraft controlled by automatic pilots; driven cars assembled in factories by robots; been cured of illnesses by pharmaceuticals, the molecular structures of which were predicted and isolated by automated processes; and used electricity generated by computer-controlled nuclear reactors. These examples are drawn from applied science, but automata also play an important role in pure science. In astrophysics, gravitational lenses have been discovered by automated computer processing of data from robotic telescopes; in biology, computer assisted shotgun gene sequencing allowed the mapping of the human genome to be completed in advance of the stated deadline. In mathematics, automated theorem provers have proved results that eluded human mathematicians, such as the theorem that all Robbins algebras are Boolean algebras.

Another aim of science, understanding, seems to be beyond the reach of automata. This deficit will not be a problem if you follow certain anti-realist traditions in the philosophy of science, such as instrumentalism, which deny that explanation and understanding are appropriate goals of science. We also know that in some other areas of activity, such as chess, computers have achieved many goals of the game, such as predicting an opponent's most likely move and winning the game, without any understanding at all. (Other goals, such as gaining an aesthetic pleasure from a beautifully executed series of moves, are absent). Nevertheless, within the hybrid scenario, humans have to understand the human/machine interface, and if the concepts on either side fail to match, problems will ensue. In particular, if machines cannot provide the appropriate global concepts, there will be a serious conceptual discontinuity at the interface.

What happens to understanding when we lack the appropriate concepts? Here is where things become interesting and allow us to address a hard question. Until now, I have not discussed the egocentric predicament – the claim that an agent can understand the world only from its own individualistic perspective. One aspect of this predicament is not as pressing for computers and instruments as it is for humans because, unlike humans, exact duplicates of individual computers and most other instruments exist. Thus, your laptop's digital camera has exactly the same perspective on the world, and representation of it, as does mine when we trade them. Objectivity as intersubjectivity is therefore easy to achieve with artifacts. But the egocentric predicament reappears within computer models where only local perspectives are available. We saw an example with cellular automata. Other examples arise in agent-based models. These use a set of methods that begin with a collection of objects, which can be individual humans that participate in economic exchanges, molecules in a gas, trees in a forest, companies in an economy, and so on. Rules for how these individual agents interact are provided, but what is not initially included is a representation of the state of the entire society, the gas, the forest, or the economy. That is, each agent has its own local perspective and initially there is no overarching theory of the entire system. Using the rules for interactions, the agents in the model are allowed to interact many times. If we are lucky, a pattern will emerge that is a property of the system as a whole. If we are lucky again, we humans will already have a concept that captures that pattern, such as the temperature in a gas, a fire in a forest, or a welfare function for the society. But what if we do not?

An ancient tradition in science and mathematics dating at least as far back as Euclid and used by luminaries such as René Descartes, Isaac Newton, David Hilbert, Bertrand Russell, John von Neumann, and Andrei Kolmogorov uses an axiomatized theory to capture the fundamental truths in domains such as geometry, classical mechanics, logic, and probability. In some cases, the axiomatization will be complete, in the sense that all truths about the subject matter can be derived from the axioms. An important feature of a complete axiomatization is thus that, in principle, everything about the subject matter can be understood by understanding the axioms. This axiomatic tradition is related to two other ideals of science, those of theoretical reduction and theoretical unification. In its most extreme but widely held form, reductionism holds that, at least in principle, all scientific theories can be derived from the theories of fundamental physics and in turn these fundamental theories unify physics. Put another way, fundamental physics is theoretically complete with respect to all other sciences.

A common feature of axiomatized theories, although one not often remarked upon, is that the necessary global predicates are either built into the axioms or can be defined in terms of concepts contained in the axioms. It is this that is not true of many agent-based models and this puts the agents in the situation of the agents with only a local perspective that we discussed earlier. Global patterns require global concepts and if we, or a machine, have no way of representing them, they will lie undiscovered. The absence of certain global predicates is thus a form of incompleteness in the theory and it calls into question the axiomatic approach as a general method for representing scientific knowledge.

The need to introduce new global concepts is widely recognized in various areas of science and it is one reason why a full reduction to fundamental physics is not possible. The method of coarse-graining in condensed matter physics foregoes a detailed description of the components of a system in favour of a higher-level description for the sake of predictive efficiency. The related area of effective field theories requires physical intuition to produce the higher level concepts that are used.

I have emphasized the role of global concepts here but it is with concepts in general that the most challenging current problems of computational science lie. Whether in the hybrid or the purely automated scenario, some way of generating new representations has to be found. Yet this very problem may in its turn be the result of a lingering anthropocentrism. For it rests on the view that science needs representations, and that representations must employ concepts. Perhaps, unlike us, computational devices need neither concepts nor representations to carry out science. Therein lies the most important moral of this essay. One lesson that Copernicus bequeathed to us, and one that we periodically ignore, is that humans should stop thinking of ourselves as the centre of the universe. If we draw the proper epistemological conclusion from that lesson, then instead of forcing epistemologically superior devices to fit their results to our limitations, we have to begin to learn how to understand on their own terms the discoveries that they make. This is a lesson that the philosophy of artificial intelligence, for one, has largely ignored.

A dominant theme of philosophy over the last two centuries has been the emphasis on concepts and descriptions as intermediaries between epistemological agents and the world. Yet some instruments and some computers confront reality non-conceptually, and the sooner we try to understand how they do it, the faster we shall learn. It will be here that we can, perhaps, finally penetrate the barriers that have stood between us and the rest of reality.

We are standing on the edge of an enormous, mist-shrouded plain from which tantalizing, partial knowledge is brought to us by surrogates. The mist parts, folds, and in places permanently retreats. It distorts sounds, renders the touch clammy, brings odd, faintly familiar smells, and perhaps even suggests that our tastes must change. To stand here and to decode these messages is enormously exciting, more so than it has been for a hundred years. It is time to grasp pieces of this strange new world.

Notes on Contributors and Acknowledgements

JULIAN BARBOUR originally planned to be an astrophysicist, but in the mid-1960s became fascinated by the foundations of dynamics. After completing a PhD at Cologne on alternative derivations of general relativity, he decided to become an independent researcher in order to avoid the publish-or-perish syndrome. For twenty-eight years he supported his family and research activities by translating Russian scientific journals. He collaborated for several years with Bruno Bertotti on the implementation of Mach's principle, on which he has authored or co-authored numerous papers. In 1989 his *Absolute or Relative Motion? Vol. 1, The Discovery of Dynamics* (Cambridge University Press) was published. In 1995 he co-edited the conference proceedings *Mach's Principle: From Newton's Bucket to Quantum Gravity* (Birkhauser), and in 1999 published *The End of Time* (Weidenfeld & Nicolson), written for scientists and lay readers, in which he argued that the quantum universe is likely to be static. Together with numerous appearances on radio and in TV programmes, this book has made him well known to members of the public interested in the foundations of science. He has recently been appointed a Visiting Professor in Physics at the University of Oxford. Many of his papers can be accessed via his website (http://www.platonia.com).

NICK BOSTROM is co-founder (with David Pearce) of the World Transhumanist Association, co-founder (with James Hughes) of the Institute for Ethics and Emerging Technologies, Director of the Future of Humanity Institute at Oxford University, UK (http://www.fhi.ox.ac.uk), and author of *Anthropic Bias: Observation Selection Effects in Science and Philosophy* (Routledge, 2002). Many of his papers can be accessed online via his website (http://www.nickbostrom.com).

GABRIEL CATREN is Director of the project 'Savoir et Système' at the Collège International de Philosophie in Paris and invited researcher at the Centre de Recherche en Épistémologie Appliquée (École Polytechnique/CNRS).

MILAN ĆIRKOVIĆ is Senior Research Associate at the Astronomical Observatory of Belgrade and Assistant Professor of the Department of Physics at the University of Novi Sad in Serbia and Montenegro. His interests include astrobiology and SETI studies, the evolution of galaxies and baryonic dark matter, the philosophy of science (especially philosophy of cosmology and quantum mechanics), future studies (in particular related to existential risks and transhumanism), science fiction, and the history of the physical sciences. Milan is co-editor, with IEET Chair Nick Bostrom, of the 2008 volume *Global Catastrophic Risks* (Oxford University Press). Many of his papers can be accessed online via his website (http://www.aob.bg.ac.yu/~mcirkovic/).

JACK COHEN is an internationally-renowned reproductive biologist. He worked in the Zoology Department at Birmingham University for thirty years, and later in the Warwick University Mathematics Institute for five, where he was made Honorary Professor. He has published about 120 research papers. His books include *Living Embryos* (Pergamon, 1963, 1967, 1980), a classic textbook that sold more than 100,000 copies; *Reproduction* (Butterworth, 1977); *Spermatozoa: Antibodies and Infertility* (Blackwell, 1978), *The Privileged Ape* (Parthenon, 1989); (with Ian Stewart) *The Collapse of Chaos* (Penguin, 1994), *Figments of Reality (Cambridge University Press, 1997)* and *What Does a Martian Look Like* (Ebury, 2002); and (with Stewart and Terry Pratchett) the bestselling *Science of Discworld* trilogy (Ebury, 1999, 2003, 2005). He acts as a consultant to top science fiction authors (e.g. McCaffrey, Gerrold, Harrison, Niven, Pratchett) designing alien creatures and ecologies. He is frequently heard on BBC radio programmes, and has initiated and participated in the production of several TV programmes for the BBC,

ITV and Channel 4. His hobbies include boomerang throwing and keeping strange animals (from *Hydra*s to mantis shrimps, and octopi to llamas).

NIGEL COOKE is a British painter widely known for his minutely detailed, large-scale canvases in which numerous smaller narratives play out amongst larger, overarching ideas. In the last few years Cooke's critically acclaimed body of work has been exhibited in solo presentations at the Moderna Museet in Stockholm, the South London Gallery in London, the Modern Art Museum of Fort Worth in Texas and at Tate Britain. Cooke was born in Manchester in 1973, studied at The Royal College of Art from 1995-1997 and received his PhD from Goldsmiths in 2004. He has been represented by Stuart Shave/Modern Art since the gallery opened in 1998.

IAIN HAMILTON GRANT is Senior Lecturer in Philosophy at the University of the West of England. He is the author of *Philosophies of Nature after Schelling* (Continuum, 2006) and of numerous articles on Kant and post-Kantian Idealism, philosophy of nature, philosophy of science and technology, and contemporary philosophy. He is currently working on a book entitled *Grounds and Powers*.

ALBERTO GUALANDI holds doctorates in Philosophy in France and Italy, and is currently a researcher attached to the University of Bologna. He has published several works, including *Le problème de la vérité scientifique dans la philosophie française contemporaine. La rupture et l'événement* (L'Harmattan, 1998); *Deleuze* (Les Belles Lettres, 1998, 2003); *Lyotard* (Les Belles Lettres, 1999, 2004) and has edited several numbers of *Discipline filosofiche*: *L'uomo, un progetto incompiuto. Vol. 1. Significato e attualità dell'antropologia filosofica* (Quodlibet, 2002), *Vol. 2. Antropologia filosofica e contemporaneità* (2002), *L'epistemologia francese e il problema del «trascendentale storico»* (with A. Cavazzini, 2006), and *Logiche del vivente. Evoluzione, sviluppo e cognizione nell'epistemologia francese contemporanea* (with A. Cavazzini, forthcoming, 2009). His current interests are centred around the philosophy of biology, philosophical anthropology and phenomenological aesthesiology.

PAUL HUMPHREYS is Professor of Philosophy at the University of Virginia. Recent publications include *Extending Ourselves: Computational Science, Empiricism and Scientific Method* (Oxford, 2004) and *Emergence: Contemporary Readings in Philosophy and Science* (co-edited with Mark Bedau, MIT Press, 2008).

JAMES LADYMAN is Professor of Philosophy at the University of Bristol, and co-editor of *The British Journal for the Philosophy of Science* (of which he was previously assistant and deputy editor). He was the Honorary Secretary of The British Society for the Philosophy of Science from 2003 to 2007. He is the author of *Understanding Philosophy of Science* (Routledge, 2002) which received a *Choice Outstanding Academic Title Award*, and, with Don Ross, *Every Thing Must Go: Metaphysics Naturalized* (Oxford University Press, 2007). He is currently writing a textbook on the philosophy of physics. In 2005 he was awarded a *Philip Leverhulme* Prize. He has published many articles on the philosophy of science and the philosophy of physics, including recently the entry on Structural Realism in *The Stanford Encyclopaedia of Philosophy*.

ROBIN MACKAY is founding editor of *Collapse*, translator of numerous articles and of Alain Badiou's *Number and Numbers* (Polity, 2007).

THOMAS METZINGER is currently Professor of Theoretical Philosophy at the Johannes Gutenberg-Universität Mainz and an Adjunct Fellow at the Frankfurt Institute for Advanced Study. He is past president of the German Cognitive Science Society and a founding board member of the Association for the

Scientific Study of Consciousness. His focus of research lies in analytical philosophy of mind, philosophy of science and philosophical aspects of the neuro- and cognitive sciences, as well as connections between ethics, philosophy of mind and anthropology. He has edited two collections on consciousness, *Conscious Experience* (Imprint Academic, 1995) and *Neural Correlates of Consciousness* (MIT Press, 2000) and one major English monograph developing a comprehensive, interdisciplinary theory of consciousness, the phenomenal self, and the first-person perspective (*Being No One – The Self-Model Theory of Subjectivity*, MIT Press, 2003). His most recent book is *The Ego Tunnel: The Science of the Mind and the Myth of the Self* (Basic Books, 2009).

CARLO ROVELLI is a member of the Institut Universitaire de France and Professor of Physics at the University of Marseille. He leads the quantum gravity research group at the Center for Theoretical Physics of Luminy. He was one of the originators of the 'loop' approach to quantum gravity, one of the main theoretical hypotheses for describing the quantum properties of space and time. He has received numerous awards, including the 1995 Xanthopoulos Award 'for his contribution to the physics of space and time'. He has published around two hundred scientific articles and the monograph *Quantum Gravity* (Cambridge University Press, 2004), as well as books for the wider public, such as *What is Time? What is Space?* (Di Renzo Editore, 2004) and *Anaximander of Miletus* (Dunot, forthcoming).

MARTIN SCHÖNFELD is a philosopher of nature at the University of South Florida in Tampa, USA. He has written on enlightenment, environment, and China. He keeps a blog on accelerating climate change and edits a climate philosophy newsletter. He is editing topic issues on the heuristic potential of climate change for *Journal of Global Ethics* and *Essays in Philosophy*. He is the author of *The Philosophy of the Young Kant* (Oxford University Press, 2000) and 'Green Kant', in Pojman, ed., *Environmental Ethics* (2008), and is now writing a book on Kantian *klimasophia*.

CONRAD SHAWCROSS is a British artist. Having featured in the prestigious *New Contemporaries* in 2001, and *New Blood* at the Saatchi Gallery in 2004, he has since exhibited internationally. Currently living and working in New York as an International Fellow for the arts based organization Location One, in 2009 he will be returning to London to become the Centenary Artist in Residence at the Science Museum, and is currently also working a major permanent commission for the UK government. Recent awards include the Art and Work awards for best sculptural installation of 2007. He is represented by Victoria Miro Gallery in the UK.

IAN STEWART is an internationally-renowned mathematician and Professor of Mathematics at the University of Warwick, dividing his time equally between research into nonlinear dynamics and furthering public awareness of mathematics. His current interests focus on the dynamics of networks. He was born in 1945 and educated at Cambridge and Warwick; he is a Fellow of the Royal Society and has four honorary degrees. His books include *Does God Play Dice?* (Penguin, 1989), *Letters to a Young Mathematician* (Basic Books, 2006), *Why Beauty is Truth* (Basic Books, 2007), and most recently *Professor Stewart's Cabinet of Mathematical Curiosities* (Basic Books, 2009), as well as (with Jack Cohen) *The Collapse of Chaos* (Penguin, 1994), *Figments of Reality (Cambridge University Press, 1997)* and *What Does a Martian Look Like* (Ebury, 2002); and (with Cohen and Terry Pratchett) the bestselling *Science of Discworld* trilogy (Ebury, 1999, 2003, 2005). His awards include the Royal Society's Faraday Medal (1995), the IMA Gold Medal (2000), the AAAS Public Understanding of Science and Technology Award (2001), and the LMS/IMA Zeeman Medal (2008). He appears frequently on radio and television, and presented the 1997 Christmas Lectures for the BBC.

KEITH TYSON is an artist who has won international acclaim for his work in many different media and reflecting diverse interests in science, philosophy and art history. Tyson has exhibited internationally, and was awarded the Turner Prize in 2002. He lives and works in London and is represented by Haunch of Venison. http://www.keithtyson.com/

Interview with Julian Barbour conducted via email by Damian Veal.

Interview with Thomas Metzinger conducted via email by Damian Veal and Ray Brassier.

Interview with Jack Cohen and Ian Stewart conducted via email by Damian Veal.

Interview with James Ladyman conducted via email by Damian Veal.

Translation of 'Errancies of the Human' by Robin Mackay.

Figures for 'Anaximander's Legacy' by Kristen Alvanson.

Thanks to Anika Carpenter and Shireen Painter at Keith Tyson Projects, to Lisa Hall at Cooke Industries, to Bryony McLennan at Victoria Miro Gallery, and to Professor J. Gassowski, Marie Allen and Beata Jurkiewicz at the University of Uppsala. Thanks also to Suhail Malik and Oliver Feltham for their suggestions for this volume, and to Alex Murray for his help in obtaining images.

Damian Veal would like to express special thanks to Robin Mackay for entrusting him with the editorship of this volume, for his tireless editorial work in preparing the volume for publication, and for commissioning and preparing the artwork and illustrations.

Special thanks also to Milan Ćirković for many helpful discussions and good advice; to Julian Barbour, Jack Cohen, James Ladyman, Thomas Metzinger and Ian Stewart for their perseverance with the interviews; to Ray Brassier for his editorial assistance; to Mike Lewis and Lydia Patton for enabling me to access online articles; and to Michael Carr for keeping Cecy and I supplied with Jake Thackray CDs, as well as solving our problem of what to watch on the box for the next decade.

Above all, thanks to Cecy, without whose love, patience and support, nothing would have been possible.

contemporary culture index

http://www.ccindex.info

"We--contemporary culture index--produce information. We spend our days with computers, querying remote databases, reading and indexing journals and periodicals. Current periodicals, deceased journals. We are creating a database."

contemporary culture index is an open-access, multi-disciplinary online database indexing international journals and periodicals.

ccindex's aim is to cover the growing need of specialized information not limited to any academic category nor to a geographical or linguistic area. Areas covered are architecture, art, cinema, cultural studies, design, literature, music, philosophy, photography and social sciences.

contemporary culture index does not pretend to be exhaustive. Aware that exhaustivity is impossible, ccindex has opted for a rigorous selection of titles in terms of their research quality; an important ambition is to connect materials that are seldom juxtaposed, in order to favour new research approaches. A high number of non-Western and European journals are not indexed in existing databases;contemporary culture index's aim is to make this valuable information its core.

Another strain of interest for ccindex is to index small and influential publications that are no longer published, especially those originating from artists or cultural producers rather than from conventional academic processes.

If you wish to review Collapse's indexed contents, please log in.

HECKER 'LIVE @ WDR'
CASSETTE | TOCHNIT ALEPH TA085

A1. NACHRICHTEN (03:05)
2. (02:17)
3. STANDARD MAP & CUSP MAP, REARRANGED PT. I (24:24)
B1. STANDARD MAP & CUSP MAP, REARRANGED PT. II (20:14)

Produced and performed by Florian Hecker
Recorded with Schöps CMC6U / MK6 microphones direct to
Soundevices 702 portable digital audio recorder at
WDR Mehrzweck-Sendestudio, Cologne on 26.09.2007

Mastered by Rashad Becker @ Audio Anwendungen
Acknowledgements: Tina Frank, Björn Gottstein, Martin Kröll

℗ Tochnit Aleph 2008   © Florian Hecker 2007
Published by Muts Song Ltd. UK

RUSSELL HASWELL 'RECORDED WHILE IT ACTUALLY HAPPENED'
CASSETTE | TOCHNIT ALEPH TA089

SIDE ONE:
A HORDE OF FLIES FEAST ON A ROTTING
PHEASANT CARCASS. (30:00:00) Miniature
Omnidirectional Microphone direct to
Sound Devices. Recorded, 2008. (mono).

SIDE TWO:
ELECTROSWAT. (13:46:23) Telephone
Pickup/Magnetic Field Fluctuation
Detector + Portable Fly Zapping Racket,
direct to MicroTrak. Recorded, 2007.
(mono).

REVERSE ELECTROSWAT (+RNE+WS+TS
+VERB). (16:00:00) Telephone Pickup/
Magnetic Field Fluctuation Detector +
Portable Fly Zapping Racket, direct to
MicroTrak. Recorded, 2007. Decomposed,
Processed + Edited, 2008. (stereo).

WWW.TOCHNIT-ALEPH.COM

Second Edition Now Available in Paperback

PHILOSOPHIES OF NATURE AFTER SCHELLING

Iain Hamilton Grant

Hardback ISBN: 0-8264-7902-2   £70.00
Paperback ISBN: 1-8470-6432-9   £24.99

A lucid and crucial account of Schelling's major works in the philosophy of nature, now available in paperback.

'The whole of modern European philosophy', wrote F.W.J. Schelling in 1809, 'has this common deficiency - that nature does not exist for it.' Despite repeated echoes of Schelling's assessment throughout the natural sciences, and despite the philosophy of nature recently proposed but not completed by Gilles Deleuze, Philosophies of Nature After Schelling argues that Schelling's verdict remains accurate two hundred years later. Presenting a lucid account of Schelling's major works in the philosophy of nature alongside those of his scientific contemporaries who pursued and furthered that work, this book does not simply aim to present Schelling's extravagant 'speculative physics' as an historical episode. Rather, Schelling's programme is presented as a viable and necessary corrective both to the rejection of metaphysics and the correlative 'antiphysics' at the ethical heart of contemporary philosophy.

"Intriguing and ambitious … Philosophies of Nature After Schelling sets a new standard for Schelling scholarship. More than this, it is an important work of philosophy in its own right." - Dustin McWherter, *Radical Philosophy* 144 (July/August 2007)

"Philosophies of Nature after Schelling is an important, indeed a groundbreaking work." - Joseph P. Lawrence, *Notre Dame Philosophy Review*, May 10, 2007

EPISODE

Pleasure and Persuasion
in Lens–Based Media

EPISODE: Pleasure and Persuasion in Lens-based Media

Edited by:
Amanda Beech, Jaspar Joseph-Lester, & Matthew Poole

Essays by:
Amanda Beech, Jaspar Joseph-Lester, Sharon Kivland,
Norman M Klein, Suhail Malik, Uriel Orlow, Matthew Poole,
& Johanna Sumiala

This new collection of essays edited by the research group Curating Video
brings together an international field of researchers from the realms of
cultural studies, visual art, psychoanalysis, and political philosophy to
explore new contexts and issues that are crucial to understanding
the experience and meaning of images. Without idealising or demonising
media culture these essays interrogate the critical status of lens-based
media, taking up the pressing dilemmas of a politics of the image
and its contemporary condition.

PRICE: £12.95
ISBN: 978-1-906441-03-6
DATE: November 2008
www.artwordspress.co.uk
www.curatingvideo.com

ARTWORDS PRESS | WWW.ARTWORDSPRESS.CO.UK

ARTWORDSPR
ESS

MONU

The Sky is not near enough *by Shumon Basar;* **Pseudo-Democracies and Pseudo-Commissions** - *Interview with Reinier de Graaf/ OMA;* **The Exotic and the Local - From Superhero to Supercity** *by Yehuda Greenfield - Gilat;* **Urbanism of the permanent Tourist** *by Deane Simpson; and more...*

EXOTIC URBANISM

#09

4 197754 112502   09

University of the West of England at Bristol

An opportunity to study in depth the great traditions of Modern European philosophy, along with its most important contemporary trends.

MA European Philosophy

The MA in European Philosophy, based in UWE's Bristol campus, allows students to pursue an interest in European Philosophy at a postgraduate level, in an inquiring environment alongside a staff with wide-ranging research interests. Study the great works of modern philosophy and their repercussions in contemporary theory and culture, through a combination of compulsory and elective modules and a dissertation on a topic of your choice.

2008-9 modules include
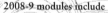
- The Post-Kantian Tradition (Hegel, Fichte, Schelling)
- Phenomenology (Merleau-Ponty)
- Contemporary French Philosophy (Deleuze, Badiou)
- Heidegger's *Being and Time*
- Kant's *Critique of Pure Reason*

University of the West of England
BRISTOL

The University of the West of England (UWE) is a modern, growing university in the thriving city of Bristol.
The MA in European Philosophy is based at UWE's St Matthias Campus, located to the Northwest of Bristol.
- For further information email iain.grant@uwe.ac.uk
- For an application pack email HLSSPostgraduate@uwe.ac.uk
- Or write to: HLSS Graduate School, Conifers, Room C001, University of the West of England St Matthias Campus, Oldbury Court Road, Bristol, BS16 2JP, United Kingdom.

See http://www.uwe.ac.uk/hlss/courses/philosophy/ for further details

Princess Lulu

Issue b, Dez. 2008 — 4 Euro

Chicago, Times, Plotter, Helvetica, DIN, **Techno**, *Löhfelm*,
RR_02*, Univers, Circuit, **Memphis**, **Gringo**, **Zeus**, The Mix

and Princess Lulu are available at:

Vienna: Secession, Song

Berlin: Pro qm, O Tannenbaum

Frankfurt a. M.: Portikus,

Munich: Kunstverein

Lausanne: Circuit

Order at:

zeitschrift@gmx.net, Meiselstrasse 29-10, 1150 Vienna, Austria

Editors:

Christian Egger, Manuel Gorkiewicz, Christian Mayer,
Yves Mettler, Magda Tothova, Ruth Weismann, Alexander Wolff

www.theselection.net/zeitschrift

Carl Bolt:
Schlossparklandschaftgestaltungselementvariationstechnikgebrauchsmaterialausdrucksformenschauspielautoparkfilm,
Cover: 16,17, Lucie Stahl: Stranger, 2008 2, Stuff, 2008 24, Untitled, 2008 29, Veloche 2008
50, Kolumne 3, Michael Dears: Snoopy Detourned 3, 10, 31 Vernisage sur le Monde 32, Denis Prisset 4,
Marion Rancaz: Ground Zero 8, Christian Egger 11, 13, 39, 43-45, David Kellner 12-15
Christian Mayer: This isn't the 15th Century 19, Monika Wista 21, Heike Bollig 22,
Princess Lulu: notes de Dance 25, 28, gelitin: pink rabbit 3rd birthday 26, Olivier Garbay: 11 60,
Battleship Latte by Christian Egger 30, Yves Mettler: Mindmap with Dance 37, Echo Park & Silverlake,
2008 40, 41, Interview: Steven Lowe by Sonia Leimer 46

RETURN OF THE ART DEAD

DEADGARDE + POST DEADART
VIDEATH + DEATHFORMANCE
DEATHORS + BIDEATHANALE
DEADSIGN + NEW MEDEATH +
DEATHPTUAL ART + SYFILIS

read it on paper and web

COLLAPSE

Journal of Philosophical Research and Development

PREVIOUS VOLUMES

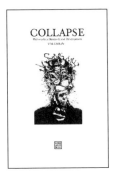